12.06
2

ESSAYS ON
PHYSIOLOGICAL EVOLUTION

Kh. S. Koshtoyants
(1900–1961)

Essays on Physiological Evolution

Honorary Editor

J.W.S. PRINGLE, D.Sc.,F.R.S.

Linacre Professor of Zoology
Oxford University

PERGAMON PRESS

OXFORD · LONDON · EDINBURGH · NEW YORK

PARIS · FRANKFURT

Pergamon Press Ltd., Headington Hill Hall, Oxford
4 & 5 Fitzroy Square, London W.1

Pergamon Press (Scotland) Ltd., 2 & 3 Teviot Place, Edinburgh 1

Pergamon Press Inc., 122 East 55th Street, New York 22, N.Y.

Gauthier-Villars, 55 Quai des Grands-Augustins, Paris 6

Pergamon Press GmbH, Kaiserstrasse 75, Frankfurt-am-Main

First edition 1965

Library of Congress Catalog Card No. 63-12462

*Based on a volume prepared by T. M. Turpayev for presentation
to Professor Kh. S. Koshtoyants on his sixtieth birthday and
published after his death in 1961 by the U.S.S.R. Academy of
Sciences, Moscow*

MADE IN GREAT BRITAIN

The authors dedicate their papers to
the memory of the eminent physiologist,
KHACHATUR SEDRAKOVICH KOSHTOYANTS

The attention of readers is drawn to the fact that Pergamon Press have published a cover to cover translation of the Soviet Journals *Pavlov Journal of Higher Nervous Activity* and *The Sechenov Physiological Journal of the U.S.S.R.* from January 1957 to the December 1961 issues. All references to issues published in English translation have been marked with an asterisk throughout the book. Copies of the English articles or of the complete journals can be obtained on request from Pergamon Press.

CONTENTS

EDITORIAL INTRODUCTION

THIS volume of essays on physiological evolution was published in Moscow in 1961. The collection was intended as a "Festschrift" for Professor Koshtoyants, but his untimely death turned it into a memorial to this great man. Its re-publication in English after an interval of three years may seem strange in this age of rapid progress, but in fact many of the articles have permanent value and those by Russian authors in particular often present summaries of results and discussion of theoretical points which are unfamiliar to Western readers. The articles by English and American contributors are now published as they were originally written except where their authors have wished to revise them to bring them more up to date. The Russian articles have been translated with care to preserve the essence of the original even if the result is not always conventional English idiom; here also authors have had opportunity for revision. The result is a collection covering a wide range of topics in comparative physiology and written with more emphasis on evolutionary aspects than is usual in contemporary English and American writing on this subject.

Dr. T. M. Turpayev has written a short biographical sketch of Koshtoyants as an introduction to the volume. I first met this remarkable man at the International Congress of Zoology in London in 1958 and we were able to arrange for him to spend two weeks in Cambridge the following year. Few of us will forget the penetrating insight he brought to bear on the problems we then discussed. It was quickly clear to us that here was not just another comparative physiologist interested in the biophysical and biochemical analysis of function in lower animals, but a real biologist wishing also to know how physiological mechanisms have come to be what they are in the course of evolution. Koshtoyants would have agreed that a full understanding of existing mechanisms is necessary to this end, but I think he would have argued that evolutionary considerations can help biochemistry and biophysics. Time and the work of his pupils will surely show that he was right.

Some of the arguments in this volume may appear uncritical to analytical physiologists. Assessing the role of a particular physiological factor in the economy of the animal as a whole is a difficult task and one which is usually shirked by experimentalists. There are two clearly different objectives, understanding of mechanism and understanding of evolutionary history; these are complementary and not antagonistic. Both are in the minds of the authors of these articles.

J. W. S. PRINGLE

K H. S. KOSHTOYANTS

SCIENTIFIC friends and pupils of Khachatur Sedrakovich Koshtoyants have joined together to mark the occasion of his sixtieth birthday by the publication of this Collection of Papers. Koshtoyants was, however, fated not to see the book: unexpected death cut off the life of this remarkable scientist. He died at the height of his powers, in a period of great creative activity and engagement in fresh fields of research.

Koshtoyants' death is a great loss to science in this country. His name has been connected with many things; not only was he an outstanding scientist who created a new trend in physiology, and a notable teacher who had trained more than one generation of young scientists; he was also an active worker in public affairs, a superb historian of science and an untiring worker for the popularization of science. And, finally, he was a brilliant and charming personality who infected those around him with his own unusual capacity for work and his truly youthful devotion to science.

Kh. S. Koshtoyants was born in 1900 in a small Armenian town, Aleksandropol (now Leninakan). At the age of 14 he started work as a pharmacist's apprentice. He was unable to obtain middle school education and had to pass the examination for the gymnasium as an external pupil, without the advantage of being able to attend lectures.

The October Revolution gave the talented youth his opportunity to obtain higher education. He completed his training at Moscow University and started independent experimental investigations in the laboratory of one of Pavlov's distinguished pupils, I. P. Razenkov. In 1928 Koshtoyants produced a special method for isolation of the pancreas without interruption of its nerve connexions with the body. This made possible the subsequent demonstration of a number of important facts relating to the effects of different pharmacological agents on the external secretion of the pancreas.

In 1929–1930 Koshtoyants conducted a series of comparative and ontogenetic experiments on the humoral regulation of the pancreas. The young physiologist's interest in the evolution of functions first became evident in these years, and this interest was greatly intensified after he had spent several months in the laboratory of the eminent comparative physiologist, Hermann Jordan, in Utrecht University.

In 1930 Koshtoyants set up the first laboratory of comparative physiology in the U.S.S.R. and started the first course of lectures on this subject in Moscow University. For the next thirty years he was engrossed in problems of evolutionary physiology, so that Koshtoyants can, along with the late

L. A. Orbeli, rightly be regarded as a founder of this branch in Soviet physiological science. He studied the evolution of function in a great number of systems (metabolism, blood, respiration, muscles, nervous system, etc.) and analysed the problems in terms of comparative, developmental and ecological physiology.

The vast quantity of material collected personally by Koshtoyants and his colleagues, together with all that had been discovered by physiologists elsewhere, was knitted together in his fundamental, two-volume textbook, *The Principles of Comparative Physiology*, a book which has been translated into a number of foreign languages.

In the 1930's Koshtoyants' main interest was centred on the origins and evolution of the functions of the nervous system. This interest was responsible for a large number of investigations undertaken to demonstrate the chemical mechanisms in processes of nerve excitation and inhibition and their phylogenetic precursors in pre-nervous stages of evolution. Koshtoyants formulated his enzymo-chemical theory of nerve excitation in 1927. In this theory excitation was regarded as a biochemical process and the effect of the mediator was thought to be the result of its inclusion in the metabolism of the innervated cell, which triggered off a chain of biochemical processes ending in the functional act specific for that particular cell.

Physiologists will readily recall the years when, throughout the entire scientific world, advocates of the chemical interpretation of synaptic transmission could be counted on the fingers of one hand. And even among these Koshtoyants was reckoned to be far to the "left" as, in his understanding of the process, the process of excitation involved not merely surface structures, but the entire metabolic complex of the cell. Today, chemical mediation is a generally accepted fact and there is ever-increasing evidence of the importance of cell metabolism in the production of excitation and inhibition. All the greater, therefore, should be the gratitude with which science remembers the solitary pioneers who, in the early days of the scientific development of this problem, drew attention to the problem itself and directed research along the right lines.

With such an approach, many links in the metabolism of nerve and effector cells were investigated in the laboratories directed by Koshtoyants and their actual relationships to the production of processes of excitation and inhibition were demonstrated. Particular attention was given to acetylcholine and the related biochemical system, to physiologically active amines and to the reactive groups in proteins; Koshtoyants was particularly interested latterly in the significance of the individual metabolites of nucleic acid metabolism. Some of these investigations, which are scattered in many papers, constituted the basis for his monograph *Proteins, Metabolism and Nerve Regulation* (1951). Shortly before his death Koshtoyants had started work on a book dealing with the biochemistry of excitation and inhibition, but he had only managed to write the first, historical chapter.

Koshtoyants' service to Soviet higher education merits special mention. In 1923, while still a University student, Koshtoyants began teaching in the capacity of lecturer and dean of faculty in the Liebknecht Industrial Paedagogic Institute. This was one of the "workers' faculties" specially organized for young workers in the years immediately following the revolution. Koshtoyants' connexion with teaching in Moscow University continued for more than thirty years: he was professor from 1930, and from 1943 he directed the Laboratory of Animal Physiology. His lectures were attended by thousands of students and were deservedly very popular: right up to the end, Koshtoyants' excitement before every lecture was just as great as it would have been had he been delivering the lecture for the first time and, consequently, his lectures were always extremely animated, full of material and quite up-to-date. They were accompanied by a profusion of often quite difficult demonstrations, for which he often called on many of his co-workers. Scores of Koshtoyants' pupils are today doing good work in the field of comparative and evolutionary physiology in the Soviet Union and other countries.

The seminar in comparative physiology held by him at the Biological Station, Tikani (Hungary), and which became a regular event, invariably attracted large numbers of junior scientists from the countries of Eastern Europe.

No matter how many tasks he had on hand, no matter how crowded his laboratories were at the time, there was always a place for young scientists from Armenia. Koshtoyants' great and constant solicitude for Armenian science was one of the manifestations of his filial devotion and gratitude to his native land. No year passed in which he did not visit Armenia. He expended much time and energy on the organization of scientific institutions in the Republic and Armenia thanked and rewarded him in return: not only was he an Academician of the Armenian Academy of Sciences but it was also here in Armenia that he was elected a Deputy of the Supreme Soviet of the U.S.S.R.

Koshtoyants' researches on the history of science, work which he referred to as his form of relaxation, gained wide publicity. His historical research displayed the same profundity and emotional involvement which was characteristic of any work he undertook. It is therefore not surprising that the fruits of this "relaxation" were splendid books on the great Russian physiologists, Sechenov and Pavlov, and a monograph, *Essays on the History of Physiology in Russia*, the latter being awarded a State Prize.

Koshtoyants' research work received wide international recognition and he was regarded as a great and respected author in world science. He was elected an Honorary Doctor of Charles University (Czechoslovakia), an Academician of the Hungarian Academy of Sciences, a Member of the Academy of the History of Science in Paris and member of a number of other foreign institutions.

He attached very great importance to personal friendships and to co-operation between scientists of different countries, being of the opinion that this helped international relationships as well as science. To realize this, one had only to see the attention with which he received foreign visitors in his Moscow laboratories at the University and Svertsov Institute. Being President of the Scientific Section of the Anglo-Russian Society, Koshtoyants did much to popularize British science and was its leading representative in the Soviet Union.

In recent years Koshtoyants was keenly interested in problems of cosmic acclimatization and it gave him great pleasure to share his knowledge with a wide audience in print, radio and television during the days of cosmic conquest. It is sad to think that Koshtoyants died only ten days before the historic moment which he had awaited so eagerly, the moment of man's ascent into outer space.

Physiological science has lost one of its outstanding representatives, one who combined in himself the knowledge of a great scientist, the high principles of the public worker and great personal charm, gentleness and goodwill. His attitude to science attracted everyone by its inexhaustible youthful enthusiasm and his capacity for work evoked amazement and admiration. The features of this enquiring, happy man will never fade from the memory of those who knew him.

T. M. TURPAYEV

LIST OF KH. S. KOSHTOYANTS' MOST IMPORTANT PUBLICATIONS

Effects of regular diets of various kinds on the secretory activity of the gastric glands. *Zh. eksp. med.* **1**, 109–128, 1928. German translation published in *Pflüg. Arch.* **220**, 4–5, 641–652, 1928.

Changes in the vasomotor properties of the blood with change in its reaction *in vitro*. *Zh. eksp. biol. med.* **8**, 21, 471–479, 1928.

History of the development of knowledge of the circulation (on the tercentenary of the publication of Harvey's book). In: *Dialectics in Nature*. A collection of papers on Marxist methodology in natural science. No. 4. pp. 69–105. Moscow 1929.

The humoral mechanism of the external pancreatic secretion. *Zh. eksp. med.* **2**, 1–2, 96–103, 1929. German translation published in *Pflüg. Arch.* **221**, 6, 751–758, 1929.

Contribution to the physiology of the embryo (embryosecretin). *Pflüg. Arch.* **227**, 3, 359–360, 1931.

Physiology and Theory of Development (Some aspects). Medgiz, Moscow 1932.

Charles Darwin (On the 50th anniversary of his death). *Probl. zhivotn.* **4**, 13–21, 1932 (Jointly with I. Ya. Zakis).

Zur Frage der Spezifizität des Sekretins. Vergleichendphysiologische Untersuchung. *Z. f. vgl. Physiol.* **18**, 1, 112–115, 1932 (Jointly with I. Ivanov, P. A. Korzhuyev, V. A. Muzheyev and S. G. Ochakovskaya).

Versuche mit dem überlebenden Pankreas. *Pflüg. Arch.* **229**, 4–5, 594–598, 1932.

On the comparative physiology of muscle tone. 1st Communication. Relationship between tone and tetany in invertebrate smooth muscle. *Biol. zh.* **2**, 6, 503–507, 1933 (Jointly with V. A. Muzheyev).

Physiological aspects of the process of smooth muscle stretching. 2nd Communication. *Biol. zh.* **2**, 6, 508–514, 1933 (Jointly with V. A. Muzheyev).

The stretch curve for the smooth muscle of the operculum of the snail poisoned with mono-iodoacetic acid. 3rd Communication. *Biol. zh.* **2**, 6, 515–518, 1933 (Jointly with V. A. Muzheyev).

On the specificity of secretin. 1st communication. Comparative physiological data. *Fiziol. zh. SSSR* **16**, 216–218, 1933 (Jointly with P. A. Korzhuyev, V. A. Muzheyev and S. G. Ochakovskaya).

Some lines for research on the history of the development of functions. In: *Some Problems of Comparative Physiology*. A collection of papers from the Laboratory of Comparative Animal Physiology, Biological Institute. Medgiz, Moscow and Leningrad 1934.

Physiological characteristics of the smooth muscle of the amphibian intestine at different periods of individual development. *Ibid.* pp. 90–97 (Jointly with V. A. Muzykantov and R. L. Mitropolitanskaya).

Functional and morphological gradients. *Ibid.* pp. 98–101.

Relationship between tone and tetany in invertebrate smooth muscle. *Ibid.* pp. 113–118 (Jointly with with V. A. Muzheyev). (A contribution to the comparative physiology of muscle tone.)

Physiological aspects of the process of stretching in smooth muscle. *Ibid.* pp. 118–125 (Jointly with V. A. Muzheyev).

The stretch curve for smooth muscle of the snail operculum poisoned with mono-iodo-acetic acid. *Ibid.* pp. 125–128 (Jointly with V. A. Muzheyev).

Trypsin of cold- and warm-blooded animals: its temperature optimum and heat-stability. *Ibid.* pp. 132–144 (Jointly with V. A. Muzheyev).

Innervation of the legs of *Phalangium opilio*. *Ibid.* pp. 160–162.

Animal physiology in the early developmental period. 1st Communication. Spontaneous motor activity in the intestine of the human embryo. *Fiziol. zh. SSSR* 17, 6, 1309–1313, 1934 (Jointly with R. L. Mitropolitanskaya).

Comparative physiology: problems and trends. Revised address to an All-Union Congress of Physiologists. June 1934. *Sorena* 8, 5–22, 1934.

Einige Probleme der Entwicklungsgeschichte der Funktionen. Probleme der theoretischen Biologie. INRA 184–242. Moscow and Leningrad 1935.

Lines of research on the evolution of function. *Fiziol. zh. SSSR* 19, 1, 1935 and *Usp. sovr. biol.* 4, 4–5, 185–210, 1935 (Special combined issue for the 15th International Congress of Physiologists, 9–17 August 1935). German translation published in *Fiziol. zh. SSSR* 19, 1, 187–211, 1935.

Physiological development of animals in the period of ontogenesis. 3rd Communication. Development of the gradient of spontaneous motor activity of the intestine in the post-embryonic development of mammals. *Fiziol. zh. SSSR* 19, 3, 682–687, 1935 (Jointly with R. L. Mitropolitanskaya).

On the physiology of mammalian skeletal muscle in different stages of individual development. *Biol. zh.* 4. 2, 237–242, 1935 (Jointly with Ryabinovskaya). German translation published in *Pflüg. Arch.* 235, 4, 416–421, 1935.

Comparative investigation on the importance of the respiratory rate in relation to the state of the central nervous system *Dokl. Akad. Nauk SSSR* 4, 9, 411–415, 1936 (Jointly with T. I. Bekbulatov). English translation published in *Dokl. Akad. Nauk SSSR* 4, 9, 423–427, 1936.

Functional correlations between lungs, gills and skin in amphibians at different stages of metamorphosis. *Byull. eksp. biol. i med.* 1, 3, 202–203, 1936 (Jointly with R. L. Mitropolitanskaya). English translation published in *Byull. eksp. biol. i med.* 1, 3, 207–208, 1936.

Adrenaline-like substances in the bodies of invertebrates (Nerve ganglia of molluscs, tentacles of *Hydra*). *Byull. eksp. biol. i med.* 2, 1, 41–43, 1936. French translation published in *Byull. eksp. biol. i med.* 2, 1, 37–39, 1936.

On the mode of action of acetylcholine as revealed by a new biological indicator and on cholinesterase in invertebrate animals. *Byull. eksp. biol. i med.* 2, 1, 37–40, 1936 (Jointly with R. L. Mitropolitanskaya). French translation published in *Byull. eksp. biol. i med.* 2, 1, 34–36, 1936.

Mode of action of chemical mediators in invertebrates (acetylcholine and potassium). *Byull. eksp. biol. i med.* 2, 3, 185–186, 1936. English translation published in *Byull. eksp. biol. i med.* 2, 3, 177–178, 1936.

The quantity of urea in the blood of ganoid fishes in connexion with problems of piscine evolution. *Byull. eksp. biol. i med.* 2, 3, 187–188, 1936 (Jointly with P. A. Korzhuyev). English translation published in *Byull. eksp. biol. i med.* 2, 3, 179–180, 1936.

The receptor function of the swim bladder of fishes. *Fiziol. zh. SSSR* 20, 2, 281–285, 1936 (Jointly with F. D. Vasilenko).

Evolution of forms of movement co-ordination in animals (Role of the sex organs). *Fiziol. zh. SSSR* 21, 5–6, 1055–1056. 1936 (Papers of the 15th International Physiological Congress, Leningrad and Moscow, 9–17 August 1935). English translation published in *Fiziol. zh. SSSR* 21, 5–6, 595–596, 1936.

The respiratory rate and the phenomena of plastic tone in amphibians and fishes. *Arkh. biol. nauk* **41**, 1, 65–69, 1936. English translation published in *Byull. eksp. biol. i med.* **1**, 1, 29–30, 1936.

Relationship Between the Functions of Autonomic and Somatic Organs in the Light of Their Evolution. USSR Acad. Sci. Press, Moscow and Leningrad 1937, 60 p.

Evolutionary physiology in the U.S.S.R. *Fiziol. zh. SSSR* **23**, 4–5, 523–536, 1937.

Influence of fluctuations in the quantity of water on the physiological properties of smooth muscle of molluscs. *Arkh. biol. nauk* **45**, 3, 113–118, 1937.

Mechanism for the formation of chemical transmitters of nerve excitation. *Dokl. Akad. Nauk SSSR* **19**, 4, 317–320, 1938. English translation published in *Dokl. Akad. Nauk SSSR* **19**, 4, 315–318, 1938.

Trophic influence of the nervous system in animal ontogenesis. *Fiziol. zh. SSSR* **24**, 1–2, 221–227, 1938.

Further investigations on the mode of formation and of destruction of the chemical factors of nerve excitation (Frog experiments) *Dokl. Akad. Nauk SSSR* **23**, 9, 950–952, 1939 (Jointly with R. L. Mitropolitanskaya). English translation published in *Dokl. Akad. Nauk SSSR* **23**, 9, 955–957, 1939.

Attempt at the analysis of symptoms of polyneuritis in B_1 avitaminosis on the basis of a chemical theory of the nerve process. *Dokl. Akad. Nauk SSSR* **24**, 4, 358–360, 1939. English translation published in *Dokl. Akad. Nauk SSSR* **24**, 4, 357–359, 1939.

A feat of daring and fearlessness (On the 360th anniversary of the birth of the English physiologist, W. Harvey). *Nov. mir* **5**, 270–277, 1939.

Eighty years of Charles Darwin's *Origin of Species. Pravda*, 24 November 1939.

Development as a problem in physiology (Some features of the evolution of functions). *Izv. Akad. Nauk SSSR*, ser. biol. **2**, 253–271, 1941.

The presence of growth substances in animal tissues. *Dokl. Akad. Nauk SSSR* **35**, 9, 328–331,1942. English translation published in *Dokl. Akad. Nauk SSSR* **35**, 9, 293–294, 1942.

The chemistry of cell respiration and growth phenomena in the weevils of oats. *Dokl. Akad. Nauk SSSR* **36**, 7, 236–238, 1942. English translation in *Dokl. Akad. Nauk SSSR* **36**, 7, 219–221, 1942.

Darwinism and the modern age. *Vestn. Akad. Nauk SSSR* **4**, 96–99, 1942.

Some new observations on the effects of benzedrine and pervitin on the nervous system. *Dokl. Akad. Nauk SSSR* **39**, 5, 216–218, 1943 (Jointly with R. L. Mitropolitanskaya). English translation published in *Dokl. Akad. Nauk SSSR* **39**, 5, 201–202, 1943.

Some chemical patterns of excitation in plants and animals. *Usp. sovr. biol.* **16**, 6, 617–626, 1943.

Disintegration and disintegrating factors in the process of evolution. *Zool. zh.* **22**, 3, 131–139, 1943.

Development of biological science in Russia. *Nature* **151**, No. 3832, 408–411, 1943.

Analysis of the modes of action of acetylcholine as a chemical factor in nerve excitation. *Dokl. Akad. Nauk SSSR* **43**, 8, 376–379, 1944. English translation published in *Dokl. Akad. Nauk SSSR* **43**, 8, 357–359, 1944.

Sechenov (2nd Edition), USSR Acad. Sci. Press, Moscow and Leningrad, 1945, 200 p.

The connection between chemical changes in the cell and electrical phenomena. *Dokl. Akad. Nauk SSSR* **47**, 6, 465–468, 1945. English translation published in *Dokl. Akad. Nauk SSSR* **47**, 6, 448–451, 1945.

The histamine–histidine decarboxylase–histaminase system in nerve tissue under different conditions. *Dokl. Akad. Nauk SSSR* **49**, 5, 390–394, 1945 (Jointly with D. Ye. Rybkina and R. L. Mitropolitanskaya). English translation published in *Dokl. Akad. Nauk SSSR* **49**, 5, 381–386, 1945.

Essays on the History of Physiology in Russia. USSR Acad. Sci. Press, Moscow and Leningrad 1946, 495 p.

Effect of acetylcholine on rhythmical contractions of skeletal muscle. *Dokl. Akad. Nauk SSSR* **53**, 3, 289–292, 1946 (Jointly with G. D. Smirnov and K. A. Laricheva). English translation published in *Dokl. Akad. Nauk SSSR* **53**, 3, 285–288, 1946.

The role of sulphydryl groups in the action of acetylcholine and of vagus inhibition on cardiac muscle. *Dokl. Akad. Nauk SSSR* **45**, 2, 181–183, 1946 (Jointly with T. M. Turpayev). English translation published in *Nature* **158**, No. 4023, 836–837, 1946.

The possible abolition of reflex inhibition of cardiac activity by action on cardiac metabolism. *Dokl. Akad. Nauk SSSR* **54**, 5, 461–464, 1946 (Jointly with S. S. Mogoras).

Mechanism of potassium action on the contractile act. *Byull. eksp. biol. i med.* **22**, 4, 3–5, 1946 (Jointly with S. A. Bishinkevich).

Nervous stimulation and cell chemistry. *Amer. Rev. Sov. Med.* **4**, 1, 45–53, 1946.

Nerve excitation and chemical processes in the cell. In: *Two Hundred and Twenty Years of the Academy of Sciences of U.S.S.R.* Jubilee Meeting of the U.S.S.R. Academy of Sciences, 15 June–3 July 1945. USSR Acad. Sci. Press, Moscow and Leningrad 1947, p. 419–434.

Comperative Investigations on the Enzymochemical Nature of Nerve Excitation and the Conclusions to be Drawn therefrom. Proceedings of All-Union Congress of Physiologists, Biochemists and Pharmacologists. Medgiz, Moscow 1947, p. 343–347.

Microphysiological investigation on the discharge of calcium ions in the heart on stimulation of sympathetic nerves. *Dokl. Akad. Nauk SSSR* **59**, 1, 199–201, 1948 (Jointly with I. A. Keder-Stepanova and V. A. Shidlovskii).

The enzymatic "permeability factor" in the phenomena of nerve excitation. *Dokl. Akad. Nauk SSSR* **60**, 6, 1105–1107, 1948.

Darwin places in England: impressions. *Nauka i zhizn'* **1**, 30–34, 1948.

Comparative investigations on the enzymochemical nature of nerve excitation and the conclusions to be drawn therefrom. In: *Problem of Soviet Physiology, Biochemistry and Pharmacology.* Proceedings of All-Union Congress of Physiologists, Biochemists and Pharmacologists. Edited by L. A. Orbeli *et al.* USSR Acad. Med. Sci. Press, Moscow 1949, p. 29–35.

Principles of Comparative Physiology. 2nd Ed., USSR Acad. Sci. Press, Moscow and Leningrad 1950, 523 p.

I. M. Sechenov, 1829–1905. Med. Lit. Press, Moscow 1950, 224 p.

Comparative investigations on cholinesterase activity in red cells exhibiting various degrees of resistance to haemolysis. *Dokl. Akad. Nauk SSSR* **71**, 1, 199–200, 1950 (Jointly with N. N. Bulatova).

Age features of cholinesterase activity in red cells. *Dokl. Akad. Nauk SSSR* **71**, 5, 979–980, 1950.

Dependence of the effects of motor and sympathetic nerves on skeletal muscle on the reactive groups in protein. *Dokl. Akad. Nauk SSSR* **72**, 5, 981–984, 1950.

Importance of sulphydryl groups in the "escape" of the heart from the depressing effect of the vagus nerve. *Dokl. Akad. Nauk SSSR* **73**, 2, 429–432, 1950 (Jointly with K. S. Logunova).

Role of the nervous system in the maintenance of the structure of muscle glycogen. *Dokl. Akad. Nauk SSSR* **75**, 6, 881–882, 1950 (Jointly with Z. A. Yanson).

Enzymochemical theory of excitation. *Fiziol. zh. SSSR* **36**, 1, 92–96, 1950.

Proteins, metabolism and nerve regulation. USSR Acad. Sci. Press, Moscow 1951, 100 p. Role of the reactive groups in proteins in nerve regulation. In: *Proceedings of 2nd International Biochemical Congress, Paris,* 1952. USSR Acad. Sci. Press, Moscow 1952, pp. 60–75. French translation published *ibid.* pp. 76–80.

Some new evidence on the reflex regulation of the external secretion of the pancreas with the operation of chemical agents. *Dokl. Akad. Nauk SSSR* **86**, 1, 197–200, 1952 (Jointly with Ts. V. Serbenyuk and Sh. I. Avrushchenko).

A possible biochemical explanation of the depressing and restoring actions of the vagus nerve on cardiac activity. *Dokl. Akad. Nauk SSSR* **88**, 2, 369–372, 1953.

Development of resting potentials in muscles in relation to controlled changes in the structure of their proteins and in their metabolism. *Dokl. Akad. Nauk Arm. SSR* **16**, 4, 123–127, 1953 (Jointly with S. S. Oganesyan).

A possible biochemical explanation for the depressing and restoring effects of the vagus nerve on cardiac activity. *Dokl. Akad. Nauk SSSR* **88**, 2, 369–372, 1953.

Dependence of the biological luminescence of the firefly on the state of the reactive groups in proteins and on metabolism. *Dokl. Akad. Nauk SSSR* **91**, 5, 1229–1232, 1953.

The activity and probable functional importance of hyaluronidase at various stages of ontogenesis in fishes. *Dokl. Akad. Nauk SSSR* **93**, 5, 937–940, 1953 (Jointly with G. A. Buznikov).

Possible abolition of the depressing effect of painful stimulation on pancreatic secretion by antihistamine preparations. *Dokl. Akad. Nauk SSSR* **95**, 2, 421–423, 1954 (Jointly with M. A. Poskonova and Ts. V. Serbenyuk).

Oscillographic examination of the central nervous system of the silkworm at various stages of development. *Zool. zh.* **33**, 4, 807–814, 1954 (Jointly with A. L. Byzov and R. L. Mitropolitanskaya).

The role of tissue sulphydryl groups in the production of spreading depression of electrical activity in the cerebral cortex. *Dokl. Akad. Nauk SSSR* **105**, 5, 1118–1120, 1955 (Jointly with Ya. Buresh).

Possible action of antihistamine preparations on conditioned reflex gastric secretion. *Dokl. Akad. Nauk SSSR* **104**, 5, 335–341, 1955.

On the nature of the periodic activity in sea anemones. *Dokl. Akad. Nauk SSSR* **104**, 662–665, 1955 (Jointly with N. A. Smirnova).

Humoral transmission of the periodic vagus influence on the heart. *Dokl. Akad. Nauk SSSR* **110**, 3, 481–482, 1956 (Jointly with M. A. Poskonova).

On the evolution of nervous system functions (phoronids *Enteropneusta*, ascidians). *Usp. sovr. biol.* **41**, 3, 306–320, 1956.

Principles of Comparative Physiology. Vol. 2. Comparative physiology of the nervous system. USSR Acad. Sci. Press, Moscow 1957, 635 p.

The role of the acetylcholine–cholinesterase system in the phenomena of galvanotaxis and the summation of stimulations in *Paramoecium*. *Biofizika* **2**, 1, 46–50, 1957.

Enzymochemical basis of vagus nerve action on the heart (at the site of potassium). *Fiziol. zh. SSSR* **43**, 7, 681–684. 1957.

Vvedenskii optimum and minimum phenomena in the nerve-muscle apparatus of molluscs. *Fiziol. zh. SSSR* **43**, 12, 1166–1169, 1957 (Jointly with Den Chzhi-chen).

To the memory of a great English physician and physiologist. At the International Congress dedicated to W. Harvey. *Nature* **12**, 71–74, 1957.

Possible role of nucleic acids in the "transmission" of nerve stimulation and in the of acetylcholine. *Dokl. Akad. Nauk SSSR* **120**, 4, 926–928, 1958.

Rhythmical electrical phenomena in unicellular organisms (*Opalia ranarum*). *Biofizika* **3**, 5, 422–425, 1958.

Enzymochemical basis of taste. *Biofizika* **3**, 6, 689–692, 1958 (Jointly with K. Rozh).

On the physiological basis of periodic activity in anodonts. *Zh. obshch. biol.* **19**, 3, 212–216, 1958 (Jointly with Ya. Shalanki).

Biochemical explanations of the abolition of the blocking effect of methylene blue on the effect of vagus nerve action. *Byull. eksp. biol. i med.* **47**, 1, 39–43, 1959 (Jointly with N. Ye. Babskaya).

Feature of the contracture of the byssus retractor muscle of *Mytilus edulis. Fiziol. zh. SSSR 45*, 7, 826–829, 1959 (Jointly with B. A. Tashmukhamedov).

Effects of β-alanine and γ-aminobutyric acid on the periodic electrical activity in nerveless organisms (*Infusoria*). *Dokl. Akad. Nauk SSSR* **127**, 3, 721–723, 1959 (Jointly with N. N. Kokina).

The work of the Cambridge physiologists. *Usp. sovr. biol.* **48**, 1, 11–115, 1959.

Interaction between cerebral and abdominal ganglia of the vine snail in the control of cardiac activity. *Fiziol. zh. SSSR 45*, 10, 1236–1241, 1959 (Jointly with N. A. Smirnova and R. Popkova).

On the origin of nervous system functions. *Zh. obshch. biol.* **20**, 5, 344–350, 1959.

Role of the forebrain in the manifestation of the "shoal group" effect in fishes. *Fiziol. zh. SSSR 46*, 9, 1030–1043, 1960 (Jointly with G. A. Malyukina and S. P. Aleksandryuk).

Ascending effects from the actions of serotonin, noradrenaline, tyramine and tryptophan on the hypopharyngeal ganglion in the snail. *Fiziol. zh. SSSR 47*, 2, 266–271, 1961 (Jointly with K. Rozh).

Nucleic acids and the conduction of rhythmical excitation in the heart. *Dokl. Akad. Nauk SSSR* **138**, 733–735, 1961.

Oecologico-physiological features of osmoregulation in the vine snail. *Zh. obshch. biol.* **22**, 4, 311–314, 1961 (Jointly with K. Rozh).

Relationship between spontaneous and reflex activity. *Zh. obshch. biol.* **22**, 5, 364–371, 1961.

Some facts and conclusions of comparative physiology in connexion with the problem of homeostasis. *Izv. Akad. Nauk SSSR*, ser. biol. 3, 377–385, 1961.

The possible role of 5-hydroxytryptamine in the motor activity of embryos of some marine gastropods. *Comp. Biochem. Physiol.* **3**, 20–26, 1961 (Jointly with G. A. Buznikov and B. N. Manukhin).

The effect of β-alanine and γ-aminobutyric acid on bioelectrical activity in *Infusoria*. In: *Inhibition in the Nervous System and γ-aminobutyric Acid*. Ed. E. Roberts. Pergamon Press, 1960, p. 128–132.

The effects of anticholinesterase substances and of acetylcholine on rhythmical electrical activity in *Infusoria* (*Opalina ranarum*). *Zh. obshch. biol.* **23**, 1, 74–76, 1962.

ON THE ORDER OF THE ONTOGENETIC DEVELOPMENT OF NERVE MECHANISMS CONTROLLING GASTRO-INTESTINAL ACTIVITY

Some Material on the Mechanism Responsible for the Development of Inhibitory Influences in Early Development

I. A. ARSHAVSKII

Institute of Normal and Pathological Physiology,
U.S.S.R. Academy of Medical Sciences, Moscow

Translated by Dr. R. Crawford

As ONE of the founders of comparative physiology in this country, Koshtoyants gave much attention to the physiology of ontogenetic development in connexion with the wider problems involved in the study of the evolution of functions. The fact that a number of physiologists in this country have engaged in systematic research on the evolution of functions in the course of both phylogenetic and ontogenetic development is due in no small measure to Koshtoyants' constant insistence on the importance of the concepts of evolutionary biology for physiological investigations.

This paper describes some experimental material obtained in our laboratory which is similar in content to the quite independent investigations carried out in Koshtoyants' laboratories. I refer to mechanisms responsible for the development of stimulating, but more particularly inhibitory, nerve influences on the motor function of the gastro-intestinal tract in the course of early development. First of all, however, the mechanisms concerned in the ontogenetic development of inhibitory influences on the activity of skeletal muscle and on cardiac activity are described briefly.

We have stated elsewhere that the features of the phenomenon of the true pessimum discovered by us in the nerve-muscle apparatus of adult warm-blooded animals are sudden transition from optimum to pessimum frequency, the development of electropositivity in the muscle, enhanced excitability and increase in the muscle's energy reserves (Arshavskii, 1956; Arshavskii and Kondrasheva, 1959). Despite the low degree of lability in the nerve-muscle apparatus in the early stages of ontogenetic development,

1

the phenomenon of the true pessimum is not observed in the early age periods. We directed our attention to the fact that the absence of a true pessimum in very young animals was associated with the absence of an exaltation phase in their nerve-muscle apparatus. The development of a true pessimum at a certain stage in ontogenetic development depends on the functional and, it would appear, structural maturation of the myoneural junction, the specific expression of this maturation being the development of an exaltation phase (Arshavskii and Rozanova, 1939; Rozanova, 1938, 1941). We linked the absence of an exaltation phase, as also the absence of a true pessimum in the very early period of development, with absence of or still inadequate structural maturation of the myoneural junction in the very early stages. Investigations by foreign and Soviet morphologists have established that complete maturation of the myoneural junction in the skeletal muscles of animals and man only occurs during postnatal development (Straus and Weddel, 1940; Whiting, 1955; Babak, 1855; Mavrinskaya, 1955; Semenova, 1955).

What then is achieved by the gradual structural maturation of the myoneural junction? The results of our investigations established that the production of a retarding effect on activity, the production of what is generally termed inhibition, requires the presence of special mechanisms, both structural and physiological. The structural mechanism, we suggest, is the presence of an intermediate link (the myoneural junction) with low lability characteristics. The physiological mechanism is the formation in this link of stationary excitation with signs of negativity, as a result of which positivity, with which is combined the accumulation of energy potentials, is created on the side of the myoneural junction in the muscle tissue itself, in the nature of conjugate perielectrotonic contrast.

This mechanism would explain the transformation which the tissues of skeletal muscle undergo in the course of ontogenetic development. We have already stated that skeletal muscle is characterized in the early stages by signs which are typical of the catelectrotonic syndrome. As the structural and functional maturation of the intermediate link (myoneural junction) advances during ontogenesis, the skeletal muscle tissue acquires characteristics which are typical of the anelectrotonic syndrome (Arshavskii, 1958; Rozanova, 1938). Increase of polarization properties would explain the significant increase in the lability of skeletal muscle potentials in the course of ontogenetic development. Skeletal muscle in the early stages of postnatal development is characterized by prolonged continuous tonic type activity. This is seen more particularly in the continuous electromyographic activity which is also recorded at times when the very young organism is in a state of so-called rest. It is as if, in the early age period, skeletal musculature functions at its "ceiling"—at the limit of its powers. This too is understandable when we consider the great energy expenditure per unit weight which is typical of the very young organism. The acquisition by skeletal muscle of electropositive, i.e. anelectrotonic, properties explains how the energy expenditure per unit weight can be reduced as, in the course of growth, the linear dimensions of the animal increase and its surface ratio is thereby relatively reduced. During ontogenetic development, therefore, skeletal musculature is first of all under continuous stimulation from the centres supplying it. It is only much later (during postnatal development) that a mechanism for inhibition of the activity of skeletal muscles develops in connexion with the structural and functional maturation of the myoneural junction. Mechanisms providing for stimulation of skeletal muscle activity appear first in the course of ontogenesis and the development of mechanisms for inhibition of its activity occurs much later.

We have established that afferent proprioceptive impulsation from the skeletal musculature, increasing in the course of ontogenetic development, leads to change in the lability of the respiratory centre as a result of which there is a gradual decrease in the natural rate of respiration as the animal grows (Arshavskii, 1959a, 1959b, 1960; Yenikeyeva, 1955). As the natural respiratory rate falls during postnatal development, there is also gradual decline in the partial pressure of oxygen in the pulmonary alveoli and, consequently in the blood plasma. When the partial pressure of oxygen reaches the level at which excitation develops in the chemoreceptors of the carotid sinus and cardio-aortic zones, the afferent impulsation from these zones determines the reflex development of constant tonic excitation in the centre for the parasympathetic innervation of the heart (Arshavskii, 1959b; Yenikeyeva, 1955). In very young animals the periods of cardiac activity are controlled by tonic influences from the centre for the sympathetic nerve supply. Thus, in respect of the heart also, of the two innervation mechanisms controlling its activity in the adult animal, it is the mechanisms which stimulate its activity which develop first in the course of ontogenesis and only much later is there development of the mechanisms inhibiting its activity. During vagal inhibition electronegativity develops in the heart in the region of the sino-auricular node. It can be postulated that there is at the same time development of negativity in the atypical tissue of the bundle of His, starting from the atrioventricular node. Electropositivity of the nature of conjugate perielectrotonic contrast develops in the actual tissue of the ventricular myocardium. Retardation of cardiac activity is thus effected through a mechanism which is exactly the same as that described above for the skeletal musculature. Vagal inhibition in the heart is merely a particular expression of true pessimum as established by us for skeletal musculature (Arshavskii, 1926, 1956a, 1956b).

Rubner's well-known law concerning energy and surface area might lead one to think that the development of constant tonic excitation in the centre for the parasympathetic supply of the heart only in the period of postnatal development represents a form of adaptation to the increasing size of the body, to the changing relationship between the body's surface area and mass. The results of our investigations enable it to be stated that the change and transformation of respiratory and cardiovascular activity in the postnatal period are determined not so much by change in the surface area of the body, associated with growth, as with change and transformation of the lability of skeletal musculature, that is on the particular features which characterize changes in the activity of the skeletal musculature in the course of the individual development of different animals.

Furthermore, it is important that consideration should be given to the following point. Not only does division of the vagus nerves or atropinization in young puppies fail to cause increase in the heart rate as in fully grown animals but, on the contrary, slowing of the heart by 20–40 beats per min can be observed in most experiments. In the early stages, therefore, when impulse influences from the vagus centre are still absent, the electrotonic type of influence from the vagus nerve does not inhibit but actually reinforces the stimulating effect which is produced by the centres for the sympathetic nerve supply in young animals.

This principle was also demonstrated by us in respect of the order in which nerve influences regulating the activity of the smooth muscle in the gastro-intestinal tract developed. In early postnatal development the smooth musculature of the stomach is controlled solely by stimulating influences through the parasympathetic nerve supply (Morachevskaya, 1941), as shown by increase in the degree of tonic contraction which can be observed even in the dog foetus (in the last third of intra-uterine development). The experiments were carried out on dog foetuses connected with the mother through the umbilical cord. This fact is of particular interest when it is compared with the results obtained with rabbits. Experiments on rabbits, carried out jointly with P. S. Kravitskaya, revealed that the walls of the stomach did not react to stimulation of the peripheral segment of a vagus nerve during the first (14–15) days of life. There was no reaction on stimulation with moderate or even with very strong induction current (Fig. 1a). The walls of the stomach only begin to react by increase in the degree of tonic contraction at the age of 15 or 16 days, and then only to very intense stimulation of the peripheral segment of the vagus nerve (Fig. 1b). The threshold for vagus nerve stimulation declines progressively as the rabbit grows older. The stimulating effect of the vagus nerve on the smooth muscle in the walls of the stomach was first demonstrated by Sokolov (1888). He also demonstrated how the parasympathetic stimulating effects developed before sympathetic inhibitory effects on gastric activity. Morachevskaya's investigations carried out in our laboratory have shown that splanchnic nerve stimulation has no effect on the motor activity of the stomach in puppies up to the age of 16–18 days. It took the form of a stimulating effect on the motor activity of the stomach from the time that the sympathetic nerve supply began to exert its effect, namely in the age period from 16–18 days to 1–1·5 months (the period during which feeding by mother's milk was still continuing). Replacement of the stimulation by the inhibitory effect of splanchnic nerve stimulation, typical of the fully grown animal, was only observed at the age of 1·5 months, that is after the puppies ceased to be fed by the mother. The inhibitory influences from the splanchnic nerve on the motor activity of the stomach became more and more pronounced as development proceeded.

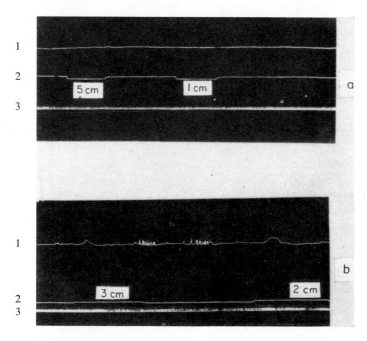

FIG. 1. Effect of vagus nerve stimulation on gastric contraction.

1—gastric contractions. 2—commencement and duration of the stimulation of the peripheral segment of the vagus nerve (the distances between the coils of the induction apparatus are shown). 3—time (sec). a—in a young rabbit aged 10 days. b—in a young rabbit aged 16 days.

Investigations carried out by Belen'kaya (1958) in Orbeli's laboratory have shown that adrenaline also has a stimulating effect, which is particularly pronounced in young rats, in the early stages of ontogenesis, and not the inhibitory effect on the motor activity of the stomach typical of fully grown animals.

What is the physiological significance of the development of inhibitory effects from the sympathetic nerve in puppies when feeding with mother's milk ceases?

Like change in respiratory and cardiovascular activity during postnatal development, the change in the activity of the gastro-intestinal tract with age should also be regarded as a consequence of the law linking energy and surface area (Helmreich, 1931). The quantitative food requirement depends on the intensity of metabolism and changes as a quadratic function in the course of postnatal development. At the same time the capacity of the gastro-intestinal cavity, like the body mass, changes as a cubic function in the course of postnatal ontogenesis. The younger the animal, the smaller is the capacity, particularly of the stomach, per unit of body surface. This would naturally explain why the young animal has to ingest food more frequently than the adult.

Shtamler's investigations (1948) in this laboratory have shown that the walls of the stomach in young puppies (up to the age of 15–16 days) are in a state of elastic tone and are still incapable of responding by reflex relaxation when the quantity of food ingested is increased. When the quantity of milk ingested exceeds the capacity of the stomach, any excess is removed by regurgitation. The gastro-intestinal component of the vomiting reflex cannot yet be produced in young puppies (Shtamler, 1948). The tone of the stomach wall gradually begins to exhibit plastic properties at the age of 16–18 days, and the stomach acquires the power to adapt its capacity to the quantity of food ingested at about the age of 1·5 months, at which time the puppy begins gradually to change to the form of food typical of fully grown dogs. The development of inhibitory sympathetic influences thus makes reflex relaxation of the stomach walls possible and food can, therefore, be ingested less frequently. Young puppies are fed with the mother's milk every two or three hours. Consideration of the law relating to energy and surface area together with the fact that the body of the young rabbit is much smaller than that of the newborn puppy would lead us to expect that feeding of the young rabbit with the mother's milk would be more frequent. This statement should still be valid even when account is taken of the higher calorific value of rabbit milk as compared with that of the dog. It has been established, however, that the rabbit feeds its young once or twice a day and the hare feeds its young once in two or three days. It has also been demonstrated that the stomach of the young rabbit can hold considerably more milk than the puppy stomach, despite the considerable difference in the sizes of their bodies. We have, as a result of special investigations, arrived at the conclusion that the properties of the stomach walls in young rabbits can provisionally be described as those of a state of "passive" plastic tone, not controlled by the nervous system. We describe the state in these terms to distinguish it from the "active" plastic tone of the stomach walls in puppies, which is controlled through the sympathetic nervous system. The above explains what an enormous influence the particular oecological conditions attaching to the life of the two different types of mammals have on the features of digestive system functioning.

We have already had occasion to draw attention to the importance which these findings of ours may have for paediatrics. In that when the sympathetic nerve supply begins to function in the stomach, it exhibits a stimulating influence, it is natural to assume that premature functioning of the sympathetic innervation, particularly if it delays the development of inhibitory influences from the sympathetic nervous system, may he responsible for the development of the phenomena described in the pathology of the breast-fed period as pylorospasm. This conclusion, reached by us as a result of our experimental findings, is in agreement with the view of Usener (1936), who suggested that the phenomena of pylorospasm developed as a result of increased reflex excitability of the autonomic nervous system and, more particularly, incomplete development of inhibiting mechanisms. We are of the opinion that the chronic tympanites which developed in the albino grey Astrakhan sheep examined by Mitropolitanskaya (1955) in Koshtoyants' laboratory was due to premature development of stimulating influences and delayed or even completely absent inhibiting effects from the sympathetic nervous system.

Investigations in our laboratory (Morachevskaya, 1941) have established that, in relation to the intestine, just as in the case of the stomach, of the two innervation mechanisms controlling its motor activity, parasympathetic influences come into operation first and sympathetic influences later in the course of ontogenetic development. When the vagus nerve was stimulated in puppies up to the age of 20 days, stimulating effects could be demonstrated in the upper third of the duodenum only. The splanchnic nerve produced no effects of any kind at this age. Stimulating effects on the motor activity of the intestine from vagus nerve stimulation were first observed at the age of 20 days, and these became particularly marked from the age of 25 days. The influence of the sympathetic nervous system, in the form of stimulation of intestinal motor activity, was first seen at the age of about 40 days. At about two months the stimulating was replaced by an inhibitory effect typical of the adult animal. As a regulator of motor activity, the vagus nerve began to exert its effect on the intestine much later in the course of ontogenetic development than on the stomach. It is of interest to compare these findings with observations on the sequence seen in the expansion of parasympathetic influences on the motor activities of the stomach and intestine in the course of phylogenesis. The following results were obtained in our original investigations (Arshavskii, 1926, 1928, 1932) on the influence of the different types of innervation on the motor activity of the intestine in the frog and lizard. In the frog the vagus nerve still had no stimulating effect whatever on the motor activity of the intestine when this effect was well marked in the stomach. In the lizard the parasympathetic influences extended to the duodenum.

We also established (in experiments carried out jointly with E. V. Morachevskaya) that stimulating influences from the *n. erigens* were the first to appear in the course of the ontogenetic development of control of the motor activity of the large intestine in the dog, these effects being noted even in the first few hours of the puppy's life, and that influences from the sympathetic nervous system could only be demonstrated later. The initial effect of hypogastric nerve stimulation, seen about the age of 16 days, was to stimulate tone. The effect of stimulation of the peripheral segment of the hypogastric nerve was already becoming inhibitory from the age of 24 or 25 days.

A point of interest is that, in experiments carried out by Plisetskaya (1958) in Orbeli's laboratory, adrenaline was found to have a depressing effect on the musculature of the hind gut in fully grown frogs, whereas both inhibitory and stimulating effects were observed in young frogs during the first few months of life after metamorphosis.

By what mechanism does the sympathetic nerve produce its inhibitory effects on the motor activity of stomach and intestine? Has this mechanism any analogy with the mechanisms responsible for inhibition in skeletal muscles and the production of vagus inhibition in the heart? The first point that strikes one is that inhibitory effects from the corresponding nerves develop much later than stimulating effects during ontogenetic development in all cases. We carried out some special experiments on fully grown dogs in which we measured the resting potentials of the duodenum and the upper part of the jejunum and also the changes produced in these potentials by stimulation of vagus and splanchnic nerves. Cotton wicks from non-polarizing electrodes were attached by means of blood clots, one to the intact surface of the intestine and the other in an incision made for the purpose into the longitudinal smooth muscle layer. The interelectrode distance ranged from 2 to 5 cm. It was found that there was a negative potential when the vagus was stimulated and a positive potential on splanchnic nerve stimulation. Sympathetic inhibition of the motor activity of the intestine was thus characterized by the development of electropositivity, just as in the case of skeletal muscles and vagus inhibition in the heart (in all cases in the effector itself). Is the development of electropositivity in the intestine (and apparently in the stomach also) a consequence of the development of electronegativity in the intermediate link on analogy with what occurs in skeletal muscle and in the heart? What should be regarded as the intermediate link in the intestine? In the case of the heart this is the atypical tissue in the sino-auricular and atrioventricular nodes. The extracardial nerves exert their stimulating and inhibiting influences primarily through the atypical tissue of the nodes. A possible suggestion is that cells of Dogiel's first type may function as the corresponding intermediate link in relation to sympathetic inhibitory influences. It could then be assumed that both the axons of preganglionic vagus neurons and the axons of postganglionic sympathetic neurons produce their effects on the intestine through these first type cells. Lavrent'yev (1946), who examined possible morphological mechanisms for the antagonistic effects of the parasympathetic and sympathetic innervations on the intestine, denies this. He considers that the axons of the first type cells and the axons of postganglionic neurons run parallel but are independent of one another and end in the terminal plexuses in the smooth muscle of the intestine. Do these terminal plexuses function as the corresponding intermediate link? This completely new suggestion will require special analysis.

What changes occur in the smooth muscle of the intestine in connexion with the order in which nerve effects develop, as just described? Let us dwell briefly on the characteristics of lability as revealed by examination of natural rhythm and the limits of stimulated acceleration of the rhythm (Morachevskaya, 1941) and also the characteristic of elastic and plastic tone.

In the dog foetus (last third of pregnancy) the natural rate of spontaneous contractions in a segment of duodenum lay between 5 and 9 min, and the

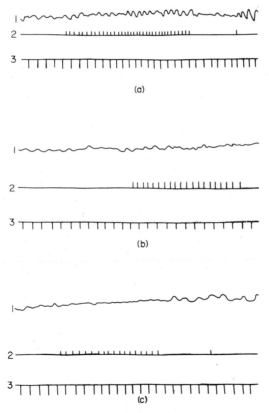

FIG. 2. Recording of the natural rate of spontaneous contractions and of the limits of stimulated acceleration.

1—contraction of the stomach. 2—rate of stimulations administered (per min) from a galvanic circuit through a rheostat. 3—time (9 sec). a—duodenum. b—jejunum. c—ileum (dog foetus).

maximum rate was from 9 to 12 min. For the segment of jejunum the natural rate ranged between 4 and 8 min, and the maximum rate from 6 to 9 min. In the ileum the natural rate was 4–7 min, and the maximum 5–8 min (Fig. 2). The lability of the intestine was thus quite low in the antenatal period when the extrinsic nerves were still without effect. There were still no spontaneous contractions in any part of the intestine in very young dog foetuses weighing 20–30 g. Koshtoyants and Mitropolitanskaya (1934) established that spontaneous movement of the intestine in man developed first in the 7th week of antenatal development, when the nerve elements of Auerbach's plexus are just beginning to appear in the intestine. Janase (1907) established that spontaneous contractions developed in the intestine of the guinea pig foetus in the 3rd or 4th week of antenatal development, and this too coincided with the first appearance of nerve elements in the intramural plexus.

The figures given above show that any gradient in spontaneous activity is hardly noticeable or, at any rate, very slight in the antenatal period (of dog foetuses). The lability of the intestine also continues to be low in the early stages of the postnatal period, up to the 20th day of life. Change in the lability of the intestine to a new and higher level was observed in puppies after the age of 20 days, when the vagus nerve first began to have a stimulating effect on intestinal motor activity. A further change in the lability of intestinal activity to a still higher level occurred at about the age of 1·5 months, when feeding of the puppy by the mother ceased entirely. The increase of lability seen in the intestine at the age of 20 days involved the duodenum and jejunum mainly. It took the form of increase in the natural rate of spontaneous contractions, raising of the limits for stimulated acceleration and, more particularly, increase in the amplitude of the individual contractions. The lability of the ileum was at this time only slightly increased, the main change here being increase in the amplitude of the individual contractions (Fig. 3).

An important point here is that predominance of the natural rate of spontaneous contractions is limited to the parts of the upper intestine in which, according to Lavrent'yev (1946), are situated the Dogiel type I cells with which the preganglionic fibres of the vagus nerve form synapses. We know that type I cells are present in smaller numbers in the lower part of the jejunum and that there are none in the ileum. This explains why there is only slight change in lability in the ileum when the lability in the upper part of the intestine undergoes considerable increase with the commencement of parasympathetic effects. What is known as the gradient of spontaneous activity in the intestine, the theory for which was suggested by Alvarez (1929), is, according to our findings, the result of differences in lability which are determined by the prominence of subordinating influences from the vagus which differ throughout the length of the intestine. These differences develop first in very feeble form during the antenatal period and their appearance coincides in time with the development of the cells of Dogiel's first type in the intramural nerve apparatus. These differences become still more pronounced with the development of extramural effects from the vagus.

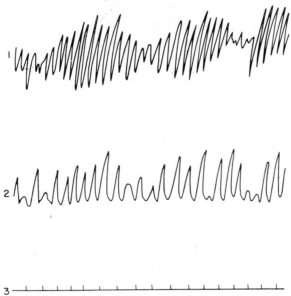

FIG. 3. Recording of the natural rate of spontaneous contractions in the duodenum (1) and at the junction of jejunum and ileum (2). 3—time (9 sec). In a 3-month old puppy (contractions recorded *in situ* by the balloon method).

On the results of comparative physiological and ontogenetic investigations Koshtoyants (1950) put forward his theory of the gradient of spontaneous activity in the intestine. In contrast to Alvarez, Koshtoyants considered that the gradient of spontaneous activity was not linear along the length of the intestine, but much more complex and repeatedly alternating. A special series of investigations was carried out to examine a phenomenon described for the intestine of fully grown dogs by Rozhanskii (1924). This was the power of the intestine to undergo shortening to the extent of 50 per cent of its original length when subjected to progressive mechanical palpatory stimulation from the pylorus to the ileocaecal valve. Our observations demonstrated that this phenomenon is absent in the antenatal period and also in the postnatal period in puppies up to the age of 20–25 days.

The features of the curve for the elastic stretch of the longitudinal muscles of the intestine, which was also described for fully grown dogs by Rozhanskii, were examined in another series of investigations. When an isolated segment of intestine from a fully grown dog was subjected to stretching by increasing weights, it was observed that at first the intestine responded by maximum increase in length even to a quite small load. This part of the intestinal reaction Rozhanskii linked with the properties of plastic tone. Subjected to further deformation by still larger loads, the intestine still responded as an elastic body. The extent of stretching was seen to be directly proportional to the load. The intestine of dog foetuses and puppies up to the age of 20–25 days was incapable of responding by active relaxation of its length with any load, which meant that the properties of plastic tone typical of the adult dog intestine were absent. The intestine of dogs aged up to 20–25 days had the properties of an elastic body (Figs. 4 and 5). The plastic properties of the intestine become particularly marked when sympathetic in-

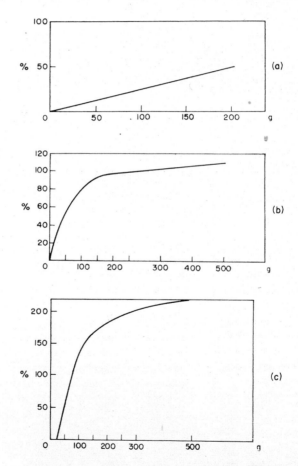

FIG. 4. Curves for the elastic stretching of the longitudinal muscles
(upper part—duodenum and part of jejunum).

a—puppy aged 3 days. b—puppy aged 30 days. c—fully grown dog. Abscissa: load
in grammes. Ordinate: percentage change in length.

hibitory influences are firmly established. The fact that the intestine in puppies up to the age of 20–25 days is incapable of undergoing shortening explains our observations that pendulum-type movements could not be produced in very young animals. This was noted by us in special X-ray investigations.

The changes in the functional state of the intestine which arise in connexion with the commencement of parasympathetic and, later, of sympathetic control of its activity thus find expression both in progressive change in lability and change in the elastic and plastic properties of the intestine. These changes take place in the corresponding transitional periods, namely at the 20th day, when the puppy's milk teeth appear and it becomes able to take mixed food, and at about the age of 1·5 months when the feeding of the puppy with mother's milk ceases entirely.

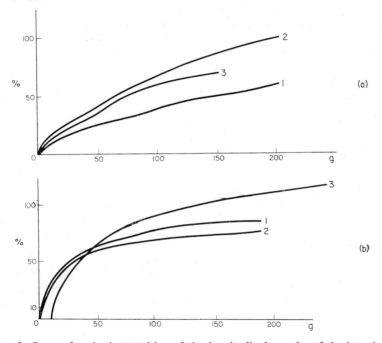

FIG. 5. Curves for elastic stretching of the longitudinal muscles of the intestine.

a—puppy aged 15 days. b—puppy aged 22 days. 1—segment from duodenum. 2—segment from jejunum. 3—segment from ileum. Remaining notation as in Fig. 4.

REFERENCES

ALVAREZ, W. C., *An Introduction to Gastro-enterology. The Mechanics of the Digestive Tract.* 2nd Ed., New York 1929.

ARSHAVSKII, I. A., Russian Physiol. J. (*Russk. fiziol. zh.*) **9**, 3–4, 453 (1926).

ARSHAVSKII, I. A., Russian Physiol. J. (*Russk. fiziol. zh.*) **11**, 1–2, 163 (1928).

ARSHAVSKII, I. A., Scientific paper of Kazan University (*Uchenyye zapiski Kazansk. gos. un-ta*) **92**, 1, 152 (1932).

ARSHAVSKII, I. A., Scientific papers of Leningrad University: biological sciences series (*Uchenyye zapiski LGU*: *seriya biol. nauk*) 22, 118 (1950).
ARSHAVSKII, I. A., Recent Advances in Biology (*Uspekhi sovrem. biol.*) 2, 193 (1956a).
ARSHAVSKII, I. A., Gagri Talks (*Gagrskiye besedy*) 2, 267 (1956b).
ARSHAVSKII, I. A., Bulletin of the U.S.S.R. Academy of Sciences, biological series (*Izv. Akad. Nauk SSSR, seriya biol.*) 1, 71 (1958).
ARSHAVSKII, I. A., *Papers of the 3rd Scientific Conference on Age Morphology and Physiology* (Trudy 3-i nauchnoi konf. po vozrastnoi morfologii i fiziologii) 212 (1959a).
ARSHAVSKII, I. A., Zoological J. (*Zool. zh.*) 38, 10, 1456 (1959b).
ARSHAVSKII, I. A., Papers of the Inst. Animal Morphology (*Trudy IMZh im. A. N. Severtsova*) 31, 35 (1960).
ARSHAVSKII, I. A. and M. N. KONDRASHOVA, Physiol. J. U.S.S.R. (*Fiziol. zh. SSSR*) 45, 2, (1959).
ARSHAVSKII, I. A. and V. D. ROZANOVA, Physiol. J. U.S.S.R. (*Fiziol. zh. SSSR*) 26, 6, 629 (1939).
BABAK, O. M., *Papers of the 2nd Conference on Age Morphology and Physiology* (Trudy 2-i nauchnoi konf. po vozrastnoi morfologii i fiziologii) 167 (1955).
BELEN'KAYA, S. E., Papers on Evolutionary Physiology (*Materialy po evolyutsionnoi fiziologii*) 3, 3 (1958).
HELMREICH, E., *Physiologie des Kindes*, Berlin (1931).
JANASE, J., *Pflüg. Arch. ges. Physiol.* 13, 117, 345 (1907).
KOSHTOYANTS, KH. S., *Principles of Comparative Physiology* (Osnovy sravnitel'noi fiziologii), Moscow (1950).
KOSHTOYANTS, KH. S. and R. L. MITROPOLITANSKAYA, Physiol. J. U.S.S.R. (*Fiziol. zh. SSSR*) 17, 6, 1309 (1934).
KOSHTOYANTS, KH. S. and R. L. MITROPOLITANSKAYA, Physiol. J. U.S.S.R. (*Fiziol. zh. SSSR*) 19, 3, 682 (1935).
LAVRENT'YEV, B. I., *Morphology of the Autonomic Nervous System*. (Morfologiya avtonomnoi nervnoi sistemy) Medgiz 1946.
MAVRINSKAYA, L. F., *Proceedings of Leningrad Congress of Embryologists* (Soveshchaniye embriologov v Leningrade. Tez. dokl.) 54 (1955).
MITROPOLITANSKAYA, R. L., *Proceedings of 8th All-Union Congress of Physiologists, Biochemists and Pharmacologists* (VIII Vses. s"ezd fiziol., biokhim. i farmakol.) 420 (1955).
MORACHEVSKAYA, YE. V., Physiol. J. U.S.S.R. (*Fiziol. zh. SSSR*) 30, 6, 681, 687 (1941).
MORACHEVSKAYA, YE. V., Physiol. J. U.S.S.R. (*Fiziol. zh. SSSR*) 39, 4, 437 (1953).
PLISETSKAYA, E. M., *Papers on Evolutionary Physiology* (Materialy po evolyutsionnoi fiziologii) 199. Izdat. Akad. Nauk SSSR. 1958.
ROZHANSKII, N. A., Scientific papers of the Physiological Laboratory, Don University, Rostov-on-Don (Trudy fiziol. labor. Donskogo un-ta, Rostov n/D) 1924.
ROZANOVA, V. D., Physiol. J. U.S.S.R. (*Fiziol. zh. SSSR*) 25, 4, 391, 403 (1938).
ROZANOVA, V. D., Physiol. J. U.S.S.R. (*Fiziol. zh. SSSR*) 30, 3, 346 (1941).
ROZANOVA, V. D., *Papers of the 2nd Scientific Conference on Age Morphology and Physiology* (Trudy 2-i nauchnoi konf. po vozrastnoi morfologii i fiziologii) 212 (1955).
SEMENOVA, L. K., *Papers of 2nd Scientific Conference on Age Morphology and Physiology* (Trudy 2-i nauchnoi konf. po vozrastnoi morfologii i fiziologii) 183 (1955).
SHTAMLER, S. M., Physiol. J. U.S.S.R. (*Fiziol. zh. SSSR*) 34, 5, 627 (1948).
SOKOLOV, D. M., Weekly Clinical Gazette (*Yezhened. klinich. gazeta*) 29, 611, 1888; *Ibid.* 30–31, 644 (1888).
STRAUSS, W. L. and G. WEDDEL, *J. Neurophysiol.* 3, 358 (1940).
USENER, M., *Zbl. Kinderheilk.* 41 (1936).
WHITING, H. P., Symp. *Biochemistry of the Nervous System* 85, New York 1955.
YENIKEYEVA, S. I., *Papers of 2nd Scientific Conference on Age Morphology and Physiology* (Trudy 2-i nauchnoi konf. po vozrastnoi morfologii i fiziologii) 219 (1959).

THE CHOLINOLYTIC PROPERTIES
OF BEE VENOM AND ITS BLOCKING
EFFECT ON GANGLIA

N. M. Artemov, T. I. Poberezhskaya and L. I. Sergeyeva

Department of Human and Animal Physiology, State University, Gor'kii

Translated by Dr. R. Crawford

Bee venom has long attracted the attention of biologists and doctors, mainly because it is used in medicine for the treatment of a number of serious illnesses. Elucidation of the theory of its physiological and therapeutic effect has, however, lagged behind its successful application in practice, and this is of course a serious obstacle to the rational and effective employment of bee venom in medicine and veterinary science.

We have attempted to fill this gap and to accumulate the experimental material, so necessary for the elaboration of a theory explaining the therapeutic effect of bee venom, in our researches on the physiological action of bee venom, begun in Koshtoyants' laboratory (Artemov and Solov'yeva, 1939; Artemov, 1941) in liaison with M. B. Krol's clinic and continued in the Department of Human and Animal Physiology, Gor'kii State University. We were guided in the accumulation of experimental evidence and in the theoretical interpretation of this evidence by general biological evolutionary principles, the importance of which in physiology was constantly stressed by Koshtoyants.

We are of the opinion that a correct understanding of the properties of bee venom and of the nature of the reaction of the mammalian and human body to it can only be arrived at if consideration is given to the historical relationship between bees and mammals, the evolutionary development of which has proceeded in close contact. In the course of the bee's evolution its venom has been perfected as a means of defence against mammals, specifically the main enemies of bees and capable of destroying not only individual working bees but also bee families as a whole. This is indicated by the adaptational features of the stinging apparatus of bees (Rietschel, 1937), by many of the instincts of bees and by the physiological properties of their venom (Artemov, 1949, 1958). There have, however, been many adaptational changes in the mammalian organism as well as the perfecting of bee venom in the course of the evolutionary

15

interaction between bees and mammals. Animals, the ordinary food of which includes bees and other poison-producing hymenoptera, have acquired quite high resistances to the venom effect and for most mammals bee venom has become a special irritant leading to the development of a number of non-specific defensive reactions (Artemov, 1958).

It was, therefore, of the greatest importance to examine the neurotoxic effect of bee venom. The power of bee venom to affect the nervous systems of various animals has been inherited by bees from wasp-like ancestors which paralyse other arthropods and their larvae by injecting their venom into the ganglia of the abdominal nerve chain. Koshtoyants (1943) regarded the state of affected arthropods as one of disintegration. We have observed the neurotoxic effect of venom, which is associated with characteristic paralyses, in a great variety of animals (annelids, molluscs, insects, amphibians, reptiles, birds, mammals) subjected to bee stings (Artemov, 1949). The venom effect was characterized by gradual development of paralysis of nerve centres and disappearance of all reflex reactions in most of the species studied. In vertebrates death from poisoning with bee venom is due to paralysis of the respiratory centre. In mammals and birds, and to some extent also in reptiles, the paralysis is preceded by a period of excitation in the form of clonic and tonic muscle spasms.

Further analysis has shown that the basis of the bee venom effect on the nervous system is its cholinolytic action. We were able to demonstrate this for the first time in experiments on the frog heart (Artemov and Solov'-yeva, 1939). It was shown that, even in relatively high dilution, bee venom abolished the acetylcholine and vagus nerve effects on the heart. This was later confirmed by experiments with natural bee venom (Artemov, 1951).

Unlike that of the cobra, bee venom has no cholinesterase activity and has no effect on the reaction between acetylcholine and cholinesterase *in vitro* (Artemov and Turilova, 1951).

All this indicates that bee venom has an atropine-like action and blocks M-cholinergic systems. It was later shown that bee venom abolished the effect of acetylcholine on the rectus muscle of the frog abdomen (Artemov, 1951). These findings demanded a comprehensive examination of the ganglion-blocking effect of venom, particularly in relation to the sympathetic ganglia. Medicine urgently requires an answer to this problem as bee venom has lately been used in illnesses requiring treatment with ganglion-blocking agents.

This paper describes the results of an investigation on the ganglion-blocking effect of bee venom on sympathetic ganglia.

METHOD

The experiments were carried out on cats in which the superior cervical ganglia and the preganglionic fibres of the sympathetic nerve were dissected out on both sides under combined ether and urethane anaesthesia.

Bee venom, diluted in Ringer's solution, was introduced into the ganglia in four ways: (1) the surface of the ganglion was painted with a 1:5000 solution of venom; (2) a 1:5000 venom solution was injected into the tissues surrounding the ganglion; (3) the ganglion was perfused with bee venom solutions of various strengths; and (4) the venom was injected intravenously. The effect of bee venom on the transmission of impulses in the ganglion was assessed from the change produced in the mechanogram of the contractions of the musculature in the third eyelid produced by electrical stimulation of the preganglionic sympathetic fibres. The contractions of the third eyelid of both eyes were recorded kymographically.

The method described by Bykov and Pavlova (1924) was used for perfusion of the superior cervical ganglion. It was perfused with Ringer's solution from a Mariotte vessel connected with a cannula inserted into the carotid artery below the superior cervical ganglion. The venom was introduced in dilutions of 1:10,000 to 1:100,000. When introduced intravenously, the venom was injected into the femoral vein in doses of up to 3 mg/kg.

In the experiments in which the sympathetic ganglion was perfused or in which the venom was injected intravenously the sympathetic nerve was stimulated with rectangular impulses, 1 msec in length, 1–12 V in amplitude and of frequencies from 50 to 150 c/s, from a multivibrator.

RESULTS

When the surface of the superior cervical sympathetic ganglion was painted with bee venom solution 1:5000, the amplitude of the third eyelid contractions was first reduced but later restored. The injection of from 0·2 to 1·0 ml 1:5000 bee venom solution into the tissues surrounding the

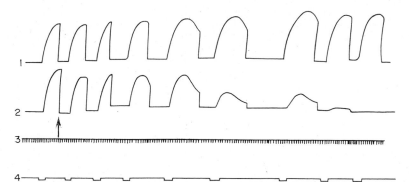

FIG. 1. Cat, 2·9 kg. Ether–urethane narcosis.

1—contraction of the "Control" third eyelid. 2—contraction of the "experimental" eyelid (superior cervical sympathetic ganglion on the same side had been treated with bee venom). 3—time (6 sec). 4—stimulation. Arrow—injection of bee venom 0·5 ml of 1:5000 solution into the tissue of the ganglion.

ganglion led to complete blocking of the transmission of nerve impulses in the ganglion in all cases. Depending on the quantity of venom injected, block developed after from 10 to 160 min. Restoration of reaction was not observed (Table 1, Fig. 1). Transient increase in the size of the third eyelid reaction was noted in a number of experiments immediately after injection of the venom but the amplitude of the contractions then began to diminish gradually and finally disappeared completely.

TABLE 1. Blocking of the transmission of excitation in a sympathetic ganglion of the cat, bee venom being introduced in different ways

Weight of cat (kg)	Action on ganglion	Dose of venom (ml)	Time to beginning of reaction (min)	Time to advent of block (min)	Time from beginning of block to recovery (min)
2·1	Applied to surface	1 : 5000	120	—	40
2·3		1 : 5000	120	—	32
2·0		1 : 5000	116	—	40
2·3		1 : 500	120	—	45
2·3		1 : 5000	110	—	38
2·6	Injected into ganglion	0·3 + 0·2 + 0·2*	45	125	—
3·9		0·4	20	35	—
2·6		0·7	5	10	—
2·9		0·5	9	19	—
2·4		0·5	15	40	—
2·3		0·3 + 0·4†	30	160	—
2·6		0·7	5	15	—
2·6		0·2 + 0·3†	25	72	—
3·2		1·0	5	10	—
3·7		1·0	3	12	—
3·4		0·7	7	22	—

  * Three injections.
  † Two injections.

Complete block of nerve impulse transmission developed when the ganglion was perfused with 1 : 10,000 venom solutions. Reduced transmission of impulses, as shown by enfeeblement of the third eyelid reaction (reduction in the amplitude of the eyelid contractions to $\frac{1}{3}$–$\frac{1}{2}$ of the original value), was seen in only 1 of 33 experiments. The time required for the development of complete block ranged from 9 to 45 min. Flushing with Ringer's solution for two hours failed to restore the conduction of excitation in the ganglion (Table 2, Fig. 2). Partial restoration of conduction was noted in only one experiment. Complete block of nerve impulse transmission developed after 18–69 min in 9 of 12 experiments in which the superior cervical sympathetic ganglion was perfused with a 1:20,000 dilution of bee venom. The reaction of the third eyelid was restored after flushing

TABLE 2. Blocking of the transmission of impulses in the superior cervical ganglion of the cat on transfusion with bee venom solutions

Weight of cat (kg)	Dilution of venom	Time to beginning of reaction (min)	Time to advent of block (min)	Time to restoration of reaction from beginning of flushing (min)
2·3	1 : 10,000	12	25	—
2·8		—	9	—
2·5		4	16	—
3·2		11	15	—
2·6		21	45	—
3·4		15	33	—
3·0		11	16	30
2·8		9	—	—
3·6		6	31	—
2·2		3	31	—
2·8		3	27	—
2·5	1 : 20,000	17	34	24
2·8		39	45	—
2·8		31	—	—
2·3		30	66	—
3·3		27	39	—
2·2		39	69	33
2·4		39	—	—
2·1		15	18	42
2·9		21	27	51
3·2		6	—	—
2·4		9	45	45
2·2		9	12	15
2·2	1 : 50,000	21	103	16
2·2		34	70	—
2·3		63	100	25
2·0		27	96	—
2·0		57	87	18

of the ganglion with Ringer's solution in half the experiments. The eyelid contraction did not, however, regain its original size. The time required for restoration ranged from 18 to 51 min from the commencement of flushing (see Table 2, Fig. 3).

Perfusion of the superior cervical ganglion with bee venom in dilutions of 1:50,000 produced blocking of impulse transmission after longer periods—from 70 to 103 min. When the ganglion was flushed through, the conduction of excitation was restored much more rapidly (after 8–25 min) and the amplitude of the eyelid contractions regained its original value in most cases (Table 2).

There was no blocking of the transmission of excitation in the ganglion in any of the experiments in which the ganglion was perfused with 1:100,000

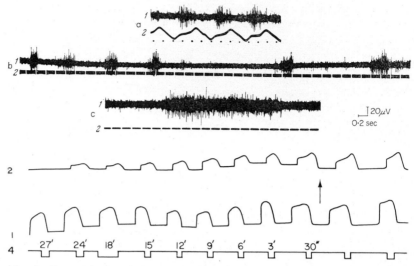

FIG. 2. Cat, 2·8 kg. Perfusion of the ganglion with a 1:10,000 solution of bee venom.

Notation as in Fig. 1. There is no time recording. The numbers indicate time after introduction of the venom. Read from right to left.

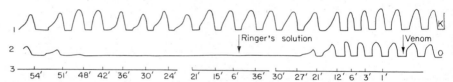

FIG. 3. Cat, 2·3 kg. Perfusion of the ganglion with bee venom solution 1:20,000.

Notation as in Fig. 1. To be read from right to left. 3—time after introduction of venom and Ringer's solution.

bee venom solution (these experiments are not included in Table 2). Table 3 gives the times at which blocking and restoration of the conduction of excitation in the superior cervical sympathetic ganglion occurred when bee venom solution 0·5–3·0 mg/kg was injected intravenously. With a dose of 0·5 mg/kg block developed at times between 15–30 sec and 4–9 min. Conduction was also restored in the ganglion after periods ranging from 3 to 15 min. With a venom dose of 1·0 mg/kg impulse conduction was blocked in the sympathetic ganglia after about 30 sec.

All these experiments thus indicate that bee venom has a powerful ganglion-blocking effect which was seen when venom was applied to the surface of a superior cervical sympathetic ganglion, when a ganglion was perfused with venom dilutions (up to 1:50,000), and when venom was injected intravenously.

TABLE 3. Blocking of the conduction of excitation in the superior cervical sympathetic ganglion of the cat on the intravenous injection of bee venom

Weight of cat (kg)	Dose of venom (mg/kg)	Time to development of block (min)	Time to restoration of reaction from beginning of flushing (min)	Remarks
2·9	0·5	4	5	Intensified respiration
2·3	1·0	0·5	5	Intensified respiration and cardiac action
	+0·5	0·25	3	
	+0·5	0·25	3	
2·8	0·5	0·25	3	
	+0·5	0·25	3	
	+0·5	0·25	3	
2·5	3·0	0·25	10	Intense panting
	+1·5	0·4	8	Convulsions, agony, death
2·4	1·0	0·5	4	
3·0	0·5	3	12	Rapid breathing, convulsions
	+0·5	2	14	
2·3	0·5	—	—	No block
	+1·0	4	4	
2·1	0·5	9	15	
	+1·5	1	14	Rapid respiration and heart action
3·0	1·5	3	7	
	+1·5	3	6	
	+1·0	2	4	
	+1·0	2	6	

To the above we can now add some new results obtained during the last two years (Artemov, 1961; Artemov et al., 1961).

We investigated lability (functional mobility) changes in the superior cervical ganglion in order to define the physiological shifts produced in the ganglia of the sympathetic nervous system when small doses of bee venom were injected into the blood. We know that the small quantity, suggested by Vvedenskii for quantitative definition of the functional state of various links in the nervous system, affords an expression of the rate of the elementary processes underlying nervous activity and it can be used as the best general index of the physiological state of the ganglion. For the measurement of lability Vvedenskii suggested the greatest number of bursts of excitation which an excitable system could reproduce per second in accurate correspondence with the rate of the stimulating impulses. This procedure involves observation of the most powerful (optimum) reaction and subsequent decline of the reaction when the rate of the stimulating impulses is increased further (frequency pessimum).

2 a*

Soviet pharmacologists (V. V. Zakusov, D. A. Kharkevich and others) consider that change in lability is the earliest and most sensitive sign of the effects of poisons on the transmission of impulses in ganglia and have used the parameter of lability successfully for investigation of the effects of pharmacological substances on the nervous system.

We investigated the changes produced by bee venom in the lability of the sympathetic ganglion in cats under urethane by periodically stimulating the preganglionic sympathetic fibres in the neck with rhythmical electrical pulses (duration 0·5 msec, tension 2 V) and recording contractions of the third eyelid. Stimulation began with suboptimum frequencies (from 10 to 30 c/s). When the contraction of the membrane reached its maximum, the rate of the stimulating impulses was then increased, with further increment in the size of the nictitating membrane contraction. Pessimum developed when frequencies of 60–100 c/s were reached and the contractions began to dimininish height. To confirm the "pessimum" nature of the reduction in the size of the contractions the frequency of the stimulating impulses was again reduced to 10–30 c/s, in which case the height of the contractions increased again.

Bee venom dilutions from 1:2000 to 1:10,000,000 were tested; from 0·0001 to 0·5 mg/kg was injected on each occasion into the cat's bloodstream.

In the first series of experiments we examined lability changes in the superior cervical ganglion resulting from the intravenous injection of bee venom, 1:2000 to 1:200,000, in doses of 0·00–0·5 mg/kg. Small doses of bee venom (0·005–0·01 mg/kg) invariably produced a considerable decline in the lability of the ganglion of 20–50 c/s. Medium doses yielded a picture of complex lability changes. Reduction in the size of the nictitating membrane contraction could sometimes be observed parallel with reduction in lability. Larger doses (0·2–0·5 mg/kg) produced still more complex changes in the functional state of the ganglion right up to complete block of impulse transmission therein. In addition, they were capable of increasing lability slightly during the first few moments before it began to decline.

Changes in the lability of the superior cervical ganglion produced by the injection of bee venom into a carotid artery through a special cannula were examined in the second series of experiments. The poison was tested in doses of 0·0001 to 1·0 mg/kg; these caused a profound decline of lability and the pessimum frequency was reduced by 10–50 c/s. Larger doses blocked impulse transmission in the ganglion; a dose of 1·0 mg/kg invariably produced tonic contraction of the cat nictitating membrane.

Bee venom in very high dilutions (up to 1:10,000,000) had thus quite a material effect on the functional state of sympathetic ganglia, reducing their lability and thereby facilitating the development of pessimal inhibition in them.

Comparison of the effect of bee venom with the actions of other ganglion-blocking substances showed that, as judged by its power to reduce lability in a sympathetic ganglion and consequently, to produce pessimal inhibition, bee venom is one of the more active gangliolytics and is superior in this respect to tetraethylammonium and hexamethonium.

It was finally shown that bee venom abolished the excitatory effect produced in a sympathetic ganglion by acetylcholine 1 : 10,000 to 1 : 100,000 injected into the carotid artery. The injection of acetylcholine produced a slow contraction of the nictitating membrane after a latent period of 5–10 sec. Bee venom 1 : 1000 to 1 : 10,000 (from 0·1 to 1·0 mg/kg) was then injected and the acetylcholine effect was then abolished in about half the cases, while a second acetylcholine injection failed to produce slow contraction of the membrane.

DISCUSSION

These, together with our earlier results, enable us to define the cholinolytic properties of bee venom. In that they exert their main action on different physiological systems, all N-cholinolytic substances are divided into two groups, namely (a) substances with a predominant "curare-like" effect on skeletal musculature and (b) ganglion-blocking substances, involving the N-cholinergic systems of autonomic ganglia (Denisenko, 1959). Bee venom must undoubtedly be placed in the latter group in that, as was demonstrated by us some time ago and later confirmed by Hoffmann (1952), its "curare-like" effect is feeble. Neumann and Habermann (1954) have also reported on the ganglion-blocking effect of bee venom.

It can, therefore, be taken as proved that bee venom is a cholinolytic with predominant ganglion-blocking action. This description of the cholinolytic properties of bee venom is, however, incomplete. We know that certain substances acting mainly on cholinergic synapses in the central nervous system have lately been isolated from the general mass of cholinolytics. The typical properties of these "central" cholinolytics are: (1) a depressing effect on conditioned reflex activity associated with weakening of internal inhibition; (2) intensification of the effect of hypnotics; (3) facilitation of electro-convulsions; and (4) stimulation of the adrenal cortex, which manifests itself by reduction in the gland content of ascorbic acid and in the development of eosinopenia in the blood (Denisenko, 1959a). It must be emphasized that bee venom has all these properties. The typical central cholinolytic effect on higher nervous activity and the stimulating effect on the adrenal cortex possessed by bee venom have been studied by us (Artemov, 1958) and the facilitation of electro-convulsions by this venom has been described by Gerlich (1950). Thus, apart from its ganglion-blocking effect, bee venom also has the other properties of a central cholinolytic. This is of considerable interest from the standpoint of evolutionary physiology. We have already mentioned that bees have come from wasplike ancestors which paralysed other arthropods by injecting their venom by means of their sting directly into the nerve ganglia of their victims. The cholinolytic properties of bee venom have been inherited by bees from their ancestors.

These findings also enable us to offer suggestions on the nature of the therapeutic action of bee venom in illnesses such as hypertensive disease, obliterative endarteritis, trophic ulcers and so on. Abroad, therapeutic preparations of bee venom have not been used in these diseases but Soviet physicians have recently expanded the indications for the use of bee venom considerably and have used bee stings and Soviet preparations of venom (Venapiolin, etc.) successfully in the treatment of these serious diseases (Fishkov, 1954; Zaitsev and Arkhangel'skii, 1956; Zaitsev and Poryadin, 1958, 1961; Antonov and Boldina, 1958; Kavetskii and Lizunova, 1957; Kononenko, 1958; Levitskii, 1960 and others).

As it is well known that the use of certain ganglion-blocking agents in these diseases gives good therapeutic results (Denisenko, 1959), it can be assumed that the good effect of bee venom is due to its power, even in small doses, to act on cholinergic systems in sympathetic nerve ganglia. And it is also quite probable that the neurons in the sympathetic ganglia which are the first to be blocked are those which are in an over-excited state as a result of continuous pathological impulsation.

We hope that this hypothesis will be found useful by clinicians for explanation of the results of bee venom treatment in hypertensive disease and obliterative endarteritis.

CONCLUSIONS

(1) Bee venom had a pronounced ganglion-blocking effect and was capable of arresting the transmission of excitation in N-cholinergic synapses in the superior cervical sympathetic ganglion of the cat.

(2) The application of a 1:5000 bee venom solution to the surface of a superior cervical sympathetic ganglion in the cat led to persistent blocking of the transmission of nerve excitation in the ganglion. Similar effects were produced by perfusion of the ganglion with bee venom dilutions of 1:10,000 to 1:50,000.

(3) The intravenous injection of bee venom led to transient blocking of excitation transmission in sympathetic ganglia in the cat.

The intravenous injection of venom in small doses (up to 0·005 mg/kg) produced appreciable reduction in the lability of the ganglion for a period of 15–30 min.

(4) The injection of bee venom 1:1000 directly into a carotid artery led to slow contraction of the nictitating membrane. Small doses of venom injected into a carotid artery reduced the lability of the ganglion considerably. This effect was seen even when venom dilutions of 1:10,000,000 were injected.

(5) Injection of venom into a carotid artery abolished the sensitivity of the ganglion to acetylcholine.

(6) These results, together with those published earlier, enable us to place bee venom in the group of N-cholinolytic substances with, predominantly, ganglion-blocking effect and some of the properties of a central cholinolytic. A theory is put forward to explain the therapeutic effect of bee venom in certain diseases.

REFERENCES

ANTONOV, I. P. and N. A. BOLDINA, *Collection of scientific papers of the Belorussian Institute for the Advanced Training of Doctors, Minsk*, **1**, 300 (1958).

ARTEMOV, N. M., *Bee Venom, its Physiological Properties and Therapeutic Applications* (Pchelinyi yad, yego fiziologicheskiye svoistva i terapevticheskoye primeneniye). Moscow–Leningrad 1941.

ARTEMOV, N. M., Scientific papers of Gor'kii University (*Uchenyye zapiski Gor'k. gos. un-ta*) **14**, 177 (1949).

ARTEMOV, N. M., Scientific papers of Gor'kii University **19**, 3; *Ibid.* **19**, 17 (1951).

ARTEMOV, N. M., *Papers by Soviet Delegates to 17th International Congress on Apiculture* (XVII Mezhdunarodnyi kongress po pchelovodstvu. Doklady sovetskoi delegatsii) p. 131 (1958).

ARTEMOV, N. M., *18th International Congress on Apiculture*, Report p. 241, Moscow 1961.

ARTEMOV, N. M., *Biol. nauki* **1**, 88 (1962).

ARTEMOV, N. M., T. I. POBEREZHSKAYA and L. I. SERGEYEVA, Scientific Papers of Gor'kii University **55**, 217 (1962).

ARTEMOV, N. M. and O. F. SOLOV'YEVA, *Byull. eksp. biol. i med.* **7**, 5 446 (1939).

ARTEMOV, N. M., L. N. TARASOVA and A. A. FILIMONOVA, *Biol. nauki* **1**, 86 (1961).

ARTEMOV, N. M. and V. TURILOVA, Scientific papers of Gor'kii University **19**, 41 (1951).

BYKOV, K. M. and A. M. PAVLOVA, *Collection of Papers Commemorating the 75th Birthday of Academician I. P. Pavlov* (Sbornik, posvyashchennyi 75-letiyu akademika I. P. Pavlova), Leningrad 1924.

DENISENKO, P. P., *Gangliolytics: Pharmacology and Clinical Applications* (Gangliolitiki, farmakologiya i klinicheskoye primeneniye) Leningrad 1959.

DENISENKO, P. P., *Scientific papers of the 9th Congress of the All-Union Society of Physiologists, Biochemists and Pharmacologists* (Trudy IX s"ezda Vses. ob-va fiziol., biokhim. i farmakol.) **3**, 209 Moscow and Minsk 1959a.

FISHKOV, YE. L., *Klin. med.* **32**, 8, 20 (1954).

FISHKOV, YE. L., *Eksp. khirurg. i anestesiol.* **4** (1961).

GERLICH, N., *Arch. Expl. Path. u. Pharm.* **211**, 97 (1950).

HOFFMANN, H. T., *Arch. Expl. Path. u. Pharm.* **214**, 523 (1952).

KAVETSKII, N. YE. and M. I. LIZUNOVA, *Kazanskii med. zhurn.* **1**, 48 (1951).

KONONENKO, I. F., Scientific papers of Kharkov Med. Inst. (*Trudy Khar'k. med. in-ta*) **37**, 138 (1958).

KOSHTOYANTS, *Zool. zh.* **22**, 131 (1943).

LEVITSKII, A. V., *Vrach. delo* **7**, 119 (1960).

NEUMANN, W. and E. HABERMANN, *Arch. Expl. Path. u. Pharm.* **222**, 367 (1954).

RIETSCHEL, P., *Zeitschr. f. Morphol. u. Okol. d. Tiere* **33**, 313, (1937).

ZAITSEV, G. P. and A. A. ARKHANGEL'SKII, *Novyi khirurgicheskii arkhiv* **5**, 42 (1956).

ZAITSEV, G. P. and V. T. PORYADIN, Apiculture (*Pchelovodstvo*) **2**, 47 (1958).

ZAITSEV, G. P. and V. T. PORYADIN, *18th International Congress on Apiculture*, Report p. 256, Moscow 1961.

THE DEVELOPMENT AND LOCALIZATION OF CORTICAL INHIBITION IN THE ELEMENTS OF THE CONDITIONED REFLEX ARC

E. A. ASRATYAN

Physiological Laboratory, Institute of Higher Nervous Activity,
U.S.S.R. Academy of Sciences, Moscow

Translated by Dr. R. Crawford

THE extremely important coordinating role of inhibition in the integrative activity of the central nervous system, and particularly of its higher divisions, has been elucidated and studied in detail by the classical neurophysiologists, Sechenov, Sherrington, Pavlov, Vvedenskii and their numerous successors. Many are also well acquainted with the facts and theories put forward by Pavlov and his pupils in relation to another important function of inhibition in the vital activity of the nervous system, namely its protective and restorative function. In addition, modern physiology has at its disposal a considerable quantity of factual evidence on the laws governing the development of inhibition in nerve structures, its interaction with excitation, its dependence on factors of various kinds, its many forms of manifestation and so on. Yet, despite the unceasing and even more rapid advance in our knowledge of inhibition, many aspects of the problem still remain unknown and neurophysiologists, following Pavlov's example, bitterly term inhibition an "accursed" problem.

One aspect of the problem which has been inadequately investigated and is still obscure is that of the original development and localization of the various forms of cortical inhibition in the elements of the conditioned reflex arc. This communication deals with this problem and contains a short exposition of some new facts arrived at by the author and his co-workers, together with some theoretical considerations deduced in large measure from these facts.

The question of the development and localization of the different forms of cortical inhibition in the elements of the conditioned reflex arc has attracted the attention of investigators ever since the development of the doctrine of higher nervous activity. Main attention has, however, been

given and is still being given to the development and localization of conditioned inhibition, the form of inhibition which is specific for the cortex
and which is most important for its activity. Until quite recently there were,
in general, two opposite views on this subject. I refer to the view enunciated
originally by Babkin (1904) and Zelenyi (1907) and subsequently upheld
by Pavlov himself that conditioned inhibition develops in cortical nerve cells
in the focus for the conditioned stimulus, and the view put forward by
Perel'tsveig (1907), Kasherininova (1909) and later supported by Anokhin
(1932), his co-workers, Khodorov (1955) and others that conditioned inhibition develops in the nerve cells of the focus for the unconditioned
stimulus.

The former view is based mainly on the well-known fact that conditioned
inhibition irradiates from the nerve structures for any one conditioned
reflex to the nerve structures of other conditioned reflexes of the same
nature, and at times, of conditioned reflexes of a different kind, that in fact,
this inhibition spreads to other related and even unrelated conditioned
reflexes. In support of this view, Roitbak (1958) cites his recent findings
that, when a conditioned reflex is extinguished, there is a sharp change in
the nature of the electrical reaction in the cortical focus for the conditioned
stimulus in response to application of the latter. No very important direct
evidence is cited in support of the latter view, and its correctness is usually
argued on indirect evidence, and primarily evidence which proves the
untenability of the former view (attention is drawn, for example, to reception of the stimulus of an inhibited conditioned reflex, etc.).

In addition to these two time-honoured views, other opinions have in the
course of time been expressed on this subject. Here we would first of all
mention the view put forward by Kupalov and his co-workers (1931, 1955)
that conditioned inhibition develops simultaneously in the cells of the foci
for both the conditioned and the unconditioned stimulus. Later, Konorskii
(1948) developed the view that cortical inhibition is a manifestation of the
activity of special inhibitory structures with an existence separate from
but parallel with the structures of excitation at cortical level, in exactly the
same way as they exist at subcortical, spinal and other levels in the integrative activity of the central nervous system. Finally, we too have expressed
certain views on the development of conditioned inhibition in the elements
of the conditioned reflex arc (1947, 1949, 1955). The essence of the view
developed by us is that conditioned inhibition develops primarily in the
elements of the actual conditioned connexion, conceived of by us as a chain
of intermediate neurons, and not in the cells of the focus for either the conditioned or unconditioned stimulus, as is held by supporters of all other
views. We do admit, however, that when the inhibition which develops
primarily in elements of the conditioned connexion is of considerable intensity, it may subsequently also involve the cortical nerve elements in the foci
for both conditioned and unconditioned stimuli. What then are the facts

and considerations on which this view is based, a view which, in general, is now supported by, for example, Skipin (1956), Maiorov (1959) with his co-workers, and some other Soviet scientists?

I would mention, before proceeding to exposition of the actual facts and considerations supporting this view, that some of them are of indirect nature; they are directed to proving that conditioned inhibition does not develop initially in either the cortical focus for the conditioned stimulus or in that of the unconditioned stimulus. Only some of these facts and considerations can be regarded as constituting a direct basis for the view we have developed.

In order to make our exposition of the subject complete and to retain chronological order, we shall deal first of all with certain well-known, long established facts which have been referred to on many occasions by other authors also in connexion with their discussion of the development of conditioned inhibition in the elements of the conditioned reflex arc. We are thinking here of the perception of the conditioned stimulus and reaction to it after inhibition of a positive conditioned reflex, that is after extinction, differentiation, delay and so on, as already mentioned. These facts constitute undeniable evidence that the inhibition which had developed under these circumstances in the arc of the conditioned reflex and which led to blocking of the conduction of excitation through it was not localized in the cortical focus of the conditioned stimulus, but somewhere in the succeeding links of the arc. Confirmation of this is apparently also provided by the seemingly trivial facts relating to the uneven course of the process of extinction or differentiation for different components in the same conditioned reflex, as for example, the salivary and motor components of an alimentary conditioned reflex. It is well known that not infrequently under these circumstances one of the components of the conditioned reflex is completely inhibited while the second can still be elicited for a considerable time. One long established fact which is of some importance in connexion with the problem we are discussing is that, when a conditioned reflex is inhibited by extinction, by differentiation or in some other way, there are no significant changes in the unconditioned reflex, and conditioned reflexes of the same kind to other stimuli are retained practically unchanged. It can, therefore, be concluded that the cortical focus for the unconditioned reflex likewise cannot be regarded as the starting point for the development of conditioned inhibition.

In addition to the facts already mentioned, which have long been known as a result of the research of many investigators, we have also at our disposal a number of facts which have been established by ourselves in conjunction with our co-workers over a number of years and which, in some respects, are more closely connected with the problem of the development of conditioned inhibition in the elements of the conditioned reflex arc. We shall now give a short description and interpretation of these facts.

In conjunction with our co-workers, we have for many years been carrying out a systematic investigation of "switching" in conditioned reflex activity (1941, 1958, 1959). The essential feature of this is that the same indifferent stimulus can, at the same time, be given two different signal significances, such as alimentary and electro-defensive, positive and negative, short-delay and long-delay and so on. This is achieved by reinforcing the particular stimulus differently under different experimental conditions (in two different rooms, at different times of the day or by two different experimenters and so on); reinforcement may be with food in one case and with electrical stimulation in the other; reinforcement is delivered at once or after a delay; there is reinforcement in the one case and none in the other, and so on.

It is not part of our task here to describe our findings and the theoretical views we have formulated on this problem as a whole. We would merely mention that this comprehensive experimental material includes findings which are closely connected with the question of the development and localization of conditioned inhibition in the elements of the conditioned reflex arc. We should like to describe these in summarized from.

We begin with a description of the very first and very demonstrative experiments of our co-workers Shitov and Yakovleva (1937). In morning experiments on dogs Shitov combined the metronome 120/min with food and elaborated an alimentary conditioned reflex to it, while Yakovleva carried out day-time experiments in the same room and on the same dogs in which the same stimulus was combined with electrical stimulation of one of the animal's paws with resultant elaboration of an electro-defensive motor conditioned reflex to the stimulus. The metronome thus acquired two signal significances, alimentary and electro-defensive, for the animals simultaneously. Usually only one of its signal significances was in evidence in any given set of circumstances, and the second was in an inhibited state. The metronome produced only the alimentary conditioned reflex in the morning experiments of one experimenter and only the electro-defensive reflex in the daytime experiments of the other. A point of interest is that when both experimenters carried out an experiment jointly, both signal significances of the conditioned stimulus manifested themselves; it produced both alimentary and electro-defensive conditioned reflexes in a somewhat irregular manner.

More recently, results similar to our original findings have been obtained by Struchkov (1955, 1956), working in our laboratory. He elaborated two different kinds of conditioned reflexes, alimentary to the sound of a buzzer and an electro-defensive reflex to tactile stimulation of the skin in dogs in one of the rooms. When these reflexes were firmly and clearly established, Struchkov proceeded to parallel experiments on the same animals in the other room, but with radical change in the nature of the experiment: in the new room he combined the tactile skin stimulus with food and the buzzer with electrical stimulation of a paw. Ultimately the dogs were able to cope even with this quite difficult task. After a phase of dual conditioned reflex reactions to each conditioned stimulus and a second phase in which the adequate reactions gradually became stronger and the inadequate reactions to each of the stimuli in a particular room declined, a state was reached in which in one room the buzzer produced only the alimentary conditioned reflex and the tactile stimulus only the electro-defensive conditioned reflex and, conversely, in the other room the buzzer produced only the electro-defensive and the tactile stimulus only the alimentary conditioned reflex.

All these observations of Shitov, Yakovleva and Struchkov indicate, in our opinion, that the production under these conditions of only one of the two different kinds of conditioned reflex which the given stimulus was capable of eliciting and the suppression of the other conditioned reflex were the result of the development of a process of inhibition in the elements of the arc for the conditioned reflex which it was the experimenter's intention to suppress. It follows, therefore, that this elaborated inhibition was located neither in the focus for the conditioned stimulus (as the stimulus produced one or other of the conditioned reflexes in each of the rooms) nor in the foci for the different kinds of unconditioned stimuli (as Struchkov's findings show that both alimentary and electro-defensive conditioned reflexes could be elicited in each of the rooms and in each experiment). By a process of exclusion, therefore, we reach the conclusion that the inhibition in these cases developed and was located in the nerve elements of the actual conditioned connexion.

It is not without interest that the two different kinds of conditioned reflexes, elaborated to the same stimulus, were in antagonistic reciprocal relationships with one another. Inhibition in a particular setting of the legitimate conditioned reflex to either stimulus (whether by extinction from an extraneous stimulus or otherwise) automatically entailed disinhibition of the other conditioned reflex to the same stimulus, usually inactive in that setting. This important fact, which was confirmed repeatedly, would appear to afford further evidence of the correctness of our conclusions on the development of inhibition in the structural elements of the conditioned connexion itself.

The results of our experiments on the switching of conditioned reflexes of the same kind but of opposite functional sign are also of considerable importance in relation to the question we are discussing. I refer to the results of earlier experiments carried out in 1938 by Shitov and Zamyetina, the essential features of which were the following. The same experimenter carried out two experiments on a dog in the same room, one in the morning and one in the afternoon, alimentary conditioned reflexes to a number of stimuli being elaborated in exactly the same manner. The only difference in these experiments was that all the stimuli without exception in the morning experiments were reinforced with food whereas in the afternoon experiments one stimulus was left unreinforced. This ultimately led to the position that the latter stimulus acquired dual signal significance: it was a positive alimentary conditioned stimulus in the morning experiments and an inhibitory alimentary conditioned signal in the afternoon experiments.

Subsequent experiments revealed that the dog could deal adequately, if not absolutely decisively, with the task when rendered much more complicated. In the morning experiments the experimenter combined a loud whistle with food and elaborated a corresponding conditioned reflex with simultaneous differentiation of a feeble whistle which was not reinforced. In the afternoon experiments the same experimenter did the opposite: he reinforced the feeble whistle with food and did nor reinforce the loud whistle. This arrangement of the experiments led to derangement of conditioned reflex activity in a number of dogs, which failed to deal with the task. The remaining dogs had great difficulty in coping with the situation and did so in rather indefinite manner. In the morning experiments the loud whistle produced a good alimentary conditioned reflex while the weak whistle either failed to produce or produced only a weak alimentary reflex. The reverse was the case in the afternoon experiments: the weak whistle produced a strong alimentary conditioned reflex and the loud whistle produced either a weak reflex or none at all.

It is our opinion that the results of these experiments likewise support the location of the elaborated chronic inhibition in the structures of the conditioned connexion. If it had been located in the cortical focus for the conditioned stimulus, the stimuli of reflexes which were inhibited in one set of experiments would not have produced reflexes in the other experiments. If this inhibition had been located in the cortical focus for the unconditioned stimulus, the position in which one stimulus produced a conditioned reflex and another stimulus close to it failed to produce a reflex would not have arisen in the experiments of the second type.

The above material on the localization of conditioned inhibition in the elements of the conditioned reflex arc was obtained by us in experiments extending over many years for the investigation of switching in conditioned reflex activity, together with other findings, a description of which is not possible here as they are not really connected with the problem we are discussing in this communication. We would merely repeat that the characteristic feature of these switching experiments was that two signal significances were imposed on the same stimulus simultaneously, the significances of signals for conditioned reflexes of different kinds, of different sign, with different delays, different strengths and so on, each of which manifested itself separately in the conditions and setting adequate for each and at different times.

We now have available some fresh evidence on the localization of conditioned inhibition, obtained in experiments of a different kind, in which the stimuli were given simultaneously the signal significances for two different kinds of conditioned reflex, alimentary and electro-defensive, but which differed from the switching experiments in that in this case the two significances of the conditioned stimulus manifested themselves parallel with one another and at the same time, under the same conditions and in the same setting. This was achieved by combining the indifferent stimulus in the experiments with food on some occasions and with electrical stimulation of one of the paws on others or by reinforcing it with the two together.

Application of the conditioned stimulus produced an alimentary conditioned reflex and an electro-defensive conditioned reflex simultaneously. It was found that the same animals could retain ordinary single conditioned reflexes to other stimuli along with the binary conditioned reflexes.

We shall not describe all the material obtained in our laboratory on these binary or dual conditioned reflexes but shall limit ourselves here to a brief description of the facts from this material which have a direct bearing on the question of the development and localization of conditioned inhibition in the elements of the conditioned reflex arc. F. K. Daurova effected extinction of the binary conditioned reflexes in a series of experiments by periodic application of the conditioned stimulus without reinforcement by food and electric current.

Her results indicated that one of the binary conditioned reflexes, namely the alimentary, could be inhibited although the second, the electro-defensive conditioned reflex, continued to be present for a considerable time. As in these experiments, unlike the switching experiments, the conditioned stimulus elicited both reflexes simultaneously in the one experiment and under the same conditions, and as there was development in these experiments not of chronic inhibition of one reflex, as occurred in the case of switching, but acute inhibition elaborated in the course of a single experimental session, the results obtained in these experiments would appear to afford particularly demonstrative and convincing proof that the conditioned inhibition developed primarily in subsequent links of the conditioned reflex arc and not in the focus for the conditioned stimulus. As when one of the binary conditioned reflexes was extinguished, single conditioned reflexes of the same nature to other stimuli remained virtually unchanged, it can be concluded that neither did this inhibition develop primarily in the focus for the unconditioned stimulus. Again, the only possible assumption is that in this case also the inhibition developed and became located primarily in the elements of the conditioned connexion itself.

Quite definite factual evidence on the localization of conditioned inhibition has also been obtained in our investigations of the last few years on the problem of duplex conditioned connexions. I should like to describe these findings to amplify the points already discussed. I should mention first of all that in the elaboration of conditioned reflexes we generally made combinations of stimuli, the unconditioned reflexes of which could be objectively and accurately accounted and recorded graphically. We therefore selected stimuli such as food, electrical stimulation of a paw, local cooling of a defined area of skin (to produce a local vasomotor reflex), the puffing of air into the eye (to produce an eyelid reflex), passive raising of a paw (to produce reflex relaxation of the extensor muscle, as revealed by electromyographic recording; subsequently, in the course of the elaboration of conditioned reflexes, the passive movement of the paw became active) and so on. We combined these stimuli in various combinations of two, in a stereotype or in alternating succession. In this way duplex conditioned connexions were generally elaborated: in the course of time each of the two combined stimuli acquired the property of eliciting the reflex of the other stimulus in the pair as a conditioned reflex in addition to its own proper unconditioned reflex. We shall not describe the features of these reflexes and all the facts we ascertained about them in detail but shall merely quote the findings which have a bearing on the localization of the conditioned inhibition in their arcs.

Our colleagues M. Ye. Varga and Ya. M. Pressman elaborated duplex conditioned reflexes in dogs by combining the puffing of air and passive raising of one paw in stereotype order. When the duplex reflex, or reflex with a duplex connexion, was elaborated, they effected extinction of one of the reflexes, checking the process of the development of conditioned inhibition in the elements of the arc of the conditioned reflex from the objective indices for the foci of the two combined stimuli. The results obtained were curious. When air was puffed into the eye without reinforcement by passive raising of a paw, there was fluctuating extinction of the reflex and ultimately the puffing of air into the eye ceased to cause flexion of the corresponding paw and might even produce the opposite movement of extension. At the same time the unconditioned reflex produced by the puffing of air into the eye, namely the eyelid reflex, was not reduced and might even be intensified, the indication being that the cortical focus was not only free from conditioned inhibition but might even be rendered more excitable.

It may be suggested that the extinction of the conditioned motor reflex was determined by the development of inhibition in the cortical focus for the motor reflex of the extremity. This, however, was not the case. When the puffing of air into the eye had ceased to elicit a conditioned reflex raising of a paw, that is when this reflex had been completely extinguished, passive raising of the paw was still capable of producing conditioned reflex blinking of the eye of more than its original intensity. Essentially the same results were also obtained when the other member of the conditioned reflex was extinguished, that is when the paw was raised passively periodically in an experiment without reinforcement by the puffing of air into the eye. In the experiments of this kind the fluctuating extinction of the conditioned reflex led ultimately to the position that the raising of a paw not only ceased to elicit a conditioned eyelid reflex but might even by followed by the opposite effect—forced and prolonged opening of the eyelids.

Furthermore, when air was puffed into the eye after the conditioned reflex had been extinguished, this produced the conditioned reflex to raising of a paw, often of greater degree than at the beginning of the experiment.

Struchkov obtained similar results with other duplex reflexes elaborated by the combination of food with either passive raising of one paw or with local cooling of a circumscribed area of skin on the side. In the experiments of the former type the giving of food produced conditioned reflex raising of a paw and passive raising of a paw elicited an alimentary conditioned reflex; in the experiments of the latter type the giving of food elicited a local cutaneous vasomotor conditioned reflex and cooling of the skin produced a conditioned alimentary reaction. When Struchkov extinguished one of the duplex conditioned reflexes, say, by periodically giving the food unreinforced by the raising of a paw, the giving of food continued to elicit an alimentary reaction after complete inhibition of the motor conditioned reflex produced by it; furthermore, passive raising of a paw at this time likewise produced an alimentary conditioned reflex. Essentially the same results were obtained when the vasomotor conditioned reflex to the giving of food was extinguished.

The results of these experiments by Struchkov and of the experiments of Varga and Pressman afford even more striking and convincing evidence than the findings of our other colleagues just described that conditioned inhibition develops and is localized primarily in the structures of the actual conditioned connexion and not at all in the cortical foci for the conditioned and unconditioned stimuli.

We admit, however, as we stated at the beginning of this paper, that when there is subsequent intensification of the conditioned inhibition in the structures in which it develops initially, it may then spread to the foci for both the conditioned stimulus and the unconditioned stimulus, or in other words, it may embrace in varying degrees all the central links in the conditioned reflex arc. The manifestation of this is weakening of the unconditioned reflex, weakening of the instinctive reaction to the conditioned stimulus, the development of a drowsy state and sleep. It will, however, have become evident from the arguments we have put forward that we put a somewhat different interpretation from the investigators mentioned earlier on those phenomena which have long been familiar to us from the great wealth of material provided by the Pavlov laboratories. Those who hold the view that conditioned inhibition develops primarily in the focus for the conditioned or in the focus for the unconditioned stimulus regard the phenomena enumerated above as the result of subsequent intensification of the initial inhibition in these foci and its spread to other cerebral structures. We differ from them and suggest that the conditioned inhibition develops initially in the structures of the conditioned connexion and, when later it becomes intensified therein, it spreads to the foci for the conditioned and unconditioned stimuli and generally to other central nerve formations. We do not, of course, exclude the possibility that inhibition may, under certain extraordinary circumstances, develop initially either in the focus for the conditioned or in that for the unconditioned stimulus, and subsequently becoming intensified in these foci, may lead to various consequences. But our material provides us with adequate grounds for considering that this is unusual and that conditioned inhibition generally develops first of all in the structures of the conditioned connexion and that it appears and undergoes intensification in the foci indicated much later.

We should like to give further support to our view by referring to the results of some new experiments carried out by our colleagues L. I. Chilingaryan and Ye. A. Romanovskaya and thus complete our exposition of the factual evidence obtained in our laboratory up to the present time on this question of the development and initial localization of conditioned inhibition in the elements of the conditioned reflex arc.

These experiments were carried out on dogs in which contact electrodes had previously been implanted on the cortical motor points for one paw, so that it was possible in chronic experiment to produce movement of the paw by electrical stimulation of the corresponding points in the cortex, to trace the changes in excitability at these points produced by various agents and factors and so on. Chilingaryan elaborated motor conditioned reflexes in such dogs by the combination of an indifferent sound with electrical stimulation of the appropriate point in the motor cortex. Romanovskaya elaborated motor reflexes in such dogs by the usual method, namely the combination of an indifferent stimulus with electrical stimulation of the paw. When the conditioned reflexes had been elaborated and rendered relatively stable, the experimenters carried out experiments for extinction of the elaborated conditioned reflexes and at the same time followed directly the course of changes in the excitability of the corresponding cortical point, comparison being made with the initial level of excitability. They obtained the following results. As the conditioned reflex underwent fluctuating extinction, the excitability of the cortical motor point was at first slightly increased after which it returned to its original level, but later, as the conditioned inhibition became more intense, it began to fall rapidly and progressively until ultimately there was marked and prolonged lowering of the level of excitability at this point below the original level. The threshold value of the stimulating current was sometimes increased to three or four times its original value or even more. By way of comparison, we would note that in ordinary control experiments, in which extinction of the conditioned reflexes was not effected, there was generally in the course of an experiment a shift in the opposite direction, with a gradual steady increase in the excitability of the cortical motor point for the paw. This is in complete agreement with the findings of many other investigators.

Although these experiments of Chilingaryan and Romanovskaya were of a preliminary nature in some degree and the results obtained will require further more detailed investigation, the actual facts established are nevertheless undoubtedly reliable as they were confirmed by a considerable number of experiments on seven dogs of different types and ages.

The results obtained in these experiments of Chilingaryan and Romanovskaya by direct means, demonstrated the absence of any essential changes in the excitability of the cortical focus for the unconditioned motor reflex in the stage of shallow extinction and considerable reduction of its excitability in the stage of deep extinction, and are therefore consistent with our other findings which we have described. They indicate more particularly that the conditioned inhibition did not develop primarily in the cortical focus for the unconditioned reflex, but developed in it later, and only when the inhibition was considerably intensified.

We now have at our disposal certain factual evidence relative to the development and localization of another form of cortical inhibition, namely ultra-boundary or prohibitive inhibition. These results were obtained by our colleague F. K. Daurova and were briefly as follows. In a series of switching experiments alimentary conditioned reflexes were elaborated in dogs to a tone of frequency 1100 c/s and loudness 45 dB in one setting and electro-defensive conditioned reflexes were elaborated to the same stimulus in another setting. The two experiments were carried out on the same day but not in any definite order. When both conditioned reflexes exhibited definite stability and clearly defined switching, Daurova set up experiments to demonstrate ultra-boundary inhibition. For this purpose she unexpectedly intensified the conditioned stimulus (tone) to 105–115 dB in both types of experiment. The results were of considerable interest: the conditioned stimulus, when considerably intensified in this way, ceased to elicit the alimentary conditioned reflex but continued to produce the defensive conditioned reflex, which meant that the conditioned stimulus produced ultra-boundary inhibition of one activity while retaining its positive signal significance for the other activity.

Essentially similar results were obtained by Daurova in the second series of experiments with binary conditioned reflexes in which she elaborated both alimentary and electro-defensive conditioned reflexes to the same tone of 45 dB in the same setting and in the same experiments. When both conditioned reflexes had attained definite stability and the conditioned stimulus produced both the conditioned reflexes with which it had been endowed simultaneously and in adequate strength, experiments were carried out to demonstrate ultra-boundary inhibition by sudden, unexpected intensification of the conditioned stimulus. The results proved to be the same as in the preceding series of experiments: the alimentary conditioned reflex disappeared but the electro-defensive reflex persisted. The following findings are not without interest. Daurova increased the food reinforcement of the tone of 45 dB (70 g meat-biscuit powder instead of 30 g in the preceding experiments) and reduced the stimulating current considerably in other series of experiments with switching and binary conditioned reflexes. When the reflexes were elaborated, following the pattern of the experiments just described, she set up experiments to demonstrate ultra-boundary inhibition by sudden marked intensification of the tone. This time the electro-defensive conditioned reflexes were inhibited and the alimentary reflexes persisted.

The general conclusion to be drawn from all these experiments is clear: as only one of the two conditioned reflexes the conditioned stimulus could produce was inhibited when it was applied in excessively strong form, it becomes obvious that the ultra-boundary inhibition which developed was not localized in the cortical focus for the conditioned stimulus, as Pavlov suggested and as is the generally accepted view, but in subsequent links of the conditioned reflex arc. In which links, is a problem which is now being investigated by Daurova.

This completes the exposition of the basic material obtained in our laboratory with a bearing on the development and location of cortical inhibition in the elements of the conditioned reflex arc. Research on these problems is still being carried out by us, subjects have been noted for future investigation, and we have also started to use electroencephalographic methods in our experiments. It is difficult to forecast what final conclusion we shall draw from the results of our new experiments on this subject. But the factual evidence we already have leads us to believe that conditioned inhibition develops and is originally located in the elements of the conditioned connexion, and not in the focus for the conditioned stimulus or the focus of the unconditioned stimulus, as other investigators believe. These findings also indicate that ultra-boundary inhibition develops and is originally located in the subsequent links of the conditioned reflex arc and not in the cortical focus for the conditioned stimulus as is at present the general opinion. We do not as yet have reliable evidence on the development and location of external or unconditioned inhibition.

In this paper we have spoken constantly of the development and location of *cortical* inhibition. This is due to the fact that we take the view that, in higher animals and man at any rate, the conditioned reflex is closed between two cortical points and the conditioned connexion is effected through cortical structures. We know that the closure of the conditioned connexion in the higher parts of the central nervous system and, consequently, the localization of the central part of the conditioned reflex arc is at the moment the subject of intense discussion. We have purposely refrained from discussing the views existing on this question for the same reasons as those which have led us to refrain from discussing the nature and mode of development of inhibition in cerebral structures. Likewise, the views held by the investigator on the site of the conditioned connexion in the cerebral structures are not of material importance in relation to the question which we are discussing.

In concluding this paper we should like to mention the great satisfaction we feel that the results of the investigations carried out in conjunction with our colleagues have enabled us in some measure to advance and, in a number of important points, to add detail to and to amplify the concepts of our great teacher, I. P. Pavlov, on the problem of inhibition—one of the most complex and important problems in higher nervous activity.

REFERENCES

ANOKHIN, P. K., Nizhegorod Med. J. (*Nizhegorodskii med. zh.*) 7–8, 1932.

ANOKHIN, P. K., *Internal Inhibition as a Problem in Physiology* (Vnutrenneye tormozhe-niye kak problema fiziologii). Moscow 1958.

ASRATYAN, E. A., Physiol. J. U.S.S.R. (*Fiziol. zh. SSSR*) 33, 1, 13 (1941).

ASRATYAN, E. A., *Collection of Papers Commemorating the 30th Anniversary of the Great October Socialist Revolution* (Sbornik, posvyashchennyi 30-letiyu Velikoi Oktyabr'skoi sotsialisticheskoi revolyutsii) 366, Moscow and Leningrad 1947.

ASRATYAN, E. A., *I. P. Pavlov. His Life and Work* (Pavlov, I. P. Zhizn' i nauchnoye tvorchestvo) 112, Moscow 1949.

ASRATYAN, E. A., J. Higher Nervous Activity (*Zh. vyssh. nervn. deyat.*) 5, 4, 480 (1955).

ASRATYAN, E. A., J. Higher Nervous Activity (*Zh. vyssh. nervn. deyat.*) 8, 3 (1958).

ASRATYAN, E. A., Lectures on Some Neurophysiological Problems (Lektsii po neko-torym voprosam neirofiziologii), Moscow 1959.

BABKIN, B. P., *Systematic research on compound nervous (mental) phenomena in dogs* (Opyt sistematicheskogo izucheniya slozhnykh nervnykh (psikhicheskikh) yavlenii u sobak), St. Petersburg 1904.

KASHERININOVA, N. A., *On conditioned salivary reflexes to mechanical stimulation* (Materialy k izucheniyu uslovnykh slyunnykh refleksov na mekhanicheskoye razdra-zheniye), St. Petersburg 1909.

KHODOROV, B. I., Reports of U.S.S.R. Academy of Sciences (*Dokl. Akad. Nauk SSSR*) 103, 6, 1119 (1955).

KONORSKII, YU. M., *Conditioned Reflexes and Neuron Organization*, Cambridge University Press 1948.

KONORSKII, YU. M., *Contemporary Problems in the Physiology of the Nervous and Muscular Systems* (Problemy sovnemennoi fiziologii nervnoi i myshechnoi sistemy) 343, Tbilisi 1956.

KUPALOV, P. S., J. Higher Nervous Activity (*Zh. vyssh. nervn. deyat.*) 5, 2, 157 (1955).

KUPALOV, P. S. and A. M. USHAKOVA, Archives of Biological Sciences (*Arkh. biol. nauk*) 31, 5, 1 (1931).

MAIOROV, F. P., Scientific papers of the Institute of Physiology (*Nauchnyye soobshche-niya In-ta fiziol. im. Pavlova*) 1 (1959).

PANKRATOV, M. A., J. Higher Nervous Activity (*Zh. vyssh. nervn. deyat.*) 9, 3, (1959).

PEREL'TSVEIG, I. YA., *On conditioned reflexes* (Materialy k ucheniyu ob uslovnykh refleksakh). St. Petersburg 1907.

ROITBAK, A. I., Scientific papers of Institute of Physiology, Georgian SSR Academy of Sciences (*Trudy In-ta fiziol. Akad. Nauk Gruz. SSR*) 11, 121 (1958).

SHITOV, F. M. and V. V. YAKOVLEVA, Bull. Exp. Biol. and Med. (*Byull. eksp. biol. i med.*) 4, 4 (1937).

SKIPIN, G. V., J. Higher Nervous Activity (*Zh. vyssh. nervn. deyat.*) **6**, 1, 22 (1956).
STRUCHKOV, M. I., J. Higher Nervous Activity (*Zh. vyssh. nervn. deyat.*) **5**, 4, 547 (1955).
STRUCHKOV, M. I., J. Higher Nervous Activity (*Zh. vyssh. nervn. deyat.*) **6**, 2, 277 (1956a).
STRUCHKOV, M. I., J. Higher Nervous Activity (*Zh. vyssh. nervn. deyat.*) **6**, 2, 282 (1956b).
STRUCHKOV, M. I., J. Higher Nervous Activity (*Zh. vyssh. nervn. deyat*). **6**, 6, 830 (1956c).
ZELENYI, G. P., *On the reaction of the dog to acoustic stimulations* (Materialy k voprosu o reaktsii sobaki na zvukovyye razdrazheniya), St. Petersburg 1907.

BIOCHEMICAL CHANGES DURING REFLEX STIMULATION

A. M. Budanova

Institute of Animal Morphology, U.S.S.R. Academy of Sciences, Moscow

Translated by Dr. R. Crawford

In 1896 Pavlov had already established that ammonia in certain dosage had a toxic effect on the body, accompanied by violent excitation. Later he gave expression to the thought: "There is no doubt that, with time, ammonia will be found to play an important part in physiology and pathology". This idea has been confirmed by the work of scientists both in this country and abroad.

Tashiro (1922) and Winterstein and Hirschberg (1925) demonstrated experimentally that stimulation of nerve *in vitro* increased the ammonia in the surrounding medium.

Torda (1953), Benitez *et al.* (1954) and others have reported increase in the ammonia content of the brain in rats and rabbits during convulsive attacks produced by various chemical stimuli.

Pravdich-Neminskii (1927) established that gaseous ammonia was discharged when a steady current was passed through nerve or muscle tissue. He also showed that nerves responded to any other form of stimulation as well as electrical stimulation by increased formation of ammonia.

Geiman (1936), Kaganovskaya and Kan (1936) and Golubtsova and Kan (1936) demonstrated increased ammonia formation on stimulation of nerves in molluscs.

The investigations of Vladimirova (1938, 1950, 1953, 1954, 1956), the object of which was to determine the behaviour of ammonia in the brain tissue of animals during various actions on the central nervous system, demonstrated increase of ammonia in the brain tissue of rats during excitation produced by both conditioned and unconditioned stimuli.

The numerous reports in the literature linking processes of excitation and inhibition with the formation of ammonia in brain, nerve and muscle tissue have been confirmed by our investigations on warm-blooded animals— rats, rabbits and dogs (Budanova, 1950–1957). These investigations were carried out, first, to determine the reasons for the development of convulsive epileptic attacks and, secondly, to study the biochemical changes occurring in the brain and tissues of animals in which convulsive states were produced by means of conditioned stimuli.

Great attention is being given at the present time to brain tissue metabolism in epilepsy.

Speranskii (1930) stated that some substance which had a toxic effect on all parts of the brain was found to have accumulated in a part of the brain which had been frozen and then thawed. This poison produced convulsive attacks in experimental animals.

The view that epilepsy is an aminotoxicosis which develops as a result of disturbance of protein metabolism occupies a special position among the numerous theories on the causes of and nature of this disease.

According to Koshtoyants, physiologically active substances which are of predominant importance in the cycle of chemical changes underlying the process of excitation are liberated in nerve tissue. He suggested that enzymochemical reactions leading to the formation of ammonia and its subsequent linkage to form amides must be of definite importance in the complex of enzymochemical reactions associated with nerve processes. In the light of these views, we carried out some experiments in which we were able to demonstrate increase of ammonia in the epileptogenic zone in the brains of dogs and rabbits (Budanova, 1950). It was thus proved experimentally that the substance described by Speranskii, which had a toxic effect on all parts of the brain and produced the epileptic attack, was in fact ammonia.

Despite fairly intense formation of ammonia, this toxic substance does not usually accumulate in the body as it is used in the biological synthesis of amides from glutamic and aspartic acids.

The metabolic changes occurring in the central nervous system and in the entire body during convulsive attacks have not as yet been clearly determined. And still less has been discovered on such changes during convulsive states of conditioned reflex origin, which are undoubtedly closer in their nature to epilepsy than the attacks produced experimentally by agents with patently destructive effects on the nervous system.

Our object was to try to get nearer to discovering the pathogenesis of the epileptic attack. We tackled the problem from both biochemical and physiological aspects.

We know that dicarboxylic acids (aspartic and glutamic) play an important part in processes of excitation, and particularly in the convulsive attack, by neutralizing the ammonia through the biological synthesis of amides. We therefore gave particular attention to these amino acids in our investigations.

Working in Pavlov's laboratory, Studentsov (referred to by Pavlov, 1951) was the first to demonstrate convulsive reactions developing in mice in response to a powerful acoustic stimulus. He observed the attacks, which began with excitation, changed to convulsive states and sometimes terminated in the death of the animal. Similar reactions have since been studied in rats and rabbits (Krushinskii *et al.*, 1949, 1950, 1954).

Golubtsova and Zhukova (1952) and Golubtsova and Nagradova (1955) found that the ammonia and lactic acid contents of the rat brain were considerably increased immediately after the attack in reflex epilepsy.

Antonitis *et al.* (1954) investigated the attacks produced in rabbits by an acoustic stimulus. Three characteristic stages were noted in the attack: (1) motor activity in the course of which the rabbit fell down; (2) tonic then clonic convulsions; and (3) gradual return to normal.

Working with reflex epilepsy in rats, we studied the ammonia–dicarboxylic acids–glutamine system.

An electric bell was used to produce epilepsy in the rats. Brain and muscle tissue were taken from normal rats and rats with reflex epilepsy for examination. The rats were killed by freezing in liquid air. The estimations of ammonia, glutamine and dicarboxylic amino acids were made by the methods described earlier (Budanova, 1950, 1952–1955).

TABLE 1. Contents of ammonia, glutamine and glutamic and aspartic acids (mg % nitrogen) in the rat brain

State	Ammonia	Glutamine	Glutamic acid	Aspartic acid
Normal	0·8	2·1	1·36	5·44
	0·9	1·1	2·16	5·85
	0·9	1·7	1·35	5·85
	0·9	1·0	1·76	3·94
	0·9	2·3	1·05	3·95
	0·9	2·0	1·50	2·45
	0·8	1·4	1·50	1·90
	0·7	1·0	1·35	4·35
	0·9	1·4	1·26	2·58
Average	0·8	1·5	1·48	4·03
Epileptic seizure in response to the bell	1·3	1·6	1·20	3·40
	1·3	1·4	1·05	3·53
	1·2	1·8	1·96	1·01
	1·1	0·7	0·80	2·89
	1·3	1·7	1·60	1·87
	1·0	1·7	0·96	1·59
	1·3	—	1·12	1·73
	1·3	1·7	0·96	1·88
	1·0	1·4	1·92	0·88
	—	2·2	1·42	2·02
Average	1·2	1·5	1·20	1·98

TABLE 2. Contents of ammonia glutamine and glutamic and aspartic acids
(mg % nitrogen) in rat muscle

State	Ammonia	Glutamine	Glutamic acid	Aspartic acid
Normal	1·3	1·5	1·36	3·26
	1·2	1·4	1·65	3·54
	1·1	1·7	1·05	3·81
	1·1	1·6	1·20	1·50
	1·0	1·7	0·90	1·49
	1·0	2·6	0·61	2·18
	0·9	2·3	1·76	2·53
	1·0	1·4	1·92	1·82
Average	1·1	1·8	1·31	2·52
Epileptic seizure in response to the bell	1·6	1·4	0·30	2·45
	1·7	1·3	0·30	2·45
	1·9	1·7	0·96	1·01
	1·9	2·1	1·28	1·30
	1·8	1·7	0·96	1·73
	1·8	2·0	1·60	2·17
	1·6	2·0	1·76	2·02
	1·5	2·1	—	—
Average	1·7	1·8	1·02	1·88

We were able to conclude from these experiments (Tables 1 and 2) that ammonia was increased, glutamic and aspartic acids were reduced and glutamine was almost unchanged in both brain tissue and skeletal muscle in reflex epilepsy.

For comparison, we give some of the results obtained by us earlier with dogs (Budanova, 1957) in which we produced conditioned reflex epilepsy and then examined the ammonia, glutamine, glutamic and aspartic acid contents (Table 3).

When we compare these results we observe undoubted features of similarity in the biological changes: we observe increase of ammonia, sharp reduction in the quantities of glutamic and aspartic acids and practically no change in the glutamine content of the blood of the dogs.

The peculiar behaviour of glutamine indicates that this substance plays some very important biological role quite apart from its participation in the neutralization of ammonia. Its constancy is most probably explained by the fact that it maintains equilibrium in the body fluids during activity of the organism. This view has also been expressed by Epshtein (1951), a co-worker with Palladin, and by the Hungarian scientists, Balazh and Shtraub (1953); they explain the constancy of glutamine by dynamic equilibrium between the formation and breakdown of the substance.

TABLE 3. Contents of ammonia, glutamine and glutamic and aspartic acids
(mg % nitrogen) in the blood of dogs

State	Ammonia	Glutamine	Glutamic acid	Aspartic acid
Normal	0·62	0·35	1·03	1·16
	0·54	0·23	1·03	1·34
	0·56	0·23	1·14	1·34
	0·57	0·36	1·09	1·21
	—	—	0·99	—
	—	—	1·04	—
Average	0·57	0·29	1·05	1·26
Attack produced with electric current	0·71	0·23	0·45	0·58
	0·71	0·23	0·45	0·58
	0·71	0·28	0·69	0·63
	0·73	0·28	—	—
	0·79	0·28	—	—
	0·76	0·20	—	—
Average	0·73	0·25	0·53	0·60
Conditioned reflex reaction to bell and to setting	0·74	0·28	0·65	0·99
	0·71	0·23	0·64	0·85
	0·68	0·20	0·69	0·85
	0·65	0·23	0·69	0·94
	0·70	0·30	0·78	0·98
	0·74	0·28	0·79	0·98
	0·68	0·30	0·70	0·86
	0·71	0·31	0·65	0·81
	—	0·31	—	—
	—	0·28	—	—
Average	0·70	0·27	0·70	0·91

CONCLUSIONS

(1) A quite definite, regular pattern was observed in the changes occurring in the contents of ammonia and dicarboxylic amino acids in brain tissue and in the blood in experimental epilepsy: ammonia was considerably increased and the dicarboxylic amino acids were almost always reduced.

(2) The changes in the contents of ammonia, glutamine and dicarboxylic amino acids developing in the blood of dogs during convulsive seizures of conditioned reflex origin were very similar to those produced by artificial unconditioned stimuli (electric current).

(3) The biochemical changes we observed during reflex epilepsy in rats were similar to those seen in conditioned reflex epileptic attacks produced in dogs.

REFERENCES

ANTONITIS, J., D. CRARY and P. SAWIN, *J. Heredity* **6**, 279 (1954).
BALAZH, T. R. and F. B. SHTRAUB, Ukrainian Biochemical J. (*Ukr. biokhim. zh.*) **25**, 17 (1953).
BENITEZ, D., G. R. PSCHEIDT and W. E. STOHE, *Am. J. Physiol.* **176**, 480 (1954).
BUDANOVA, A. M., Reports of the U.S.S.R. Academy of Sciences (*Dokl. Akad. Nauk SSSR*) **75**, 875 (1950).
BUDANOVA, A. M., Papers of the Institute of Animal Morphology, U.S.S.R. Academy of Sciences (*Trudy IMZh. im. a. N.. Severtsova Akad. Nauk SSSR*) **6**, 38 (1952).
BUDANOVA, A. M., Problems of Medical Chemistry (*Voprosy med. khimii*) **1**, 190 (1955a).
BUDANOVA, A. M., Bulletin of the U.S.S.R. Academy of Sciences, Biological Series (*Izv. Akad. Nauk SSSR, seriya biol.*) **6**, 82 (1955b).
BUDANOVA, A. M., J. Higher Nervous Activity (*Zh. vyssh. nervn. deyat.*) **7**, 554 (1957).
EPSHTEIN, S. F., Ukrainian Biochemical J. (*Ukr. biokhim. zh.*) **32**, 416 (1951a).
EPSHTEIN, S. F., Bull. Exp. Biology and Medicine (*Byull. eksp. biol. i med.*) **1**, 156 (1951b).
FERDMAN, D. L., Recent Advances in Biology (*Uspekhi sovrem. biol.*) **14**, 191 (1941).
FERDMAN, D. L., S. F. FRENKEL' and A. I. SILAKOVA, Biochemistry (*Biokhimiya*) **7**, 43 (1942).
GEIMAN, YE. YE., Physiol. J. U.S.S.R. (*Fiziol. zh. SSSR*) **20**, 846 (1936).
GOLUBTSOVA, A. V. and T. P. ZHUKOVA, Bull. Exp. Biology and Medicine (*Byull. eksp. biol. i med.*) **2**, 187 (1952).
GOLUBTSOVA, A. V. and I. L. KAN, Bull. Exp. Biology and Medicine (*Byull. eksp. biol. i med*) **1**, 129 (1936).
GOLUBTSOVA, A. V. and N. K. NAGRADOVA, Bull. Exp. Biology and Medicine (*Byull. eksp. biol. i med.*) **9**, 39 (1955).
KAGANOVSKAYA, S. N. and I. L. KAN, Bull. Exp. Biology and Medicine (*Byull. eksp. biol. i med.*) **1**, 495 (1936).
KOSHTOYANTS, KH. S., Recent Advances in Biology (*Uspekhi sovrem. biol.*) **18**, 617 (1943).
KOSHTOYANTS, KH. S., Bull. of the U.S.S.R. Academy of Sciences (*Izv. Akad. Nauk SSSR, seriya biol.*) **2**, 171 (1945).
KOSHTOYANTS, KH. S., *Collection of Papers Commemorating the 30th Anniversary of the Great October Revolution* (Yubileinyi sbornik, posvyashch. 30-letiyu Velikoi Oktyabr'skoi revolyutsii). Izdat. Akad. Nauk SSSR (1947).
KOSHTOYANTS, KH. S., Reports of the U.S.S.R. Academy of Sciences (*Dokl. Akad. Nauk SSSR*) **60**, 6 (1948).
KOSHTOYANTS, KH. S. and Ts. V. SERBENYUK, Reports of the U.S.S.R. Academy of Sciences (*Dokl. Akad. Nauk SSSR*) **104**, 795 (1955).
KRUSHINSKII, L. V., Recent Advances in Biology (*Uspekhi sovrem. biol.*) **28**, 108 (1949).
KRUSHINSKII, L. V., Recent Advances in Biology (*Uspekhi sovrem. biol.*) **33**, 74 (1954).
KRUSHINSKII, L. V., D. A. FLEYEV and A. N. MOLODKINA, J. of G. Biology (*Zh. obshchei biol.*) **11**, 104 (1950).
PAVLOV, I. P., Archives of Biological Sciences (*Arkh. biol. nauk*) **4**, 191 (1896).
PAVLOV, I. P., *Complete works* (Poln. sobr. soch.) **4** (1951).
PRAVDICH-NEMINSKII, V. V., Bulletin of the Biological Research Institute, Perm University (*Izv. Biol. nauchno-issled. in-ta pri Permskom gos. un-te*) **5**, 421 (1927).
SPERANSKII, A. D., *The Epileptic Attack* (Epilepticheskii pristup) Medgiz (1932).
TASHIRO, S., *Am. J. Physiol.* **60**, 519 (1922).
TORDA, G. I., *Pharmacol. Expl. Therap.* **107**, 197 (1953).
VLADIMIROVA, YE. A., Physiol. J. U.S.S.R. (*Fiziol. zh. SSSR*) **25**, 930 (1938a).
VLADIMIROVA, YE. A., Physiol. J. U.S.S.R. (*Fiziol. zh. SSSR*) **24**, 915 (1938b).
VLADIMIROVA, YE. A., Problems of Medical Chemistry (*Voprosy med. khimii*) **2**, 2 (1950a).

VLADIMIROVA, YE. A., Bull. Exp. Biology and Medicine (*Byull. eksp. biol. i med.*) **29,** 219 (1950b).

VLADIMIROVA, YE. A., Bull. Exp. Biology and Medicine (*Byull eksp. biol. i med.*) **30,** 345 (1950c).

VLADIMIROVA, YE. A., Bull. Exp. Biology and Medicine (*Byull. eksp. biol. i med.*) **31,** 288 288 (1953).

VLADIMIROVA, YE. A., Reports of the U.S.S.R. Academy of Sciences (*Dokl. Akad. Nauk SSSR*) **95,** 905 (1954).

VLADIMIROVA, YE. A., Reports of the U.S.S.R. Academy of Sciences (*Dokl. Akad. Nauk SSSR*) **106,** 937 (1956).

WINTERSTEIN, H. and C. HIRSCHBERG, *Biochem. Z.* **156,** 138 (1925).

YUDAYEV, N. A. and M. A. KREKHOVA, Problems of Medical Chemistry (*Voprosy med. khimii*) **1,** 24 (1955).

THE ORIGINS OF PATTERNED NERVOUS DISCHARGE*

Theodore Holmes Bullock†

University of California, Los Angeles

The output of single neurons and of groups of neurons is normally probably always patterned, i.e. temporally and spatially distributed in a meaningful, non-random way. One way of stating the function of the nervous system, or of any significant part of it, is that it formulates appropriately patterned messages in code. The question how this formulation takes place is surely one of the core questions of general neurology. Curiously, it has received little direct attention although a great body of related information is known.

The question of the mechanism of formulation of meaningful pattern in the discharge of nerve cells is in turn basic to the origins of pattern and timing in all nervously mediated actions and behavior. I shall deal here chiefly with the relative roles of central nervous automaticity versus feedback from the periphery (the effectors or the actions they cause). Some recent findings on the intimate neuronal events of automaticity are included at the end. For this discussion, temporal pattern can be regarded as more basic than spatial pattern, and I shall consider only this aspect. Given either one, a suitable system can provide the other but it seems more likely that in actuality spatial patterns are not so often the real origin of temporal patterns as they are the consequence, in the nervous system.

The present essay does not attempt a review of the pertinent literature. However, it is important to note that in effect the last word on the subject was spoken by Sir James Gray in the 1950 S.E.B. symposium on "Physiological Mechanisms in Animal Behaviour."

"The whole problem of central versus peripheral control of muscular activity is obviously extremely complex, and for any particular observer there must nearly always be some element of bias in favour of the view which provides the more satisfactory picture of the particular material with

* Reprinted from *Behaviour*, **17**, 1, and published by kind permission of N. V. Boekhandel en Drukkerij V/H. E. J. Brill, Leiden, Netherlands.

† Aided by grants from the National Institute of Neurological Diseases and Blindness and The Office of Naval Research. Based on a paper delivered to the International Ethological Conference, Cambridge, England, September, 1959.

which he is most familiar. To my mind, the role of the proprioceptors in amphibian ambulation seems to be sufficiently clear to doubt the necessity of introducing conceptions of central control for which there is, at present, no direct experimental evidence. How far we are justified in attempting to extend this picture to mammals is more doubtful. For present purposes, however, the main conclusion must be that the existence of centrally controlled patterns of locomotion should be regarded as non-proven..." (Gray, 1950, p. 124).

I would underline that it is difficult to find fault with the elegant work and cautious arguments of Gray and Lissmann (summarized in the article referred to) except in matters of emphasis and of selection of examples. But it is just here I believe where there has grown up a climate of opinion, not fully explained by a literal reading of these authors, which is so one-sided, emphasizing peripheral as opposed to central control, as to call for restoration of a balance.

Theoretically, temporal pattern may be expected to arise in one of two general ways: by following timing cues from peripheral causes or timing cues from central pacemakers.

A. Timing cues from peripheral causes are exemplified by ordinary reflexes. Except in a few special cases, the input pattern of impulses is greatly "distorted" in the output, that is, the central nervous system formulates an appropriate output which is only dependent on the input for triggering. Commonly a large number of unsynchronized input impulses, arriving at a given neuron cause a smaller number of rhythmic output impulses. The peripheral cause which confers the timing may be an environmental event as in an eye-blink to an approaching object (Fig. 1, A). (It may even be a bodily factor of non-nervous nature, as when a fly's wing buzzes more rapidly upon being cut short and more slowly when loaded. Other evidences indicates this is not due to sensory feedback but is purely mechanical.)

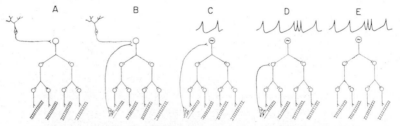

Fig. 1. Diagrams of types of pattern formulation. The three levels of neurons are understood to represent branching chains in whose junctions integrative properties may alter the actual impulses and deliver them spatially as well as temporally distributed, to the effectors (bottom).

A and B are shown with receptors, C, D and E with spontaneous pacemakers giving simple or grouped discharges. B and C have proprioceptive feedback acting on the trigger neuron, D only on the shaping of the pattern. Further explanation in the text.

Probably the most common peripheral cause of rhythmic patterns in terrestrial animals is sensory feedback from proprioceptors (Fig. 1, B). Any case belongs in this category where a feedback loop exists which actually starts the next cycle of events before some central pacemaker does (Fig. 1, C). From this requirement the difficulty of distinguishing categories in practice is obvious, but the distinctions are nevertheless real.

A subcategory of some interest must be those patterns derived from receptors with maintained background discharge. The function connecting input and output may become complex. This is probably not the unusual but the usual case, especially if we take into account maintained background discharge of some of the central neurons in the pathway. A related class consists of actions which depend on the presence of a tonic input from certain receptors to sustain the central excitatory state, even when those receptors are presumably not necessary for their sensory-informational contribution or for timing the pattern ("*Stimulationsorgane*" of von Buddenbrock and others).

Although in this general class the rhythmically recurring patterns are peripherally determined by feedback which is essential to the rhythmicity, the diagram (Fig. 1, B) shows that there must usually be some triggering signal to start the rhythm from a resting condition. This may be a sensory input other than feedback or a centrally arising command.

Now most actions triggered by input signals contain elements of pattern not in the input. Consider eye movements, swallowing, coughing, a cricket's chirp, a grasshopper's hop, a squid's color change, taxes and instincts, not to speak of more complex behavior. From the feeding movements of a sea anemone to formation of a word in human speech, the predetermined central contribution to the pattern is enormous even if the initiation follows a peripheral cue. Our examples have been confined to motor acts but is it not just as likely that the output of most central masses of organized neurons constituting an integrating level is also patterned in a way not contained in its input? A pre-existing pattern, awaiting first permissive input and then triggering input to release it, may reasonably be inferred to be, not universal, but frequent.

B. Timing cues from central pacemakers are another way of triggering patterned output. In principle it should be no surprise to find that a perfectly coordinated sequence of reciprocal activation of antagonistic muscles forming an adaptive action can arise purely centrally. For in only one uncomplicated feature does this differ from the picture just drawn for reflexes, namely that a central timer is provided which rings an alarm at intervals, releasing a predetermined mechanism.

The timer or pacemaker or central automaticity is by definition not dependent on phasic peripheral cues but it always depends on certain steady state conditions, e.g. temperature and ionic and organic milieu. It is highly likely that the automaticity often depends also on steady state or background impulses, as it were, to keep it awake. Under certain steady conditions an isolated heart beats, a respiratory center discharges in an isolated brain stem (Salmoiraghi and Burns, 1958), an embryo moves its limbs in a coordinated way when there are no reflex arcs formed (Weiss), a resting millipede starts to walk, a ctenophore abruptly changes the direction of its ciliary metachronal wave, a hovering fish moves now this fin, now that. Wells (1950) concluded that the rhythmic movements of *Arenicola* are neither responses to environmental cues nor to the internal needs they normally satisfy. Still one can be sure some state or substance has accumulated to a threshold and caused the alarm to ring. This is exactly what we mean by spontaneity: the determination by internal factors of when the alarm shall ring to a steady application of energy or accumulation of something.

Besides the clear cases of neurogenic cardiac rhythms there are other rhythmic processes which have been recorded electrically from the central nervous system, after experimentally isolating it from the periphery. The isolated ventral nerve cord of the beetle, *Dytiscus* is a classical case (Adrian, 1931). The respiratory neurons in vertebrates have already been referred to above (see also Oberholzer and Tofani, 1960). Hughes and Wiersma (1960) have found persistence of the rhythmic discharge of motoneurons to a swimmeret in crayfish after isolation of the abdominal cord from the periphery. Miller (1960) and Wilson and Weis-Fogh (1962) find the breathing and flying rhythms of a locust to be central and not dependent on any phasic input. The evidence is strong that the rhythm of swimming pulsations in medusae is of nervous origin and it may be supposed that the rhythm of tentacle activity of certain alcyonarian polyps is also (Horridge, 1956, 1959). Peristaltic creeping in the earthworm probably arises as a central rhythm and is not dependent on phasic input although its spread along the animal depends on tonic input from tactile receptors or proprioceptors. Parapodial creeping in *Nereis* is even more dependent on intrinsic nervous automaticity. Swimming in the leech, *Hirudo* seems likely also to come from a neurogenic rhythm rather than from chain reflexes as is clearly the case for the walking movements of this animal. The theoretical alternative of a spontaneous rhythm modulated in frequency by feedback, that is by phasic input, is probably common (Fig. 1, C). It can properly be called a central automatism, since removal of the phasic input can alter but not stop the rhythm. The feedback may also be competent to maintain the rhythm, if it were possible to stop the spontaneity, and may in some cases take control by having time constants for a higher frequency than the autochthonous one. Examples which have actually been shown to belong to this class rather than one of the others cannot at present be given.

The feedback may only modulate the form but not the frequency of the rhythm by affecting not the pacemaker but its followers (Fig. 1, D).

The disturbances in walking in a tabetic or a blinded man show the effect of missing feedback on the form a distinct from the occurrence of a pattern.

The feedback in any of these cases may be from follower neurons and not only from the periphery. It may be a complex mixture including positive and negative, specific (from one muscle) and less specific (from many muscles), fast and slow-adapting influx and may be more or less dependent on higher central influences (Eccles and Lundberg, 1958).

Central automatism without feedback (Fig. 1, E), at least of immediate role in timing, is not unreasonable. Of course an eventual feedback is inevitable—the success or failure of the action for the biological welfare of the organism will influence the evolution of the mechanism. We know of such purely central cases. In fact, several kinds of cases are known.

(1) Some pacemakers are fixed frequency alarm clocks as far as normal sensory influence is concerned. The weak electric organs of gymnotid fish like *Eigenmannia* discharge at a constant frequency of about 350 per sec, day and night, uninfluenced by excitement, food or other fish but only by temperature among factors so far tested (Lissmann, 1958; Coates *et al.*, 1954, Bennett and Grundfest, 1959). The electric discharge of *Torpedo* (Albe-Fessard and Szabo, 1954) and the sound production in the cicada, *Graptosaltria* (Hagiwara and Watanabe, 1956) involve fixed frequency motoneuron firing and sensory input can determine only the duration of a burst.

(2) More commonly, the neurons between pacemaker and effector are integrative followers, modifying the details of the temporal pattern within each cycle. In each heart beat of a lobster a complex burst of several dozen impulses arises in a pacemaker neuron of the cardiac ganglion, even when the ganglion is isolated from the heart. It fires many times during a burst, and the other neurons—followers—fire repeatedly, each in a different pattern, for example starting a high frequency and declining. The actual frequencies, time courses, durations and numbers of impulses are individually characteristic and recur consistently for hundreds of heart beats (Maynard, 1955, Bullock, 1958).

This has been analyzed in some detail and the conclusion reached that a primary patterned burst arises in a single cell, the pacemaker, not dependent on feedback of spikes from other cells to formulate it. Intracellular mechanisms, presumably two or more interacting processes must be postulated.

These, then, are the main alternative sources of initiation of pattern. It is probable that each of them actually occurs in certain cases. In most cases it has not been unequivocally determined which category is involved, e.g. locomotion in insects, fish and terrestrial vertebrates. The methodology necessary is similar to that used in the analysis of control system, viz. the interruption of, or injection of a spurious signal into, selected parts of the presumptive loop. To accomplish this in a known manner, for example to cut all the sensory feedback without disturbing other elements, such as reducing some essential tonic input, is technically difficult because most nerves are mixed. As a result the literature, though abundant, is conflicting and in most instances inadequate for a satisfactory evaluation.

Some statements are readily established, however. When the action never occurs until released by external stimuli, it can be said to be a pure case of peripheral timing. Although "never" is a hard requirement to satisfy, possibly many reflexes such as the lateral giant fiber startle responses in earthworm and crayfish are examples and, barring the discovery of very complete "vacuum" mating and feeding, without mate or prey, the finer movements of copulatory organs or mouthparts may be. But in view of the known occurrence of vacuum activity (see Verplanck, 1957), this cannot be assumed without careful examination in any given case. The importance of the central elements in determining the shape and course of such responses is clear upon consideration of the simplicity of the timing trigger in the stimulus situation. Wiersma (1952) speaks of push-button responses, exemplified by giant fiber-mediated escape movements. These are peripherally timed but it is not good English to speak of peripherally "controlled." If my enemy strikes, he may precipitate my action but he does not control it!

When the action is obviously disturbed in pattern by cutting some sensory pathways, it can be said that peripheral elements at least play a role in shaping the pattern. The hind limbs of a frog with all dorsal roots contributing to them severed, are somewhat abnormal in details of righting and hopping though these movements can be performed remarkably well. A mantid makes errors in striking at prey after neck proprioceptors are cut. The immediate change of gait of insects upon amputation of some of the legs and the restoration of normal gait, in some experiments, by gluing pegs onto the stumps, points to the same conclusion in these instances (Hughes, 1958).

But it cannot be said that the rhythm itself, apart from its detailed form, is peripheral or feedback-determined unless rigorous experiments show the rhythm fails when nothing but timing cues in the input are cut off. The experiments of Gray and Lissman (1940, 1946) on ambulation in toads appear to have shown just this. A toad continued to show stepping movements with all dorsal roots cut but one, the minor cutaneous tenth dorsal root, but stopped when that was cut. The probability that the minimum essential input was phasic, providing a timing cue rather than merely tonic, was indicated by the behavior of preparations with three of the limbs plus the dorsal musculature immobilized by section of their motor roots and the fourth limb left at first intact, but with its nerve supply exposed. Relatively weak stimuli to any limb sufficed to elicit a clear ambulatory rhythm. But when the dorsal roots of the intact limb were severed, all rhythmic response disappeared, even to strong stimuli. The previously intact limb still gave specific reflex responses but only monophasically. "It is difficult to draw any conclusion other than that when (phasic) proprioceptor impulses from other limbs are effectively excluded, the impulses arising in the proprioceptor endings of the intact limb are essential for the maintenance of the ambulatory" rhythm. (Gray, 1950, p. 117.)

Similar experiments on other species are extremely desirable, for both the just mentioned results and those to the opposite effect in the list on p. 48 seem clear and some relation to species or type of movement seems required. The use of additional technics is also desirable, for example, interrupting ventral roots and looking for rhythmic discharge in their central stumps by electrical recording. Still another technic of servo-loop analysis, that of injecting artificial signals has also been little used. Von Holst manipulated the fins of a fish and adduced evidence that this did not determine or even seriously influence the rhythm normally controlling that fin, since the rhythm could still be seen as usual superinposed on the separate rhythm of another subordinate fin.

Another type of evidence pointing to pattern formulation by central neurons, even without any reafference (feedback) is the literature on b r a i n stimulation in unanesthetized animals, a technic now in use by many authors. In predisposed humans, Penfield has found that certain regions of the cortex can be crudely stimulated electrically and complex, vivid audio-visual experiences triggered. The subject reports a scene as though reliving it, each time and only while the electrical stimulus is applied to that spot. Less complex but normally coordinated movements occur in lower forms. Although many regions of the brain are "silent" or yield simple jerks or twitches, particular loci call up entirely normal-appearing sequences such as chirping or antenna-cleaning in crickets (Huber, 1957), compulsive drinking in a goat (Andersson, 1953), stuffing imaginary seeds into the mouth in a pocket mouse (Strumwasser and Cade, 1957), crowing and many other actions in chickens (Holst and St. Paul, 1960).

The category of patterned movements represented by most of the responses just mentioned ("fixed action patterns") is of special interest for our problem. Other familiar examples are sneezing, jumping, spitting, stinging, swallowing, seizing, displaying and the like. They are in general not rhythmic like heartbeats and locomotion, but brief and episodic and suggest in certain cases rather less o p p o r t u n i t y for f e e d b a c k c o n t r o l of the pattern than in others. This could well be studied with the technics already mentioned. Mittelstaedt (1957) provides a review of a few cases already examined from the point of view of control circuits. The central origin, which is the aspect of interest here, is found in such diagrams as "higher command" or an equivalent term. It seems at present likely that for many relatively complex behavioral actions the nervous system contains not only genetically determined circuits but also genetically determined physiological properties of their components so that the complete act is represented in coded form and awaits only an adequate trigger (Bullock, 1957), either internal or

3 a*

external. In the former event we have a built-in tendency to spontaneous discharge under suitable steady state conditions, which may include deprivation of external releasers and gradual increase of probability of release, by weaker stimuli or eventually "in a vacuum", without external trigger.

Closer understanding of the mechanism of pattern formulation by feedback, or more generally, by circulating signals in circuits with loops, presents one class of problems. Chiefly, these are the determination in given cases of the form of the circuit, the kinds of functions performed where signals are integrated and the time constants. Examples of such analyses are Mittelstaedt (1957), Hassenstein and Reichardt (1956), Lettvin and Maturana (1959), Hubel and Wiesel (1959). These and other cases illustrate the role of connections and coupling functions in formulating patterns of impulses in consequence of some initial event. But although reverberating circuits are known, I do not think of an instance where reverberation confined within the nervous system is known to be the basis of a maintained rhythm.

Quite a different class of problems is posed by the mechanism of pattern formulation based on true spontaneity. At the present stage it is exciting simply to see the signs of this, therefore to be able to study its locus and character. In the lobster cardiac ganglion and in some other cases, we now have—as a result of the ultramicroelectrode which penetrates an active cell without significantly changing its activity (monitored by external recording electrodes)—an intimate view of the truly spontaneous activity of single neurons. We even have evidence of the confinement of the pacemaker to a limited part of a neuron for there can be two separate rhythms in one cell at one time and we can say that sometimes the electrode is near, at other times it is far from the pacemaker region. We find both true relaxation oscillation and simple pendulum oscillation. Either can give, as a special case, grouped bursts of impulses from a single cell (Bullock and Terzuolo, 1957, Bullock, 1959). This finding is of particular interest for it means that not only simple triggers can arise spontaneously but even patterned clusters of nerve impulses, like the more complex repeated patterns of a snare drum, can arise within a single neuron. Presumably this requires the interplay of two or more separate processes and perhaps distinct parts of the cell. But these are questions still in the future.

SUMMARY

In sum, sensory input is of decisive importance—in creating the permissive steady state centrally (making the frog want to jump), in directing action adaptively (aiming his jump), and in perfecting details during the action in some cases (probably more in mantid fly catching than in frog jumping). But central patterning is the necessary and often the sufficient condition for determining the main characteristic features of almost all actions, whether stimulus triggered or spontaneous.

Recent neurophysiological evidence shows that primary temporal pattern of impulse sequence, as in regular bursts may arise spontaneously within localized pacemaker regions of one single neuron. Or pattern may be formulated between cells by complex combinations of specific connections using the integrative properties of neurons to cause output patterns that are different from but some function of input: thus delays, rates of rise and fall of several kinds of synaptic potentials on the same cell, their spatial spread and summation, facilitation, after-excitation and -inhibition.

The primary factor in the special case of rhythmically recurring patterns like locomotion, breathing and heartbeats, is apparently sometimes central automaticity and sometimes phasic input from proprioceptive feedback consequent upon the execution of the preceding phase. The feedback may modify the details of form or frequency even in the cases where it is not necessary to maintain the rhythm. Tonic input may be important in keeping up a central excitatory state without providing essential timing cues. The general conclusion is pluralistic: pattern arises in different ways, but in almost all, the details of temporal and spatial distribution of impulses, as distinct from the triggering, are basically central. When we find peripheral triggering or modulation, we can speak of peripheral determination or influence but hardly of peripheral control of behavior.

Nervous systems are not like present day computers, even complex ones, but have oscillators and built-in stored patterns; they do not give outputs predictable by their inputs or externally controlled "instructions."

REFERENCES

ADRIAN, E. D., Potential changes in the isolated nervous system of *Dytiscus marginalis*. *J. Physiol.* **72**, p. 132–151 (1931).

ALBE-FESSARD, D. and T. SZABO, Étude microphysiologique du neurone intermédiare d'une chaîne reflexe disynaptique. *C. R. Soc. Biol.* **148**, p. 281–283 (1954).

ANDERSSON, B., The effect of injections of hypertonic NaCl-solutions into different parts of the hypothalamus of goats. *Acta physiol. Scandinav.* **28**, p. 188–201 (1953).

BUDDENBROCK, W. VON, Sinnesphysiologie. *Vergleichende Physiologie* **1**, Birkhauser, Basel (1952).

BENNETT, M. V. L. and H. GRUNDFEST, Electrophysiology of electric organ in *Gymnotus carapo. J. gen. Physiol.* **42**, p. 1067–1104 (1959).

BULLOCK, T. H., The trigger concept in biology. In *Physiological Triggers and Discontinuous Rate Processes*, T. H. BULLOCK, ed. Amer. Physiol. Soc., Washington (1956).

BULLOCK, T. H., Parameters of integrative action of the nervous system at the neuronal level. In *The Submicroscopic Organization and Function of Nerve Cells*, H. FERNÁNDEZ-MORÁN and R. BROWN, eds. *Exper. Cell. Res.* Suppl. 5, p. 323–337 (1958).

BULLOCK, T. H., Initiation of nerve impulses in receptor and central neurons. In *Biophysical Science, Revs. Mod. Physics* **31**, p. 504–514 (1959) (also Wiley, New York).

BULLOCK, T. H. and C. A. TERZUOLO, Diverse forms of activity in the somata of spontaneous and integrating ganglion cells. *J. Physiol.* **138**, p. 351–364 (1957).

COATES, C. W., M. ALTAMIRANO and H. GRUNDFEST, Activity in electrogenic organs of knifefishes. *Science* **120**, p. 845–846 (1954).

ECCLES, R. M. and A. LUNDBERG, Integrative pattern of Ia synaptic actions on motoneurones of hip and knee muscles. *J. Physiol.* **144**, p. 271–298 (1958).

GRAY, J., The role of peripheral sense organs during locomotion in the vertebrates. *Symp. Soc. Exp. Biol.* **4**, p. 112–126 (1950).

GRAY, J. and H. W. LISSMANN, The effect of de-afferentiation upon the locomotor activity of amphibian limbs. *J. exp. Biol.* **17**, p. 227–236 (1940).

GRAY, J. and H. W. LISSMANN, Ambulatory reflexes in spinal amphibians. *J. exp. Biol.* **17**, p. 237–251 (1940).

GRAY, J. and H. W. LISSMANN, Further observations on the effect of de-afferentiation on the locomotory activity of amphibian limbs. *J. exp. Biol.* **23**, p. 121–132 (1946).

GRAY, J. and H. W. LISSMANN, The coordination of limb movements in the amphibia. *J. exp. Biol.* **23**, p. 133–142 (1946).

HAGIWARA, S. and A. WATANABE, Discharges in motoneurons of cicada. *J. cell. comp. Physiol.* **47**, p. 415–428 (1956).

HASSENSTEIN, B. and W. REICHARDT, System-theoretische Analyse der Zeit-Reihenfolge und Vorzeichenauswertung bei der Bewegungsperzeption des Rüsselkäfers *Chlorophanus*. *Z. Naturf.* **11** b, p. 513–524 (1956).

HOLST, E. VON and U. ST. PAUL, Von Wirkungsgefüge der Triebe. *Naturwissenschaften* **18**, p. 409–422 (1960).

HORRIDGE, G. A., The responses of *Heteroxenia* (Alcyonaria) to stimulation and to some inorganic ions. *J. exp. Biol.* **33**, p. 604–614 (1956).

HORRIDGE, G. A., The nerves and muscles of medusae. VI. The rhythm. *J. exp. Biol.* **36** p. 72–91 (1959).

HUBEL, D. H. and T. N. WIESEL, Receptive fields in the cat's striate cortex. *J. Physiol.* **148** p. 574–591 (1959).

HUBER, F., Sitz und Bedeutung nervöser Zentren für Instinkthandlungen beim Männchen von *Gryllus campestris* (L.). *Z. Tierpsychol.* **12**, p. 12–48 (1955).

HUGHES, G. M., The coordination of insect movements. II. The effect of limb amputation and the cutting of commissures in the cockroach (*Blatta orientalis*). *J. exp. Biol.* **34**, p. 306–333 (1957).

HUGHES, G. M. and C. A. G. WIERSMA, The coordination of the swimmeret movements in the crayfish, *Procambarus clarkii* Girard. *J. exp. Biol.* **37**, 657–670 (1960).

LETTVIN, J. Y., H. R. MATURANA, W. S. McCULLOCH and W. H. PITTS, What the frog's eye tells the frog's brain. *Proc. I.R.E.* **47**, p. 1940–1951 (1959).

LISSMANN, W. H., On the function and evolution of electric organs in fish. *J. exp. Biol.* **35**, p. 156–191 (1958).

MAYNARD, D. M., Activity in a crustacean ganglion. II. Pattern and interaction in burst formation. *Biol. Bull.* **109**, p. 420–436 (1955).

MILLER, P. L., Respiration in the desert locust. *J. exp. Biol.* **37**, p. 224–278 (1960).

MITTELSTAEDT, H., Prey capture in mantids. In *Recent Advances in Invertebrate Physiology*. Univ. of Oregon, Eugene (1957).

OBERHOLZER, J. H. and W. O. TOFANI, The neutral control of respiration. In *Handbook of Physiology*, Sect. I, *Neurophysiology*, vol. 2, p. 1111–1129 (1960).

SALMOIRHAGI, G. C. and B. D. BURNS, Rhythmicity of breathing—a study with extracellular microelectrodes. *Fed. Proc.* **17**, p. 139 (1958).

STRUMWASSER, F. and T. CADE, Behavior elicited by brain stimulation in freely moving vertebrates. *Anat. Rec.* **128**, p. 630–631 (1957).

VERPLANCK, W., A glossary of some terms used in the objective science of behavior. *Psych. Rev.* **64** (Suppl. no. 6, part 2), p. i–viii, 1–42 (1957).

WEISS, P., Experimental analysis of coordination by the disarrangement of central-peripheral relations. *Symp. Soc. Exp. Biol.* **4**, p. 92–111 (1950).

WELLS, G. P., Spontaneous activity cycles in polychaete worms. *Symp. Soc. Exp. Biol.* **4,** p. 127–142 (1950).

WELLS, G. P., *The sources of animal behaviour*. An inaugural lecture delivered at University College, London, 5 May 1955. H. K. Lewis, London (1955).

WIERSMA, C. A. G., Neurons of arthropods. *Cold Spring Harbor Symp. Quant. Biol.* **17,** p. 155–164 (1952).

WILSON, D. M. and T. WEIS-FOGH, Patterned activity of co-ordinated motor units studied in flying locusts. *J. exp. Biol.* **39,** 643–667 (1962).

THE IMPORTANCE OF POTASSIUM IONS IN THE MECHANISM OF SPREADING CORTICAL LEÃO DEPRESSION

J. Bureš, O. Burešová and I. Křivánek

Physiological Institute, Czechoslovakian Academy of Sciences, Prague

Translated by Dr. R. Crawford

THE question of whether potassium ions can, under certain circumstances, play the part of mediator was investigated by Koshtoyants and his colleagues in the peripheral synapse (Koshtoyants, 1957; Koshtoyants and Salanki, 1958). The need for an understanding of the mediator role of potassium in the central nervous system has become more urgent in the last few years in connexion with analysis of the phenomenon of spreading cortical depression (SD). Electrical, mechanical, thermal and chemical stimuli of sufficient strength, acting directly on the surface of the cortex, reduce electrical activity at the point of their application. The reduced electrical activity spreads through the cortex at a rate of 2–5 mm/min in all directions (Leão, 1944a). Maximum depression persists for several minutes in each cortical region and electrical activity is completely restored only after 10–20 min. The front of the wave of depressed electrical activity is associated with slow potential change—surface electronegativity which attains an amplitude of 5–10 mV and which is replaced after 1–2 min by less marked electropositivity (Fig. 1). In the presence of spreading depression there is reduction both of spontaneous and evoked EEG activity, change in the excitability of motor regions, etc. All this indicates that during spreading depression there is profound disturbance of the normal physiological functions of the cerebral cortex, which is also revealed by considerable impairment of conditioned reflex activity (Burešová, 1956; Bureš and Burešová, 1960).

Despite the fact that spreading depression has received a great deal of attention in the course of the last 15 years (Marshall, 1959), the mechanism of this interesting phenomenon still remains obscure. The fact that spreading depression could be produced with potassium chloride led to the assumption that potassium ions were concerned in this phenomenon. This paper describes experimental results obtained in our laboratory during the last 5 years in the course of an attempt to verify this hypothesis.

58

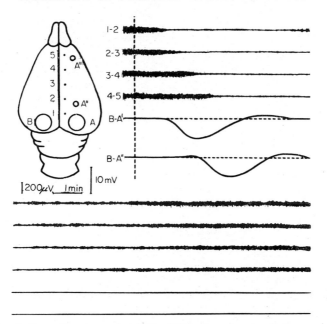

FIG. 1. Spreading depression in the EEG of a rat under dial narcosis.

1–5: needle electrodes. B, A′, A″: calomel electrodes for the recording of the steady potential. Dotted vertical line: application of 1 per cent KCl through trephine opening A.

POTASSIUM IONS AS A FACTOR PRODUCING DEPRESSION

The experiments were carried out on albino rats aged 2 or 3 months, narcotized with dial (40 mg/kg). Large trephine openings (diameter 5 mm) for the application of solutions and smaller openings for the application of calomel electrodes to record slow potential changes were made over both hemispheres. In most of the experiments EEGs were also recorded with needle epidural electrodes (Fig. 1). The threshold concentrations producing spreading depression were determined for the various substances in the following manner. The substances to be examined were applied to the cortex in increasing strengths (with intervals of 30–40 min between applications) until spreading depression developed. The results were processed statistically by the Probit method or by the moving averages method (Finney, 1950; Weil, 1952).

Substances producing spreading depression can be divided into three groups.

(1) Substances producing depolarization of the cell membranes by changing the ion composition in the extracellular space. K^+ is a typical example of this group.

(2) Substances which disturb cell metabolism as, for example, 2,4-di-nitrophenol, NaCN, monoiodoacetic acid, etc.; when exposed to the action

of these substances the cell cannot maintain high gradients of ion concentrations between the intracellular and extracellular space.

(3) Amino acids producing depression (glutamic acid, aspartic acid, glutamine, asparagine). The mode of action of these substances is unknown.

Table 1 gives the threshold concentrations of the most important substances producing spreading depression. Obviously, if we are to determine

TABLE 1. Threshold concentrations of certain substances causing spreading depression

Substance	Number of experiments	$\log ED\,50 \pm \sigma \log ED\,50$	ED 50
KCl	50	$-1\cdot097 \pm 0\cdot024$	0·080 M
2,4-dinitrophenol	47	$-3\cdot68 \pm 0\cdot26$	$2\cdot08 \times 10^{-4}$ M
NaCN	53	$-2\cdot82 \pm 0\cdot09$	$1\cdot51 \times 10^{-3}$ M
Monoiodoacetic acid	46	$-2\cdot05 \pm 0\cdot02$	$8\cdot86 \times 10^{-3}$ M
1-asparagine	50	$-1\cdot26 \pm 0\cdot07$	0·055 M
1-glutamine	62	$-1\cdot11 \pm 0\cdot05$	0·077 M
1-glutamic acid	52	$-0\cdot65 \pm 0\cdot06$	0·224 M
1-aspartic acid	56	$-1\cdot05 \pm 0\cdot05$	0·089 M

which substance is the mediator of spreading depression, that substance must not only be present in the brain but must also cause spreading depression in a concentration which is physiological. In this light greatest attention should be given to potassium ions and amino acids. Yet it would hardly be possible to ascribe mediator function to any of these substances solely on the basis of the threshold concentrations producing spreading depression.

Experiments in which the development of spreading depression was blocked afforded more information. A feature which demanded attention was the great variety of substances producing spreading depression, with no differences whatever in the nature of the spreading depression produced. One gained the impression that the different stimuli produced different chain reactions converging ultimately through a common link to the process of spreading depression. A substance which interfered with one of these chain reactions also suppressed the depressor effect of the corresponding stimulus but was without influence on the effects of other stimuli. The blocking effect became more universal the nearer it was to the terminal common link of the different chain reactions. We have demonstrated in an investigation carried out jointly with Koshtoyants (Bureš and Koshtoyants, 1955) that glutathione could prevent development of the spreading depression produced by sublimate but did not alter the effectiveness of KCl. Glycylglutamine blocked the depressor effect of glutamine but had no effect on spreading depression produced by KCl. In contrast, divalent cations, particularly those of magnesium and calcium, blocked the effects of all substances producing spreading depression. A typical experiment illustrating the blocking effect of $CaCl_2$ is shown in Fig. 2. In view of the well-known antagonism between potassium and divalent cations in peripheral excitable structures (Shanes, 1958), it is suggested that the common end-link in the action of substances producing spreading depression is increase in the extracellular concentration of K^+ resulting from disturbance of the permeability of the cell membrane.

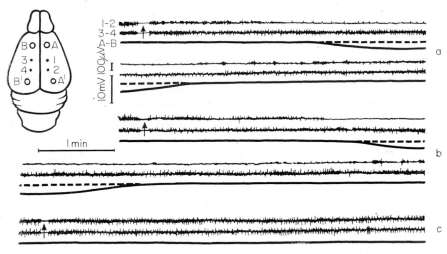

FIG. 2. Effect of Ca ions on spreading depression produced by application of 2 per cent KCl solution. Arrow: application to the region A' of a 2 per cent KCl solution containing various concentrations of $CaCl_2$.

a—0·86 per cent. b—1·08 per cent. c—1·29 per cent. The positions of the individual EEG leads are shown in the diagram. The slow potential was recorded between the region A and B.

Further proofs of this hypothesis were obtained by comparison of the relative effectiveness of the blocking effects of Mg^{++} and Ca^{++}. When the same concentration of potassium chloride (2 per cent) was used, $MgCl_2$ prevented the development of spreading depression in concentration about three times lower than that of $CaCl_2$ (Table 2). A similar relationship between the effective strengths of Mg^{++} and Ca^{++} could also be observed in relation to blocking of the spreading depression produced by an accurately dosed mechanical stimulus (Zacharova and Zachar, 1958).

This constancy of the relationship between the effectiveness of the blocking actions of Mg^{++} and Ca^{++} would appear to be connected with the fact that these ions exert their influence on the same link—the liberation of K^+ from neurons.

THE SPREAD OF DEPRESSION

The fact that spreading depression jumps across the sulci in the cortex (Marshall *et al.*, 1951) and that incision of the cortex does not prevent its spread (Sloan and Jasper, 1950) indicates that the spread does not depend on the continuity of nerve connexions. These observations are consistent with the hypothesis that the mode of spread is humoral. Grafstein (1956) observed that spreading depression, produced in an isolated strip of cat cortex, spreads more rapidly towards the cathode than towards the anode. From this she concluded that spread was due to positively charged particles, movement of which towards the cathode was accelerated by the electrical field. This favours the "potassium" nature of spreading depression and is inconsistent with the view that amino acids constitute the mediator of spreading depression, as movement of these would be accelerated in the opposite direction.

Almost at the same time we established (Bureš and Burešová, 1956) that the spread of depression could be prevented by the local application of Ca^{++} or Mg^{++}. The amplitude of the wave of steady potential associated with spreading depression was reduced almost to zero in a region of the cortex treated with divalent cations (Fig. 3). The Ca and Mg ion concentrations reducing the amplitude of the negative potential by 50 per cent were estimated. Table 2 shows that magnesium ions were about three

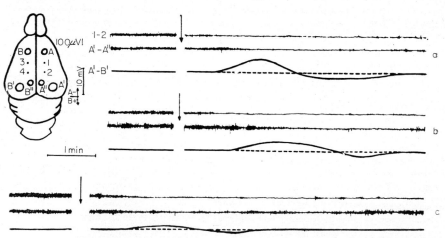

Fig. 3. Blocking of spreading depression in a region of the cortex protected by CaCl₂ solution.

1, 2, 3, 4: steel needles for EEG recording. A′A″, B′B″: trephine openings for the application of CaCl₂, the EEG leads and the recording of the slow potential changes. A, B: trephine openings for the application of 1 per cent KCl. 100 μV—calibration for EEG, 10 mV—for the recording of steady potential. Upward deflection of the potential indicates negativity in the hemisphere A. Applications: a—NaCl 0·9 per cent; b—CaCl₂ 1 per cent; c—CaCl₂ 1·5 per cent. Arrow— introduction of 1 per cent KCl at A.

times more effective than calcium ions. The processes responsible for the development of depression and for its spread are, therefore, apparently identical.

TABLE 2. Effect of divalent cations on the development and spread of spreading depression

Blocking substance	50% block of the development of spreading depression caused by 2% KCl	50% reduction in amplitude of wave of negative potential associated with spreading depression
$MgCl_2$	0·041 M	0·042 M
$CaCl_2$	0·123 M	0·119 M
Ca^{++}/Mg^{++}	2·97	2·83

Development of the spreading depression produced by application of 2 per cent KCl solution to the surface of the brain could be suppressed with Ca^{++} and Mg^{++} in the concentrations required for 50 per cent reduction of the negative wave of spreading depression. It is impossible, however, to assess the concentrations of K^+ responsible for the development of spreading depression in the cortex from this comparison as the spread of depression took place in all layers of the cortex, whereas the divalent cations were applied to the surface. It could, however, be observed that, soon after the application of $CaCl_2$, the slow potential wave changed its sign to positive in the area of application, while remaining negative in the deeper layers of the cortex.

MOVEMENT OF IONS DURING SPREADING DEPRESSION

All proofs of the importance of K^+ in the development and spread of depression have hitherto been indirect. They require confirmation by direct observations on the movement of K ions during spreading depression so that it can be determined whether they can actually play any important part in the spread of depression. There are many methodological difficulties associated with the investigation of electrolytes in the brain. Determination of the total ion content of brain tissue does not afford any indication of their distribution between extracellular and intracellular spaces, which must be of decisive importance in any attempt to explain spreading depression. We have devised a method for examination of ion composition in the extracellular space. The surface of the cortex is bathed through an epidural fistula (Bureš and Křivánek, 1958, 1960). The bathing fluid (isotonic saccharose or choline chloride) is passed at a constant rate (130 ml/min) through a cannula inserted into a trephine opening, 5 mm in diameter, over the occipital pole of the hemisphere. The K^+ and Na^+ ion concentrations in the bathing fluid are increased during the contact with the surface of the cortex. These concentrations are determined by means of a flame photometer. It was shown that the liberation of K^+ was increased by

TABLE 3. Changes in the concentrations of K^+ and Na^+ in the fluid irrigating the surface of the cortex at the time of spreading depression (SD)

	Substance causing SD	Washing fluid	Number of animals	Normal (meq/l.)	During SD (meq/l.)	Change (%)	Statistical reliability
Irrigation of place of development of SD	K^+ 2,4-dinitro-phenol	Saccharose	11	0·021 ± 0·001	0·041 ± 0·006	+91	0·020 ± 0·005 $p < 0·01$
	K^+ 2,4-dinitro-phenol	NaCl	21	0·027 ± 0·001	0·044 ± 0·008	+63	0·017 ± 0·002 $p < 0·01$
	Veratrine	Saccharose	13	0·023 ± 0·004	0·059 ± 0·006	+156	0·036 ± 0·006 $p < 0·01$
	Na^+ 2,4-dinitro-phenol	Saccharose	11	0·215 ± 0·034	0·289 ± 0·035	+34	0·074 ± 0·023 $p < 0·05$
	Veratrine	Saccharose	14	0·284 ± 0·024	0·369 ± 0·052	+30	0·085 ± 0·055
Irrigation of area of origin of SD	K^+ 2,4-dinitro-phenol	Saccharose	16	0·024 ± 0·001	0·037 ± 0·003	+54	0·013 ± 0·0028 $p < 0·01$
	Na^+ 2,4-dinitro-phenol	Saccharose	15	0·256 ± 0·023	0·315 ± 0·031	+25	0·059 ± 0·0197 $p < 0·01$

65–90 per cent as a result of the addition of effective concentrations of 2,4-dinitrophenol to the bathing fluid and that liberation of Na^+ was increased by 30 per cent (Table 3). Similar changes were also seen in regions of the cortex through which a wave of spreading depression was passing. While the rise in the concentration of Na^+ can be explained by increased blood supply at the time of the spreading depression (Leão, 1944 b; Burešová, 1957), the increased concentration of K^+ is apparently due also to the outflux of potassium from the cells.

The correctness of this view was confirmed by ^{42}K experiments (Křivánek and Bureš, 1960). Investigations dealing with the incorporation of radioactive isotopes in brain tissue indicate that potassium exchange in the brain proceeds very slowly, so that the specific activity of potassium in the brain does not even reach 10 per cent of the potassium activity in the plasma one or two hours after the intraperitoneal injection of ^{42}K. If the increased liberation of K^+ is due to its exit from the cells, the larger fraction of inactive K^+ in the total quantity liberated should manifest itself by a lower specific activity.

^{42}K in isotonic sodium chloride solution was injected intraperitoneally in doses of 0·3–0·5 μc per animal in a series of rat experiments. Bathing of the cortex was started 50 min after the injection at a rate of about 60 ml/min. The bathing was effected with saline for 40 min and then with saline containing 2,4-dinitrophenol for a further 40 min. The corresponding results are represented in Fig. 4. The increase in the concentration of K^+ in the bathing fluid collected during spreading depression was not accom-

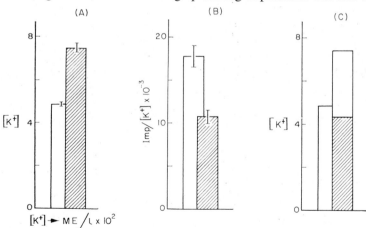

FIG. 4. Changes in the K^+ concentration (A) and specific ^{42}K activity (B) in the bathing fluid (0·9 per cent NaCl) during spreading depression caused by 2,4-dinitrophenol.

White columns—control values. Shaded columns—experimental values. C—Provenance of K^+ passing into the bathing fluid. The same values as in A. Shaded part of the column—potassium of extracellular origin. Unshaded part—potassium of intracellular origin.

panied by a proportional increase in radioactivity, so that this indicated that the source of K⁺ was not in the plasma. Calculation showed that the K⁺ increase could have come from intracellular reserves. Increased outflow of intracellular potassium during spreading depression was also observed by Brinley *et al.* (1960) using a different modification of washing the brain cortex. The cerebral cortex was first locally treated with a ^{42}K solution and then washed with Ringer solution. The activity of the washing solution increased considerably during spreading depression. On the assumption that most of the ^{42}K was localized intracellularly, this indicates increased outflow of potassium.

Van Harreveld and Schade (1959) studied the ion shifts during spreading depression. Employing an ingenious histochemical method they demonstrated accumulation of Cl⁻ in the dendrites and bodies of cortical neurons in the region of maximum negativity. These findings amplify their earlier results (Van Harreveld and Ochs, 1956, 1957; Van Harreveld, 1957, 1958), which showed that the resistance of the cortex and the volume of the somato-dendritic parts of neurons were increased during spreading depression.

These findings suggest that the permeability of the cell membrane is increased for all ions during spreading depression and that the ions begin to move in the direction of their concentration gradients. But the entry of Na⁺ into the cell is apparently more intense than the exit of K⁺ and, so that an electroneutral state will be preserved on both sides of the membrane, the entry of Na⁺ is accompanied by the entry of Cl⁻. The increase in the concentration of electrolytes within the cell leads to equalization of the osmotic gradients by transfer of water from the extracellular to the intracellular space. This reduces the conductance of the extracellular space and increases the volume of the neurons.

CAN CHANGES IN THE CONCENTRATION OF K⁺ IN THE EXTRACELLULAR SPACE MEDIATE SPREADING DEPRESSION?

It can be taken as established that the concentration of K⁺ in the extracellular space increases during spreading depression. What is the role of this change in the mechanism of spreading depression? In our preceding experiments the perfusing fluid was collected over periods of 20 min. It is unlikely that the discharge of K⁺ was uniform over this period. It can be postulated that the maximum increase in the extracellular concentration of K⁺ coincided in time with the wave of negative potential and that the liberation of K⁺ declined in the intervals between waves. In a special series of experiments, therefore, we collected samples of the perfusing fluid every 2 min and at the same time recorded changes in steady potential in the area perfused. Figure 5 represents a typical experiment and shows that the liberation of K⁺ during spreading depression coincided in time with the wave of cortical negativity.

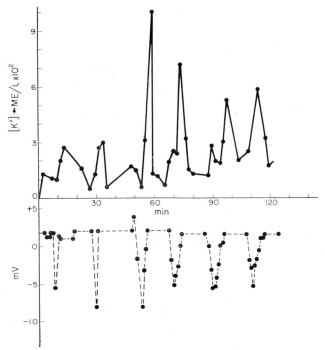

FIG. 5. Changes in the concentration of K$^+$ in the washing fluid (0·9 per cent NaCl) accompanying negative slow potential waves of spreading depression.

In these experiments the K$^+$ content was increased 2·6 times (average) and in some cases even 5 times during the wave of cortical negativity. Similar values can also be arrived at from the findings shown in Table 3. During a 20-min perfusion the liberation of K$^+$ was increased by 54 per cent in the region through which the wave of depression was passing. The EEG indicates that one or two waves of depression with total durations of 2–4 min passed through the perfusion region during this period. The concentration of K$^+$ in the extracellular space was only increased during these 2–4 min and a concentration 3–5 times greater than the normal concentration of K ions in the extracellular space was reached at the peak of the negativity. The view that ion shifts only occur during the slow potential change is also supported by Van Harreveld's findings of histological changes only in the region corresponding to the wave of negative potential.

As the changes in the concentration of ions in the bathing fluid would appear to be directly proportional to the changes in the extracellular space, it can be postulated that at the peak of the negative wave of spreading depression the concentration of K$^+$ in the corresponding region is at least increased to 20–25 mM. The K ion concentration producing spreading depression on the surface of the brain is 70 mM, but this may be reduced under certain conditions to 25–30 mM (Bureš and Burešová, 1960). The maximum extracellular concentration of K^+ developing at the time of spreading depression must, however, be higher than the values given (the explanation being inertia of the method employed for estimation of K) and, conversely, the threshold concentrations for superficial application would appear to be higher than the actual effective concentrations developing in the immediate vicinity of cortical neurons.

The experimental material described leads us to believe that the most probable explanation of spreading depression of cortical activity is as follows. Spreading depression is accompanied by the discharge of potassium ions from the nerve cell and the accumulation of K^+ in the extracellular medium in a concentration sufficient to excite adjacent neurons.

REFERENCES

BRINLEY, F. J., E. R. KANDEL and W. H. MARSHALL, J. Neurophysiol. 23, 246 (1960).
BUREŠ, J. and O. BUREŠOVÁ, Utilization of reversible depression of the cortex (by means of spreading depression) for study of conditioned reflexes. International Colloquium on EEG of higher nervous activity [Primeneniye obratimogo ugneteniya kory mozga (s pomoshch'yu rasprostranyayushcheisya depressii) dlya izucheniya uslovnykh refleksov. Mezhdunarodnyi kollokvium po EEG vysshei nervnoi deyatel'nosti] (in press) Moscow 1960.
BUREŠ, J. and KH. S. KOSHTOYANTS, Reports of the U.S.S.R. Academy of Sciences (Dokl. Akad. Nauk SSSR) 105, 1118 (1955).
BUREŠ, J. and O. BUREŠOVÁ, Physiol. Bohemosl. 5, 195 (1956).
BUREŠ, J. and O. BUREŠOVÁ, Activation of latent foci of spreading cortical depression in rats. J. Neurophysiol. (In press).
BUREŠ, J. and J. KŘIVÁNEK, Washing of brain surface by epidural fistula—a method for study of brain electrolytes in vivo. International Symposium über den Mechanismus der Erregung, Berlin 1958.
BUREŠ, J. and KŘIVÁNEK, J., Physiol. Bohemosl. 9, 488 (1960).
BUREŠOVÁ, O., Physiol. Bohemosl. 5, 350 (1956)
BUREŠOVÁ, O., Physiol. Bohemosl. 6, 1 (1957).
FINNEY, D. J., Probit Analysis. Cambridge University Press, London 1950.
GRAFSTEIN, B., J. Neurophysiol. 19, 154 (1956).
KOSHTOYANTS, KH. S., Physiol. J. U.S.S.R. (Fiziol. zh. SSSR) 43, 68 (1957).
KOSHTOYANTS, CH. S. and J. SALANKI, Acta Biol. Acad. Sci. Hung. 8, 361 (1958).
KŘIVÁNEK, J. and J. BUREŠ, Physiol. Bohemosl. 9, 494 (1960).
LEÃO, A. A. P., J. Neurophysiol. 7, 359 (1944a).
LEÃO, A. A. P., J. Neurophysiol. 7, 391 (1944b).
MARSHALL, W. H. Physiol. Rev. 39, 239 (1959).
MARSHALL, W. H., D. F. ESSIG and S. J. DUBROFF, J. Neurophysiol. 14, 153 (1951).
SHANES, A. M., Pharmacol. Rev. 10, 165 (1958).
SLOAN, N. and H. JASPER, J. Neurophysiol. 2, 59 (1950).
VAN HARREVELD, A., Am. J. Physiol. 191, 233 (1957).
VAN HARREVELD, A., Am. J. Physiol. 192, 457 (1958).
VAN HARREVELD, A. and S. OCHS, Am. J. Physiol. 187, 180 (1956).
VAN HARREVELD, A. and S. OCHS, Am. J. Physiol. 189, 159 (1957).
VAN HARREVELD, A. and J. P. SCHADE, J. Cell. and Comp. Physiol. 54, 65 (1959).
WEIL, C. S., Biometrics 8, 249 (1952).
ZACHAROVÁ, D. and J. ZACHAR, Čsl. fysiol. 7, 190 (1958).

SOME PATHWAYS IN THE EVOLUTION OF INTEROCEPTIVE SIGNALLING

V. N. CHERNIGOVSKII

Institute of Physiology, U.S.S.R. Academy of Sciences, Leningrad

Translated by Dr. R. Crawford

IT IS well known that the evolutionary approach has been extremely fruitful in the analysis of a number of physiological functions. It has in many cases permitted a fuller and more profound understanding of the features of physiological processes in higher animals and has revealed how they have been developed. A striking example of this is afforded by the numerous and fruitful investigations of Koshtoyants and his pupils and co-workers.

Conclusions as to the possible ways in which a physiological system has evolved may be reached if the investigator has adequate comparative physiological and anatomical material at his disposal. Not infrequently, the accumulated evidence of palaeontology may afford him considerable assistance. Material from embryology and the results of research on the ontogenesis of physiological functions may also be used with success. Unfortunately, all these approaches can only be utilized to a small extent in attempts to understand the evolution of interoceptive signalling. The main obstacle is the scantiness of information in the absence of systematic research in this field. This makes it extremely difficult today to present anything like a complete picture of the evolutionary development of interoceptive signalization.

In the pages that follow we shall, therefore, discuss what are essentially only possible ways in which chemoreception and mechanoreception have been evolved in the interoceptive zone of the carotid sinus.

Koch (1931) was the first to point out that the presence of receptors in the region of the carotid sinus, aortic arch and pulmonary artery must be connected with the fact that all these vessels in mammals are derivatives of the primitive branchial arteries. It will be evident from what follows that this view has been confirmed by many investigations and, more particularly, by evidence of the evolution of chemoreception in the carotid body. We shall first of all examine the latter. Kohn (1900) had already stated that the carotid body is composed of two rudiments. The inner consists of tissue resembling cavernous tissue, is permeated by capillaries and passes directly into the wall of the artery. The outer rudiment consists of nervous system elements. Vinnikov (1946, 1958) and his co-workers have shown that glomus tissue cultures give a typical glial type of growth and that this tissue has apparently originated from the ganglionic plate in the region of the branchial vessels. It can thus be assumed that the carotid reflexogenic zone as a whole

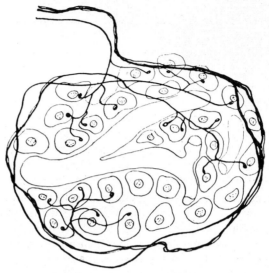

Fig. 1. Schematic representation of the relationship between sensory nerve endings, capillaries and cells in the carotid body (after B. I. Lavrent'yev).

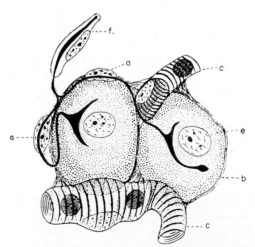

Fig. 2. Schematic representation of the relationships between sensory nerve endings, capillaries and cells in the carotid body.

a—Schwann cells. b—membranes of epithelioid cells. c—capillary. e—epithelioid cell. f—sensory nerve fibre with intracellular endings (after Castro).

consists of two rudiments, a vascular element proper, formed by the branchial arteries and possibly, a placode of the glossopharyngeal nerve. Vinnikov places the interoceptors in a special group of "tertiary" receptors (1946, 1958).

According to Vlados-Priimak (1958), the carotid body in rats is formed from a mesenchymal rudiment, an outgrowth of the wall of the common carotid artery into which, at later stages in development, cells migrate from the caudal part of the superior cervical sympathetic ganglion (spongioblasts, poorly differentiated neuroblasts, less frequently more mature neuroblasts). In the definitive stage the vessels of the carotid body retain the structure of an arteriovenous anastomosis but its cells have become differentiated into special "epithelioid" cells.

The detailed structure of the carotid body has been studied by Lavrent'yev (1943) and, somewhat later, by Castro (1951). Figures 1 and 2, which have been borrowed by us from the works of these authors, show that typical epithelioid cells are disposed round the capillaries to form continuous sheaths. The sensory nerve endings are within the cells and, consequently, chemical stimuli circulating in the blood reach the nerve endings after penetrating into the cells. This idea of the intracellular situation of nerve endings is far from being shared by all morphologists, although it corresponds most closely with the ideas of physiologists on the mode of action of chemical stimuli (Chernigovskii, 1943, 1947; Belen'kii, 1952).*

The carotid body has been demonstrated as a fully developed morphological structure in mammals—man, chimpanzee, orang-outang, dog, cat, rabbit, guinea pig, albino rat, albino mouse, horse, cow, sheep, pig (Smirnov, 1945), birds and reptiles—in the gecko *Hemidactylus flaviviridis* Ruppel (Bhatia and Dyal, 1933), and in the monitor lizards, *Varanus monitor* (Chowdhary, 1951), *Varanus varius* (Adams, 1952).

Adams is of the opinion that the carotid body in reptiles contains cells similar in structure to the epithelioid cells of the glomus caroticum of mammals. The carotid body is absent in fishes and the larvae of caudate and acaudate amphibians.

In fully grown amphibians the division of the common carotid artery into internal and external arteries is replaced by a special structure, the vascular labyrinth (Gefässlabyrinth), which has been studied in detail by Pischinger (1934) and other authors (Palme, 1934; De Boissezon, 1939; Smirnov, 1944; Chowdhary, 1951).

The vascular labyrinth only appears in the course of the metamorphosis of the larvae of caudate and acaudate amphibians, being formed from a large number of vascular anastomosis between the primitive arterial arch and the carotid artery. The formation of the vascular labyrinth is

---

* Details of the morphology of the carotid body in various animals can be found in the monograph of A. A. Smirnov (1945).

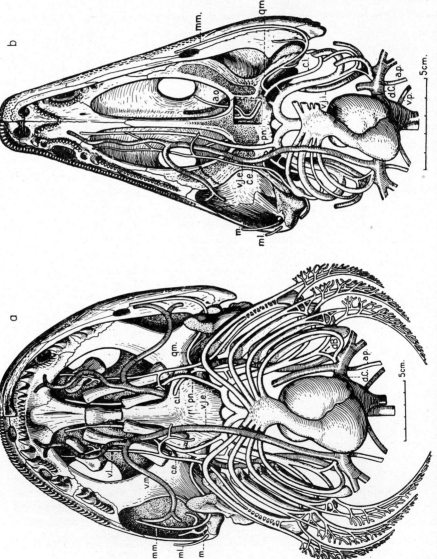

Fig. 3. Reconstruction of the vascular system.

a—dinosaur: neoteric form of *Beuthosuchus*. ap—pulmonary artery. ce—external carotid artery. ci—internal carotid artery. dB—ductus Botallii. dC—duct of Cuvier. mm—medial mandibular artery. pn—palatonasal artery. qm—quadratomandibular artery. vje—external jugular vein. vl—lingual vein. vm—mandibular vein. m—muscular branch. ml—lateral mandibular artery. b—*Beuthosuchus*. ao—orbital artery. (After Bystrov.)

apparently a regular process connected with the loss of branchial respiration and transition to pulmonary respiration in some vertebrates.

Bystrov (1939) made an attempt to reconstruct the vascular system of one of the dinosaurs which he regarded as a neoteric form of *Benthosuchus*. He suggested that, in remote geological epochs, the transition of the animal from branchial to pulmonary respiration was accompanied by reduction of the branchial vessels and appearance of the special structure, the vascular labyrinth. A similar process can be traced in the metamorphosis of axolotl into *Ambystoma*.

We reproduce Bystrov's reconstruction of the vascular system of a dinosaur and *Benthosuchus* in Fig. 3a and b.

As regards the innervation of the vascular labyrinth in the frog, Palme (1934) demonstrated nerve fibres in its wall. The most complete macroscopic study of the nerve supply to the vascular labyrinth in the frog is that of Smirnov (1944) from whose paper we have borrowed Fig. 4. This shows that the vascular labyrinth is supplied by branches of the glossopharyngeal nerve, which are, in fact, the sinus nerve.

Later, Neil *et al.* (1950) studied the nerve supply of the vascular labyrinth by physiological methods. We shall describe their findings on physiological effects produced by stimulation of the various nerves later. Figure 5, which is taken from their paper, shows that the relationships found by them are in complete agreement with the picture described earlier by Smirnov.

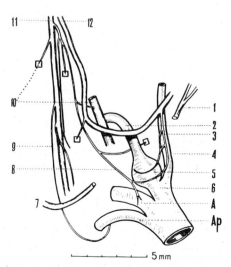

FIG. 4. Nerve supply of the vascular labyrinth in the frog *Rana temporaria*. Male. Right side.

1, 7—first spinal nerve. 2—internal carotid artery. 3—sinus nerve. 4—external carotid artery. 5—vascular labyrinth. 6—common carotid artery. 8—depressor nerve. 9—recurrent branch of vagus nerve. 10—muscle. 11—vagus nerve. 12—glossopharyngeal nerve. A—aorta. Ap—pulmonary artery. (After Smirnov.)

In the light of these findings, the presence in frogs of a structure analogous to the glomus caroticum of birds and mammals is of very great interest.

Some authors (De Boissezon, 1939; Chowdhary, 1951; Adams, 1952) state that cells are present in the region of the vascular labyrinth which are similar to the epithelioid cells in the mammalian, carotid body. Careful examination of Fig. 5 will show, however, that the structures receiving their

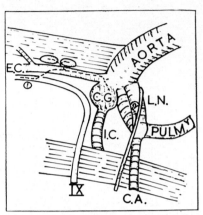

FIG. 5. Diagram of the anatomical relationships between the sinus nerve, the nerve supplying the pulmo-cutaneous trunk and the corresponding vessels in the frog (*R. temporaria*).

Right side. The sinus nerve is indicated by the interrupted line 1 and the pulmo-cutaneous trunk by the interrupted line 2. Two epithelial bodies are shown close to the external carotid artery. A branch of the sinus nerve (dot-dash) goes to the epithelial bodies; EC—external carotid artery. IC—internal carotid artery. CG—carotid "gland" (vascular labyrinth). CA—cutaneous artery. LN—laryngeal branch of the vagus nerve (recurrent nerve). IX—glossopharyngeal nerve. (After Neil, Strom and Zotterman.)

nerve supply from the sinus nerve, which were regarded by Neil *et al.* as the analogue of the mammalian carotid body, are situated close to the external carotid artery. The attempts of these authors to record impulses in the very delicate nerves on chemical stimulation of receptors in this structure (injection of lobeline) were unsuccessful. This negative result cannot, of course, be regarded as conclusive in that, as the authors very reasonably point out, the nerve branches to the "carotid body" could easily have been damaged in the dissection of the vessels.

As the results obtained by Neil *et al.* were indefinite, investigations of a similar nature were carried out in our laboratory on bony fishes of the carp family*, frogs, tortoises and mammals (Kravchinskii, 1945a, b, c; Kulayev and Beller, 1948).

Here we shall speak only of the results which have immediate bearing on the phylogenesis of chemoreception.

* Details of the species used will be found in the author's original papers.

Kravchinskii applied cocaine solution to the branchial vessels of fishes and showed that this led to rapid and irreversible arrest of respiration, the development of a shock-like state and the death of the animal. He produced the same results by dividing the branches of the vagus nerve to the gills. By applying lobeline and adrenaline solutions Kravchinskii demonstrated the great sensitivity of the nerve endings to these two substances. Lobeline in dilution 10^{-7} accelerated respiration in fishes from 80 to 160/min. But larger quantities of the stimulus led to depression of respiration. Adrenaline 10^{-6} stimulated respiration.

Investigations on frogs showed that the application of nicotine (0·2 per cent) and potassium cyanide (10^{-3}) tampons to the trunk and region of division of the aorta produced respiratory changes. Nicotine applied to the trunk and division of the aorta arrested respiration. Applied to the aortic trunk it accelerated respiration.

Potassium cyanide, applied to the trunk and the aorta, caused intensification and acceleration of respiration. Kulayev and Beller (1948) applied nicotine solutions (10^{-4}) directly to the vascular labyrinth in the frog and observed arrest first of respiration and then of the heart.

There is obviously no point in entering on a detailed discussion of the exact points from which Kravchinskii and Kulayev and Beller produced the various respiratory changes. Examination of Figs. 4 and 5 will show that the vascular labyrinth and the aortic arch are in such close proximity and that the depressor nerve is so closely connected with the sinus that it is hardly possible to speak of local stimulation at any of these levels. The chemical stimuli almost certainly acted on several points at once.

Such are the main facts concerning the evolution of the chemosensitive properties of the carotid body. There can hardly be any doubt that the chemosensitive properties of the branchial vessels was in fact the immediate precursor of chemoreception in the carotid body. If these views are accepted, the following considerations may be of some importance. In the branchial vessels we apparently have an example in which chemoreceptive properties are not as yet connected with a definite tissue of the type of the epithelioid cells in the carotid body. The development of a special tissue apparently took place after the development of pulmonary respiration. So far as can be judged from the evidence available, the vascular labyrinth also has chemosensitive properties. It can be assumed that these features are probably also peculiar to the special bodies of Neil, Strom and Zotterman.

In the course of evolution chemosensitive properties were presumably only retained to any significant extent by the receptors in the mammalian carotid body, which acquired specific and high sensitivity to oxygen deficiency in arterial blood. The vascular labyrinth was reduced to arteriovenous anastomoses, which afforded the chemoreceptors in the carotid body closer contact with the blood.

Unfortunately, it is impossible at the present time to form even an approximate conception of the evolution of chemoreceptors in tissues (Chernigovskii, 1943). The only point that is clear is that tissue chemoreception can be demonstrated even in the earliest stages of postnatal development. The experiments of Komarov (1951) in our laboratory and, later, those of Pal'gova (1952, 1954), co-workers of Prof. A. P. Polosukhin, have shown that reflexes from intestinal chemoreceptors can be demonstrated in kittens within a few hours after birth.

It would be rash, however, to utilize these findings for assessment of the ways in which tissue chemoreception has evolved, although they are indeed of importance when considered in relation to the ontogenetic development of interoception. The factual evidence at present available is insufficient even for schematic presentation of the general features of the evolution of tissue chemoreception.

Let us examine the possible stages in the evolution of mechanoreception (pressoreception). Two main types of mechanoreception can be distinguished in the fully grown mammal. First, there is mechanoreception in the viscera which are constantly subject to changes in volume by virtue of their particular physiological function (gastro-intestinal tract, urinary bladder, etc.). Secondly, there are the blood-vessels which are capable of periodic change in volume. There is a lack of reliable evidence on the evolution of mechanoreception in the hollow, smooth-muscle organs. A certain amount of work has been done on the evolution of mechanoreception in the vascular system.

Numerous investigations have served to establish the embryogenesis of the large vessels which are most important in relation to reception. In mammals the third pair of arterial arches gives origin to the carotid artery. The embryonic connexion with the dorsal aorta (ductus caroticus) disappears completely in mammals but can still be observed in snakes and lizards. The fourth pair of arterial arches gives origin to the aortic arches which are still present in fully grown amphibians and reptiles. In birds the left arch is reduced and the right is retained. In mammals, on the other hand, the right arch is reduced and the left retained. The sixth pair of branchial arches gives the pulmonary artery. Its embryonic connexion with the dorsal aorta (Botallo's duct) is absent in mammals, although it sometimes persists as a developmental abnormality. On the other hand, Botallo's duct is constantly present in fully grown caudate amphibians, in *Halteria* and in tortoises. Thus, the main interoceptive vascular zones in mammals (carotid sinus, aortic arch and pulmonary artery) are derivatives of the branchial arteries (Shimkevich, 1928; Shmal'gauzen, 1947).

Such clear evidence on the embryogenesis of the main vessels naturally compels us to see the precursors of the vascular interoceptive zones of mammals in the branchial vessels. This has been confirmed by a number of experimental investigations.

First of all, McWilliam (1885) stimulated the branchial vessels in fishes and the corresponding nerves mechanically and apparently observed slowing of the heart. Later, Lutz (1930) and Lutz and Wyman (1932a, b, c) investigated reception in the branchial vessels of fish (*Mustelus canis* and *Squaius acanthias*) and showed that increase of pressure in the branchial arteries led to a reflex fall of blood pressure and inhibition of cardiac activity. It is also shown that electrical stimulation of the first 4 branchial nerves led to reflex inhibition of cardiac activity. Subsequently, Irving *et al.* (1935) recorded increase of impulse discharge in the 4 branchial nerves on change of pressure in the branchial vessels.

Later, Mott (1951) studied similar reflexes in eels (*Anguilla anguilla*). She applied electrical stimulation to the central end of the ninth and tenth pairs of cranial nerves and observed slowing of the heart and a fall of pressure in the ventral aorta. She obtained similar results by artificially increasing the pressure in the first branchial arch. She also noted increased spontaneous impulse discharge in the peripheral ends of the ninth and tenth cranial nerves when the pressure in the ventral aorta was raised artificially.

There is, therefore, no doubt that the branchial vessels are actually the reflexogenic interoceptive zones in vertebrates with branchial respiration. The physiological evidence has been supported by morphological investigations (Boyd, 1936, 1941) demonstrating the existence of receptors in the branchial vessels. The findings described have also been completely confirmed by observations on amphibians.

As far as we know, Nikiforovskii (1913) was the first to prove the presence of special afferent fibres producing depressor effects on stimulation of the central end of the vagus nerve in the frog. Subsequently, Kuno and Brucke (1914) repeated his experiments and observed a fall of blood pressure in the frog when the central end of the vagus nerve was stimulated. Later, Meyer (1927) stimulated the central end of the glossopharyngeal nerve in the frog and noted inhibition of the cardiac contractions.

The macromorphology of the nerve supply to the vascular labyrinth in the frog, based on the work of Smirnov and of Neil, Strom and Zotterman, has already been given in Figs. 4 and 5. This can be supplemented by Carman's (1955) findings of similar relationships in the New Zealand frog (*Hyla aurea*).

The most complete physiological findings are those of Neil, Strom and Zotterman. Recording impulses in the sinus nerve of the frog (*Rana temporaria*), they observed definite increase of impulse discharge in the nerve when there was increase of pressure in the carotid artery. These experiments left no doubt that the vascular labyrinth is the analogue of the carotid sinus in mammals.

No less important are the findings of Neil, Strom and Zotterman in an examination of the impulses arising on change of pressure in the pulmocutaneous trunk. Recording from the laryngeal branch of the vagus nerve

(Fig. 5,2), they observed definite groups of discharges, the development of which coincided with the cardiac contractions, an observation which affords further confirmation of the presence of interoceptive zones in the vascular system of the frog.

Existing evidence thus indicates that the interoceptive zones, demonstrated in certain mammalian vessels, have undoubtedly been formed on the basis of pressoreceptor mechanisms in the branchial arteries. But these findings refer only to three zones (aorta, carotid sinus, pulmonary artery) and leave us in the dark as to the presence of mechanoreceptors in other parts of the vascular bed. It is somewhat difficult to form a sufficiently clear opinion on this question at the present time as a number of the investigations dealing with reception in the vessels of different vertebrates have been restricted almost entirely to the animals which are generally used in physiological laboratories (cat, dog, rabbit). Reflexogenic zones situated along

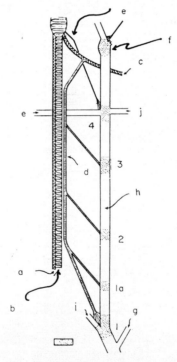

FIG. 6. Reflexogenic, pressor–depressor zones situated along the right common carotid artery in the rabbit.

a—sympathetic nerve. b—vagus nerve. c—superior laryngeal nerve. d—depressor nerve and, leaving it, branches supplying the individual zones. e—nerve coming directly from the ganglion nodosum to the reflexogenic zone (common carotid nerve). f—carotid sinus. g—left common carotid artery. h—right common carotid artery. i—subclavian artery. j—superior thyroid artery. k—dorsal muscular artery. 1, 1 a, 2, 3 and 4—individual reflexogenic zones situated along the common carotid artery.
(After Bose and Green.)

the right common carotid artery of the rabbit from a point 2 cm proximal to the carotid sinus, recently demonstrated by Green (1953, 1954) and by Bose and Green (1954) may possibly be of some importance. The zone nearest to the carotid sinus is supplied by a special nerve coming directly from the ganglion nodosum of the vagus nerve. The other zones receive fibres from the depressor nerve. These relationships are shown diagrammatically in Fig. 6. Similar zones have recently been described by Bianconi and Green (1959) in the region of the brachiocephalic trunk in the cat.

We know of only three papers presenting evidence of the existence of receptors in the heart and vessels of the frog which are not derivatives of the branchial arteries.

Davydov (1940) studied reflex changes in cardiac activity of frogs produced by stimulation of vascular mechanoreceptors. He perfused the vessels of the posterior extremities and showed that increase of pressure (by 25–30 cm H_2O) produced a transient negative isotropic effect which was immediately replaced by a positive effect. Employing a special method to increase pressure in the venous sinus, Davydov observed peculiar changes in cardiac tone, in the form of reduced diastolic relaxation. Neil and Zotterman (1950) showed that auricular contraction evoked bursts of impulses in the vagus nerves.

Lukshina and Ugolev (1957) have recently shown that increase of pressure in the ventricle of a heart completely isolated from all vessels but with its nerve connexions intact led to increase of vascular tone and reduced outflow from an anterior abdominal vein. The same effect was observed when pressure was increased in the atria. The authors observed the most intense reaction when pressure was increased in all divisions of the heart. The increase of pressure required to produce a reflex was quite small (15–25 mm H_2O).

There has thus been extremely little investigation of the nature of reception in peripheral vessels and it is clear that the views we have expressed on the evolution of mechanoreception in vessels other than those developing from the branchial arteries can only be quite provisional.

Orbeli (1934) once expressed the thought that depressor reactions constitute a later and phylogenetically younger stage in the evolution of vascular tone. Pressor tone and pressor reflexes, through change in which reflex regulation of the circulation is effected, are in his opinion primary. Investigations on the establishment of depressor reflexes from the carotid sinus in the course of growth apparently constituted one of the elements on which Orbeli based this opinion. We, too, have expressed agreement with Orbeli's view (Chernigovskii, 1943).

Attention should, nevertheless, be drawn to investigations in which it has been shown that depressor reflexes can be observed in newborn animals within the first hours and days of life. Mikhaleva (1947, 1956) has shown in a series of investigations that stimulation of the central end of the vagus nerve in puppies elicits definite depressor reactions. In our laboratory Komarov studied the age features of reflexes from mechanoreceptors in the carotid sinus and established that compression of one common carotid artery produced pressor reactions and respiratory stimulation in kittens and puppies during the first few hours after birth. The reactions scarcely differed in any respect from those seen in fully grown animals.

The pressor reaction produced by compression of a carotid artery in fully grown animals is generally regarded as the result of temporary loss of the tonic depressor impulsation from receptors. Inasmuch as this reaction was also observed in newborn animals, it would appear that both pressor and depressor reflexes are already present in them.

These facts are not sufficient, however, to throw doubt on the correctness of the opinion that depressor reflexes generally and reflexes from the carotid sinus in particular are of later development. However, evidence concerning the ontogenetic development of vascular tone is not a very reliable basis on which to build a theory of the phylogenesis of pressor–depressor reflexes. In any case the facts are not clear enough for any decisive conclusion.

The possible ways in which mechanoreception in the cardiovascular system may have evolved can nevertheless be traced with a certain degree of reliability on the evidence afforded by factual material, but the latter is quite inadequate for any opinion about mechanoreception in the lungs and digestive tract. Findings which are of great interest on receptor function in the swim-bladder (Vasilenko and Koshtoyants, 1936; Vasilenko and Livanov, 1936; Koshtoyants, 1936, 1937; Sokolov, 1953, 1956) cannot be used to explain the evolution of mechanoreception in the lungs in view of the patent disputability of the genetic relationships between the swim-bladder and lungs. Only the results obtained by Neil, Strom and Zotterman, given by the authors in the paper already referred to, can be considered in this relationship. They were able to record definite impulses from the pulmonary branches of the vagus nerve in the frog when the lungs were stretched by air. They suggest that the presence in the frog lungs of receptors reacting to stretching constitutes a definite stage in the evolution of the Hering–Breuer reflex which is so characteristic of mammals. In their opinion the reflexes in frogs on stretching of the lungs function as a peculiar defence mechanism, protecting the lungs from excessive stretching as in these animals the filling of the lungs with air is not connected with movements of the thorax as in mammals, but with vibrations of the floor of the mouth. Unfortunately, information on the development of mechanoreception in the lungs is also limited to these findings*.

* One organ which we have not examined among receptors for mechanical stimulation is the somewhat peculiar one known as the organ of the lateral line. Its physiology has now been fairly fully investigated (Sand, 1937; Malyukina, 1954, 1955). Although this organ is quite a curious mechanoreceptor, its evolution has no relationship with the types of mechanoreceptors which have been examined in this paper.

REFERENCES

ADAMS, W. E., *Anat. Rec.* **113**, 1 (1952).

BELEN'KII, M. L., *Pharmalogical Analysis of the Significance and Mechanism of the Chemical Sensitiveness of Receptors in the Carotid Body* (Farmakologicheskii analiz znacheniya i mekhanizma khimicheskoi chuvstvitel'nosti retseptorov karotidnogo klubochka), Leningrad 1952.

BHATIA, M. L. and J. DYAL, *Anat. Anzeig.* **76**, 417 (1933).

BIANCONI, R. and J. GREEN, *Arch. Ital. de Biol.* **97**, 47 (1959).

BOSE, J. and J. H. GREEN, *J. Physiol.* **124**, 43 (1954).

BOYD, J. D., *J. Anat.*, **71**, 137 (1936).

BOYD, J. D., *J. Anat.*, **76**, 248 (1941).

BYSTROV, A. P., *Acta Zoologica* **20**, 125 (1939).

CARMAN, J. B., *J. Anat.* **89**, 503 (1955).

CASTRO, F., *Acta Physiol. Scand.* **22**, 14 (1951).

CHERNIGOVSKII, V. N., *Afferent System of the Viscera* (Afferentnyye sistemy vnutrennykh organov) (1943).

CHERNIGOVSKII, V. N., Advances in Biology (*Usp. sovrem. biol.*) **23**, 215 (1947).

CHOWDHARY, D. S., *Anat. Rec.* **107**, 235 (1951).

DAVYDOV, I. N., Physiol. J. U.S.S.R. (*Fiziol. zh. SSSR*) **28**, 524 (1940).

DE BOISSEZON, P., *J. Med. Bordeaux* **13**, 341 (1939); cited by HEYMANS and NEIL. *Reflexogenic areas of the cardiovascular System.* London (1958).

GREEN, J. H., *J. Physiol.* **122**, 70 (1953).

GREEN, J. H., *J. Physiol.* **123**, 41 (1954).

IRVING, L., D. Y. SOLANDT and O. M. SOLANDT, *J. Physiol.* **84**, 187 (1935).

KOCH, E., *Die reflektorische Selbststeuerung des Kreislaufes*, Leipzig 1931.

KOHN, A., *Arch. f. Mikroskop. Anat.* **56**, 819 (1900).

KOMAROV, YE. I., *On the Physiology of Interoceptive Unconditioned Reflexes in Newborn Animals* (Materialy k fiziologii interotseptivnykh bezuslovnykh refleksov u novorozhdennykh zhivotnykh), Leningrad 1951.

KOSHTOYANTS, KH. S., Physiol. J. U.S.S.R. (*Fiziol. zh. SSSR*) **21**, 1055 (1936).

KOSHTOYANTS, KH. S., *Relationship between Functions of Autonomic and Active Organs in the Light of their Evolution* (O sootnoshenii funktsii vegetativnykh i animal'nykh organov v svete ikh evolyutsii) (1937).

KRAVCHINSKII, B. D., Physiol. J. U.S.S.R. (*Fiziol. zh. SSSR*) **31**, 11 (1945a).

KRAVCHINSKII, B. D., Physiol. J. U.S.S.R. (*Fiziol. zh. SSSR*) **31**, 25 (1945b).

KRAVCHINSKII, B. D., Physiol. J. U.S.S.R. (*Fiziol. zh. SSSR*) **31**, 120 (1945c).

KULAYEV, B. S. and N. N. BELLER, Collection of scientific papers of students of the V.M.M.A. (V sb. "*Nauchnyye raboty kursantov i slushatelei VMMA*"). **4**, 24 (1948).

KUNO, J. and I. BRUCKE, *Pflüg. Arch.* **157**, 117 (1914).

LAVRENT'YEV, B. I., J. General Biol. (*Zh. obshch. biol.*) **4**, 232 (1943).

LUKSHINA, H. I. and A. M. UGOLEV, Bull. Experimental Biology and Medicine (*Byull. eksp. biol. i med.*) **1**, 6 (1957).

LUTZ, B. R., *Biol. Bull. Wood's Hole* **59**, 170 (1930).

LUTZ, B. R. and L. C. WYMAN, *Biol. Bull. Wood's Hole* **62**, 100 (1932a).

LUTZ, B. R. and L. C. WYMAN, *Biol. Bull. Wood's Hole* **62**, 17 (1932b).

LUTZ, B. R. and L. C. WYMAN, *Science* **75**, 590 (1932c).

McWILLIAM, J. A., *J. Physiol.* **6**, 192 (1885).

MALYUKINA, G. A., *On the Physiology of the Lateral Line Analyser in Fishes.* (Materialy k fiziologii analizatora bokovoi linii ryb), Moscow 1954.

MALYUKINA, G. A., J. Higher Nervous Activity (*Zh. vyssh. nervn. deyat.*) **5**, 426 (1955).

MEYER, F., *Pflüg. Arch.* **215**, 545 (1927).

MIKHALEVA, O. A., Physiol. J. U.S.S.R. (*Fiziol. zh. SSSR*) **33**, 547 (1947).

MIKHALEVA, O. A., In: On evolutionary physiology. (V sb. "*Materialy po evolyutsionnoi fiziologii*") **1**, 209, 230 and 246 (1956).

MOTT, J. C., *J. Physiol.* **114**, 387 (1951).

NEIL, E., L. STROM and Y. ZOTTERMAN, *Acta Physiol. Scand.* **20**, 338 (1950).

NEIL, E. and Y. ZOTTERMAN, *Acta Physiol. Scand.* **20**, 160 (1950).

NIKIFOROWSKY (NIKIFOROVSKII), P., *J. Physiol.* **45**, 459 (1913).

ORBELI, L. A., Papers of the Military Medical Academy (*Trudy Voenno-med. akademii*) **1**, 33 (1934).

PAL'GOVA, L. YE., Bull. Experimental Biology and Medicine (*Byull. eksp. biol. i med.*) **33**, 20 (1949).

PAL'GOVA, L. YE., Bull. Experimental Biology and Medicine (*Byull. eksp. biol. i med.*) **38**, 7 (1954).

PALME, F., *Ztschr. Ges. Exper. Med.* **113**, 514 (1934).

PISCHINGER, A., *Ztschr. f. Anat.* **103**, 547 (1934).

SAND, A., *J. Physiol.* **89**, 47 P (1937).

SHIMKEVICH, V. M., *Course of Comparative Vertebrate Anatomy* (Kurs sravnitel'noi anatomii pozvonochnykh zhivotnykh), Moscow 1928.

SHMAL'GAUZEN, I. I., *Principles of Comparative Anatomy* (Osnovy sravnitel'noi anatomyi) (1947).

SMIRNOV, A. A., Papers of the Naval Medical Academy (*Trudy Voyenno-Morskoi med. akad.*) **3**, 81 (1944).

SMIRNOV, A. A., *The Carotid Reflexogenic Zone* (Karotidnaya refleksogennaya zona), Leningrad (1945).

SOKOLOV, V. A., Papers of the Institute of Physiology (*Trudy In-ta fiziologii im. Pavlova*) **11**, 352 (1953).

SOKOLOV, V. A., *Proceedings of Congress on Evolutionary Physiology of the Nervous System* (Tez. i ref. dokl. Soveshchaniya po evolyutsionnoi fiziologii nervnoi sistemy) 149 (1956).

VASILENKO, F. D. and KH. S. KOSHTOYANTS, Physiol. J. U.S.S.R. (*Fiziol. zh. SSSR*) **20**, 281 (1936).

VASILENKO, F. D. and M. N. LIVANOV, Bull. Experimental Biology and Medicine (*Byull. eksp. biol. i med.*) **2**, 280 (1936).

VINNIKOV, YA. A., *J. General Biol.* (*Zh. obshch. biol.*) 7, 345 (1946).

VINNIKOV, YA. A., *Proceedings of 6th All-Union Congress of Anatomists, Histologists and Embryologists* (Tez. dokl. VI Vses. s"ezda anatomov, gistologov i embriologov) 18, Kiev 1958.

VLADOS-PRIIMAK, E. KH., *Proceedings of 6th All-Union Congress of Anatomists, Histologists and Embryologists* (Tez. dokl. VII Vses. s"ezda anatomov, gistologov i embriologov) 450, Kiev 1958.

ACETYLCHOLINE METABOLISM
IN RADIATION SICKNESS

N. N. DEMIN

Moscow

Translated by Dr. R. Crawford

NUMEROUS investigations have established that various kinds of change in neurohumoral regulatory processes are important in the pathogenesis of radiation sickness (Lebedinskii, 1955; Livanov, 1956; Krayevskii, 1957; Gorizontov, 1958; Livanov and Biryukov, 1959; Livanov and Kondrat'yeva, 1959). These changes involve biochemical, physiological and morphological deviations from the normal which are characteristics of this particular pathological process.

The enzymochemical theory of excitation and inhibition formulated by Koshtoyants and his co-workers (Koshtoyants, 1944, 1945, 1950, 1951, 1952) can be used with great advantage for investigation of the trophic function of the nervous system. Koshtoyants based his work on the important hypothesis that the biological agents connected with the functional activity of the nervous system must play a direct part in the cycle of metabolic changes in the innervated tissues, thereby linking the metabolism of the nerve elements closely with the metabolism of effector organs into a single functional dynamic system.

The effect of ionizing radiation on the intimate metabolism of the naturally occurring chemical factors which participate in the mechanisms responsible for the activity of nerve elements is also of considerable interest in this connexion. As one such substance, we selected acetylcholine for investigation.

Acetylcholine has numerous functions in the body. The activity of cholinergic nerve structures is linked with it. This constitutes the outstanding role of acetylcholine in the functioning of many central and peripheral nervous mechanisms, in the control of blood-vessel tone, of the rhythm of cardiac activity, the motor activity of the digestive tract, the activities of exocrine and endocrine glands, and in the control of muscular activity. The formation of acetylcholine is not, however, confined to nerve tissue. It is present in muscle, liver, the nerveless placenta and other organs. As a "local hormone", acetylcholine would appear to be of great

importance for regulation of the physicochemical state of various inter-
phase boundaries in cells and to influence their polarization and permeability. Also, acetylcholine may have important influences on the activity of
a number of highly important enzyme systems (Demin, 1953, 1955a, b;
Demin and Kuznetsova, 1958) and on oxidation processes (Demin, 1953;
Gremels, 1936, 1937; Labbe and Rubinstein, 1933; Franck et al., 1948;
Welsh, 1948; Welsh and Hyde, 1944). It also has some effect on the activity
of sulphydryl groups (Demin, 1953, 1955c, d; Demin et al., 1955; Turpayev,
1955; Nistratova and Turpayev, 1959).

Some reduction of cholinesterase activity both in the blood serum and
in a number of tissues has been observed at relatively late periods after
irradiation in most cases of radiation sickness (Ponomarenko, 1956;
Kuznetsova, 1957; Petrovnina, 1958; Luthy, 1953; Burn et al., 1952;
Conard, 1952; Florsheim and Morton, 1954; Doull, 1954; French and Wall,
1957). Fluctuations in cholinesterase activity have been noted in the early
period after irradiation, with initial increase of activity (Ponomarenko, 1956;
Petrovnina, 1958; Baglioni and Piemonte, 1947; Korneyeva, 1959).

Extensive researches on the metabolism of acetylcholine have been carried
out by Petrovnina (1958) in relation to both external and internal irradiation.
It was found that both cholinesterase and choline-acetylase activity increased initially and then declined in the brain tissues of rats with radiation
sickness; later, choline-acetylase activity increased again but cholinesterase
activity declined further; this was associated with an increased content of
acetylcholine. Similar fluctuations in cholinesterase activity and acetylcholine contents were established by Petrovnina for other tissues also (lungs,
liver, spleen). The initial increase of cholinesterase activity could be preceded by a still earlier slight reduction.

It should, however, be remembered that the cholinesterase activity of
biological materials is built up from the activities of several esterases with
similar actions and that acetylcholine is present in the tissues in the form
of fractions in various combinations with different biochemical and micro-
morphological components of the cell. Shastin et al. (1960) have established
that the activities of different cholinesterase in different organs may undergo
dissimilar changes after exposure to radiation.

This paper describes the results of some of our personal experiments in
research on acetylcholine metabolism in radiation affections.

Our attention was attracted more particularly to the problem of linked
acetylcholine. It should be stated that very little work has been done on
this subject in normal biochemistry. It has been suggested that bound
acetylcholine is a stage in the production of free acetylcholine, a form of
precursor, and that bound acetylcholine is a biologically inactive form of
acetylcholine deposited in tissues. It is, however, possible to adduce a
number of considerations which indicate that bound acetylcholine, which

is inaccessible to attack by cholinesterases, is not biologically passive. It is, in fact, when combined at one or other time with biological formations that acetylcholine manifests its activity.

According to some reports tissue acetylcholine is bound to lipoproteins, particularly in mitochondria and microsomes; it can also be fixed by other structures.

Working with rats, our laboratory has carried out the following estimations: total cholinesterase activity, the activity of the specific enzyme acetylcholine esterase, the activity of non-specific cholinesterases and also the contents of free (with reservations!) and bound acetylcholine in the tissues of the liver, brain and small intestine in normal animals and animals after irradiation with lethal dosage of 800 r (Korneyeva, 1959; Demin and Korneyeva, 1960; Korneyeva, 1961).

Total cholinesterase activity was estimated with acetylcholine as substrate, specific acetylcholine esterase activity being assessed from the destruction of acetyl-β-methylcholine and non-specific cholinesterase activity from the destruction of benzylcholine.

Quite a number of different methods for estimation of bound acetylcholine, based on the denaturation of proteins and the destruction of lipid formations, have been suggested. Having evaluated these methods both theoretically and practically, we decided on heating without the introduction into the sample of any other substances with the exception of cholinesterase inhibitors.

There is at present no sufficiently sensitive chemical or physicochemical method for the quantitative estimation of acetylcholine in low biological concentrations; sensitive, but not very accurate, biological tests have to be used. In this investigation we used the dorsal muscle of the leech as the test object for acetylcholine. Extracts, the acetylcholine in which had been destroyed by a cholinesterase preparation, served as controls. The tissue samples to be examined were extracted with Ringer's solution at pH 7·6, either in the cold (for estimations of free acetylcholine) or after heating (for total acetylcholine estimations). The quantity of bound acetylcholine was the difference between total and free acetylcholine.

It was found that in the normal animal the contents of free and bound acetylcholine varied considerably in the tissues examined. As judged by the absolute contents of the two fractions, the quantities of acetylcholine in the small intestine and brain were respectively 200 and 100 times greater than the quantity in the liver. According to our findings, in normal rats the total cholinesterase activities in the tissues of the small intestine and brain were twice that in the liver, while acetylcholine esterase activity in the liver was but half the non-specific cholinesterase activity. Acetylcholine esterase activity was slightly higher in the small intestine and three times greater in the brain than the non-specific cholinesterase activity.

4 a*

Radiation sickness in rats led to certain changes in the content of free acetylcholine and in the acetylcholine esterase and non-specific cholinesterase activities of the tissues from the organs examined.

The early period in the development of acute radiation sickness in rats was characterized by a considerable reduction in the content (almost disappearance) of free acetylcholine in the liver two hours after irradiation, with gradual and apparent return to normal on the second day after exposure. The content of free acetylcholine was also reduced in the brain, but the reduction was relatively slight and was only seen two days after irradiation. The content of bound acetylcholine generally remained fairly steady, particularly in the brain, although the range of its fluctuations was increased in the liver.

Acetylcholine esterase activity in liver and brain tissue tended to be increased 2, 24, 48 and 72 hr after irradiation whereas non-specific cholinesterase activity was subnormal at these times. Acetylcholine esterase activity in small intestine tissue was slightly below normal at all periods after irradiation and non-specific cholinesterase activity was above normal 2 and 24 hr and below normal 48 and 72 hr after irradiation.

A special series of experiments (Demin and Korneyeva, 1960; Korneyeva, 1961) established that the shift in acetylcholine metabolism which developed in the body of the rats after whole-body γ-irradiation in dosage of 800 r could be demonstrated as early as 10 min after exposure. It was also shown that significant changes in acetylcholine metabolism developed (in rats) even after 100 r γ-irradiation, which was not accompanied by any serious pathological signs and still less by the death of the experimental animals. In this case also the changes in the contents of the different acetylcholine fractions and in cholinesterase activity in the various tissues began to develop very early—almost immediately after irradiation.

The abnormalities in acetylcholine metabolism after exposure to a dose of 100 r were, however, somewhat different from those seen after lethal irradiation.

Our findings indicate that the irradiation of rats (even with non-lethal doses) led to quite early changes in acetylcholine metabolism which were more particularly connected with changes in the activities of both specific and non-specific cholinesterase in the various organs. The changes in brain tissue were of particular interest. A certain correlation could be noted in the rats between the tendency for the content of free acetylcholine to be reduced and increase of acetylcholine esterase activity.

Acetylcholine metabolism in acute radiation sickness has also been studied by us (Demin et al., 1961) in monkeys (Macaca rhesus). These animals were exposed to whole-body irradiation, some with X-rays 700 r and the others with γ-radiation 600 r.

Generally, therefore, these findings indicate that there was a considerable · increase of total cholinesterase activity during the first three days, with a subsequent trend towards normal values, in the tissues examined in the monkeys (small intestine, liver and brain) and that non-specific cholinesterase activity in the blood serum tended to fall gradually. The increase of non-specific cholinesterase activity was particularly evident in the small intestine and liver (it was almost doubled on the third day after irradiation).

The changes in acetylcholine content were dissimilar in the intestine and liver. The bound acetylcholine content was increased in both tissues (almost at once after irradiation) to almost double. The free acetylcholine content was increased sharply—almost four times—on the first day in the tissue of the small intestine but remained almost unchanged at this time in the liver; on the third day the free acetylcholine content was somewhat reduced in the small intestine (but not to normal values) and was increased in the liver. It should be emphasized here that the level of bound acetylcholine content can be regarded as almost independent of cholinesterase activity whereas cholinesterase can readily attack free acetylcholine on contact.

It can be concluded that acetylcholine metabolism in monkeys was just as acutely disturbed in acute irradiation sickness as in other animals.

The general inference that can be drawn is that acetylcholine metabolism is considerably intensified in a number of tissues during the first days after irradiation.

In view of the probable trophic effect of bound acetylcholine, its increased content in tissues may also have a positive influence on metabolism in radiation sickness.

Appreciable abnormalities in acetylcholine metabolism were also observed as remote consequences of acute radiation sickness in monkeys irradiated two or three years before examination. Total cholinesterase activity tended to be high in the tissues of the small intestine and liver of monkeys which had recovered from acute radiation sickness, this tendency being particularly marked in the liver; no signs of increase could be observed in brain tissue. The increased total cholinesterase activity in the tissue of the small intestine was associated with a considerable increase in the activity of acetylcholine esterase only, whereas in the liver both the specific and non-specific cholinesterase activities were increased, particularly the former. All the experimental animals showed considerable increases in the contents of both free and linked acetylcholine in the tissues of the small intestine, liver and brain. Non-specific cholinesterase activity in the blood serum of monkeys which had recovered from sickness was slightly lower than in healthy animals.

Rabbits were used as the experimental animals in one series of our experiments. Shaternikov studied the effect of strong external irradiation with the γ-rays of ^{60}Co on total cholinesterase activity and the free and bound acetylcholine contents of the brain immediately after irradiation. Estimations were made 10, 30 and 60 min after the commencement of irradiation; the corresponding doses were then 5000, 15,000 and 30,000 r.

Reduction of cholinesterase activity was observed in the 10th min of irradiation. This was associated with a sharp increase (more than twofold) in the content of free acetylcholine. Cholinesterase activity had regained normal values after 60 min of irradiation; with this was associated apparent return of the free acetylcholine concentration to normal. The bound acetylcholine content, which is not directly dependent on cholinesterase, was sharply reduced even after 10 min with these increasing doses of irradiation.

Convulsions generally developed in the rabbits towards the end of the irradiation. It is interesting to compare these results with the findings of Tower and Elliott (1953), who noted that the bound acetylcholine content of brain tissue was also reduced in convulsions. According to these authors, there was also reduction in the content of bound acetylcholine in the epileptogenic zones of the cortex. Potassium and local pH changes may possibly play an important part in the liberation of acetylcholine from the bound state. Changes in potassium content and pH have been noted in excitation; the pH changes may be associated with intensified breakdown of acetylcholine.

Under normal conditions there are generally only traces of acetylcholine in the blood plasma. Small quantities of acetylcholine have sometimes been found in the plasma at times of intense organ activity, described as "cholinergic activity", as for example in digestive glands (Razenkov, 1937). Acetylcholine has often been demonstrated in the blood of the portal vein but the liver retains it effectively. Acetylcholine has sometimes been demonstrated in the plasma in pathological conditions. Al'pern et al. (1944, 1949) attached great significance to this in the pathogenesis of a number of illnesses.

Working on angiostomized dogs in our laboratory, Smirnov and Shaternikov (1960) found that acetylcholine was present only in traces in arterial blood and blood leaving the intestine and liver.

Acetylcholine began to appear in the blood leaving the intestine as early as two hours after fasting dogs had been irradiated with the γ-rays of ^{60}Co, 300 r, but the liver retained it completely. The quantity of acetylcholine was considerably increased on the third day and in some dogs at this time acetylcholine not only "slipped through" the liver but could even be demonstrated in the arterial blood. The quantity of acetylcholine in the blood of the portal vein was somewhat reduced on the seventh day, but sometimes even at this time the liver was still unable to retain it completely. This "escape" of acetylcholine through the liver was observed in one dog only on the tenth day after irradiation. Acetylcholine was present in the blood of the portal vein (but in somewhat less quantity than on the third day) in all the dogs right to the end of the observation.

This flow of acetylcholine to the liver in radiation sickness cannot but have some effect on liver function. The entry of acetylcholine into the liver may possibly also have a positive effect, inasmuch as we know, for example, that acetylcholine stimulates the deposition of glycogen, promotes greater energy economy in metabolism and so on. The biological significance of this acetylcholine, which is exogenic as far as the liver is concerned, is still undetermined.

It should be pointed out that Kainova (1960) working in our laboratory, has demonstrated considerable intensification of the metabolism of various phospholipids in the liver during the first days after irradiation. In view of the findings of Hokin and Hokin (1954, 1955, 1958, 1959) on the power of acetylcholine to stimulate phosphate and phospholipid metabolism in a number of tissues and the constant entry of acetylcholine into the liver from the blood in animals suffering from radiation sickness observed by us, we carried out *in vitro* experiments to study the possible connexion between these facts (Demin and Kainova, 1961). It was found that acetylcholine in dilutions of from 10^{-10} to 10^{-2} inhibited the metabolism of various phospholipids in slices of liver from normal animals, whereas in concentrations of 10^{-10} to 10^{-7} it increased (almost twofold) the intensity of lecithin and cephalin metabolism in slices of liver from irradiated animals (but had practically no effect on replacement of inosite phosphatides and sphingomyelins).

All the published evidence and the findings we have described in this communication indicate that ionizing irradiation leads to considerable changes in acetylcholine metabolism. These occur both at the time of the irradiation and in the course of the development of acute radiation sickness, and may even be in evidence several years after severe affections. There are associated changes both in the activity of the enzymes catalysing the breakdown of acetylcholine and in the quantities of the acetylcholine fractions in the tissues. In view of the high biological activity of acetylcholine in nerve and other tissues, it is suggested that a number of features in the pathogenesis of radiation sickness are directly connected with changes in acetylcholine metabolism. These disturbances would appear to constitute some of the earliest links in the mechanisms for the radiation effect on the body. Basically, the radiation changes in acetylcholine metabolism probably reflect compensatory reactions in the irradiated organism.

REFERENCES

AL'PERN, D. YE., *Chemical Factors of Nerve Excitation in the Human Organism* (Khimicheskiye faktory nervnogo vozbuzhdeniya v organizme cheloveka), Moscow 1944.

AL'PERN, D. YE. (Editor). *Humoral Factors in the Reactivity of the Nervous System* (Gumoral'nyye faktory reaktivnosti nervnoi sistemy), Kharkov 1949.

BAGLIONI, T. and A. PIEMONTE, *Boll. Soc. Ital. Biol. Sper.* **23**, 372 (1947).

BURN, J., P. KORDIK and R. MOLE, *J. Physiol.* **116**, 5, 1952; *Brit. J. Pharm.* **7**, 58 (1952).

CONARD, R., *Am. J. Physiol.* **170**, 418 (1952).

DEMIN, N. N., *Biochemical Activity of Acetylcholine* (Biokhimicheskaya aktivnost' atsetilkholina), Moscow 1953.

DEMIN, N. N., Bull. of U.S.S.R. Academy of Sciences (Biological series) (*Izv. Akad. Nauk SSSR, seriyabiol.*), **6**, 67 (1955a).

DEMIN, N. N., Ukrainian Biochem. J. (*Ukr. biokhim. zh.*) **27**, 460 (1955b).

DEMIN, N. N., Biochemistry (*Biokhimiya*) **20**, 317 (1955c).

DEMIN, N. N., *Proceedings of 8th All-Union Congress of Physiologists, Biochemists and Pharmacologists* (Tez. dokl. VIII Vses. s"ezda fiziol., biokhim. i farmakol.), Moscow 1955.

DEMIN, N. N. and A. S. KAINOVA, *Radiobiology* (Radiobiologiya) (1961).

DEMIN, N. N. and N. V. KORNEYEVA, *Proceedings of 1st Biochemical Conference of the Baltic Republic and Belorussia* (Tez. dokl. I Biokhim. konf. Prebalt. resp. i Belorussii), Tartu 1960.

DEMIN, N. N., N. V. KORNEYEVA and V. A. SHATERNIKOV, Biochemistry (*Biokhimiya*) **26** (1961).

DEMIN, N. N. and I. V. KUZNETSOVA, *Contemporary Problems of Nervism in Physiology and Pathology*. A collection commemorating the 70th birthday of Academician A. D. Speranskii (Sb. "Sovremennyye voprosy nervizma v fiziologii i patologii", posvyashch. 70-letiyu akad. A. D. Speranskogo), p. 405, Moscow 1958.

DEMIN, N. N., S. N. NISTRATOVA and L. S. ROZANOVA, Reports of the U.S.S.R. Academy of Sciences (*Dokl. Akad. Nauk SSSR*) **100**, 597 (1955).

DOULL, J., *Pharm. Expl. Theor.* **110**, 14 (1954).

FLORSHEIM, W. H. and M. E. MORTON, *Am. J. Physiol.* **176**, 15 (1954).

FRANCK, C., R. GRANDPIERRE, P. ARNOULD and P. DIDON, C. R. *Soc. Biol.* **142**, 79 (1948).

FRENCH, A. B. and P. E. WALL, *Am. J. Physiol.* **188**, 76 (1957).

GORIZONTOV, P. D., Collection: *Pathological Physiology of Acute Radiation Sickness.* (V sb. "Patologicheskaya fiziologiya ostroi luchevoi bolezni), p. 5, Moscow 1958.

GREMELS, H., *Arch. Expl. Path. Pharm.* **182**, 1 (1936).

GREMELS, H. and P. ZINNITZ, *Arch. Expl. Path. Pharm.* **188**, 79 (1937).

HOKIN, M. R. and L. E. HOKIN, *J. Biol. Chem.* **209**, 549 (1954).

HOKIN, L. E. and M. R. HOKIN, *Biochem. et Biophys. Acta* **16**, 229 (1955).

HOKIN, L. E. and M. R. HOKIN, *J. Biol. Chem.* **233**, 822 (1958).

HOKIN, L. E. and M. R. HOKIN, *J. Biol. Chem.* **234**, 1387 (1959).

KAINOVA, A. S., Biochemistry (*Biokhimiya*) **25**, 540 (1960).

KORNEYEVA, N. V., *Collection of Abstracts on Radiation Medicine for 1957* (Sbornik referatov po radiats. med. za 1957 g.), p. 38, Moscow 1959.

KORNEYEVA, N. V., *Radiobiology* (Radiobiologiya) (1961).

KOSHTOYANTS, KH. S., Reports of the U.S.S.R. Academy of Sciences (*Dokl. Akad. Nauk SSSR*) 43, 376 (1944).

KOSHTOYANTS, KH. S., Bull. of U.S.S.R. Academy of Sciences (Biological series) (*Izv. Akad. Nauk SSSR, seriya biol.*) **170** (1945).

KOSHTOYANTS, KH. S., Physiol. J. U.S.S.R. (*Fiziol. zh. SSSR*) **36**, 92 (1950).

KOSHTOYANTS, KH. S., *Proteins, Metabolism and Nerve Regulation* (Belkovyye tela, obmen veshchestv i nervnaya regulyatsiya), Moscow 1951.

KOSHTOYANTS, KH. S. (Editor). *Collection of Papers from the Laboratory of General and Comparative Physiology.* Papers of the Inst. Animal Morphology, U.S.S.R. Academy of Sciences (Sbornik rabot Labor. obshchei i sravnitel'noi fiziologii. Trudy IMZh im. Severtsova Akad. Nauk SSSR) **6** (1952).

KRAYEVSKII, N. A., *Outline of the Pathological Anatomy of Radiation Sickness* (Ocherki anatomii luchevoi bolezni), Moscow 1957. English translation in preparation by Pergamon Press.

KUZNETSOVA, N. YE., *Proceedings of Conference on pathogenesis, treatment and prevention of radiation sickness, marking the 40th anniversary of the Socialist Revolution* (Tez. dokl. konf., posvyashch. 40-i godovshchine Sotsialisticheskoi revolyutsii, po probleme "Patogenez, klinika, terapiya i profilaktika luchevoi bolezni"), p. 6, Leningrad 1957.

LABBE, M. and M. RUBINSTEIN, *C.R. Soc. Biol.* **112**, 1040 (1933).

LEBEDINSKII, A. V., *Papers by the Soviet Delegation to the International Conference on Peaceful Uses of Atomic Energy, Geneva*, 1955. (Doklady sovetskoi delegatsii na Mezhdunarodnoi konf. po mirnomu ispol'zovaniyu atomnoi energii), Moscow 1955.
LIVANOV, M. N., Med. radiology (*Med. radiol.*) 1, 1, 19 (1956).
LIVANOV, M. N. and D. A. BIRYUKOV, *Proceedings of 2nd International Conference on the Peaceful Uses of Atomic Energy, Geneva, 1959* (Trudy Vtoroi Mezdunarodnoi konf. po mirnomu ispol'zovaniyu atomnoi energii), Geneva 1959.
LIVANOV, M. N. and I. N. KONDRAT'YEVA, Med. radiology (*Med. radiol.*) 4, 9, 3 (1959).
LUTHY, H., *Radial. Clinica* 22, 491 (1953).
NISTRATOVA, S. N. and T. M. TURPAYEV, Biochemistry (*Biokhimiya*) 24, 171 (1959).
PETROVNINA, YE. N., *Changes in the Acetylcholine-cholinesterase-choline-acetylase System in Organs of Animals Affected by Ionizing Radiation* (Izmeneniya v sisteme atsetil-kholin-kholinesterasa-kholine-acetylase in organakh zhivotnykh, porazhennykh ioni-ziruyushchei radiatsei), Moscow 1958.
PONOMARENKO, N. YE., Med. radiology (*Med. radiol.*) 1, 5, 13 (1956).
RAZENKOV, I. P. (Editor), *Control of the Activity of Digestive Glands* (K mekhanizmu regulyatsii deyatel'nosti pishchevaritel'nykh zhelez), Moscow and Leningrad 1937.
SHASTIN, R. N., F. KH. KUCHERYAVYI and T. V. KRANTIKOVA, Med. radiology (*Med. radiol.*) 5, 7, 88 (1960).
SMIRNOV, K. V. and V. A. SHATERNIKOV, Reports of the U.S.S.R. Academy of Sciences (*Dokl. Akad. Nauk*) SSSR 131, 961 (1960).
TOWER, D. B. and K. A. C. ELLIOTT, *J. Appl. Physiol.* 5, 375 (1953).
TURPAYEV, T. M., Biochemistry (*Biokhimiya*) 20, 456 (1955).
WELSH, J. H., *Bull. Johns Hopkins Hosp.* 83, 568 (1948).
WELSH, J. H. and J. E. HYDE, *Proc. Soc. Expl. Biol. Med.* 55, 256 (1944).

THE REACTION OF FISH TO CHANGE
IN THE SALINITY OF THE MEDIUM

A. G. GINETSINSKII, V. F. VASIL'YEVA and YU. V. NATOCHIN

Institute of Evolutionary Physiology, U.S.S.R. Academy of Sciences, Leningrad

Translated by Dr. R. Crawford

THE salinity of the water is one of the basic ecological factors determining the distribution and migration of fish—that economically extremely important class of lower vertebrates. Physiologists studying the evolution of functions have been attracted by the osmoregulating systems of fishes as an example of great plasticity in the mechanisms providing for the continued existence and advancement of animals through the geological upheavals of the past. It is not surprising, therefore, that an extensive literature, both individuals papers and reviews, has been devoted to questions connected with osmoregulation in fishes (Koshtoyants, 1940; Korzhuyev, 1938; Smith, 1932; Prosser, 1950; Brown, 1957).

Yet, this problem is still far from being completely understood. This applies particularly to the mechanisms for the reaction of fishes to change in the salinity of the water and this was, in fact, the subject of this investigation.

METHOD

The fishes studied were the freshwater perch and pike (*Perca fluviatilis, Esox lucius*), skates (*Raja clavata, Trigon pastinaca*) and marine bony fishes (*Spicara smaris, Odontogadus merlangus*).*

Inulin (2 ml/100 g of a 10 per cent solution) was injected intramuscularly into the fish 12 hours before an experiment. The urine was expressed from the bladder by gentle massage of the abdomen and the genito-urinary orifice was then sutured before the fish was placed in the water to be examined. The fishes were removed from the aquarium after a certain time. The tail was cut off with scissors; blood from the divided vessels was collected in a test tube and after clotting was centrifuged. With fishes weighing

---

* The investigations on marine fishes were carried out at the Sevastopol Biological Station of the U.S.S.R. Academy of Sciences, to the Directorate of which we express our sincere gratitude for making the work possible.

about 30–40 g, serum sufficient for all biochemical estimations could be obtained in this way. The abdominal cavity was opened carefully, the urinary bladder which had filled up was punctured and all the urine secreted during the period of investigation was collected and measured. In the case of the skates, which have no urinary bladder, the urine was collected directly from the ureters. To achieve this, the cloaca was stretched and a specially constructed cannula was introduced, its expanded funnel-shaped end being fixed over the ureteral orifices with a tobacco-pouch suture. The cannula was connected to a light, thin rubber receptacle for the urine, which did not impede swimming. As the urine receptacle filled up it was removed and replaced with a fresh one. At the same time segments of the long tail were removed and the required quantities of blood obtained. Haemorrhage was arrested by the application of a ligature to the entire tail. A fish could thus be used for several experiments.

The following urine and serum estimations were made: (1) inulin concentration (resorcin method for calculation of the extent of filtration); (2) osmotic pressure (cryoscopy); (3) sodium concentration (flame photometry); and (4) chlorides (silver nitrate titration).

The activity of succino-dehydrogenase, the enzyme dehydrogenating succinic acid, was determined in kidney sections and in the leaflets of the gills by a histochemical method (reaction with neotetrazolium).

Urine secretion and filtration were calculated in terms of 100 g body weight per hour.

Similar estimations were made with fishes taken from natural waters after they had been kept for three or four hours in the experimental media (fresh waters and waters with increased salinity).

EXPERIMENTAL RESULTS

Freshwater Fishes

Under natural conditions the osmotic pressure in the blood of the perch averages 279 mM, which corresponds to a freezing point of $-0.52°C$. The greatest deviation from the average value observed was 16 per cent. The deviations in most cases were not more than ± 10 per cent.

When the fishes were kept in hypertonic solution with salinity greater than 268 mM. $(-0.5°C)$, the osmotic pressure of the blood began to increase. Urine secretion began to diminish appreciably from this point and it ceased entirely when the salinity exceeded $-0.75°C$. The freezing point of the blood then ranged between $-0.64°$ and $-0.69°C$, the average being $-0.66°C$ (Fig. 1).

The rise in the freezing point was apparently connected with the entry of sodium salts from the hypertonic solution, a point which was confirmed by direct estimation. The concentration of this ion in the blood plasma arose from 90 to 130 meq/l. (in pike).

There was no change in the concentration of osmotically active substances introduced by the kidney into the medium of high salinity. The freezing point of the urine remained at a constant level but exhibited fluctuations equivalent to $-0.1°$ around the average value (Fig. 1). The corresponding sodium concentration also remained virtually unchanged, averaging about 4 meq/l.

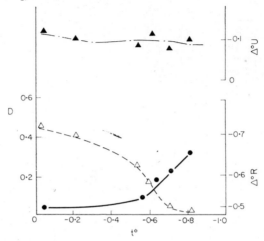

Fig. 1. Reaction of the perch in a hypertonic medium (average experimental values).

Ordinate D; $\triangle$—diuresis (ml) per 100 g body weight/hr. Ordinate R: replace by solid black circle—blood freezing points. Ordinate U: ▲—urine freezing points. Abscissa: freezing point of the experimental medium.

Elasmobranchs

Because of the high urea content, the osmotic pressure of the blood in elasmobranchs exceeds that of sea water. In these, as in freshwater fishes, the maintenance of a constant blood composition is based on the discharge of osmotically free water (Smith, 1931, 1936; Kempton, 1953). Our observations on Black Sea skate afford a clear illustration of these well-known features of elasmobranchs.

Table 1 shows that the osmotic pressure in the blood of skates was 30 per cent higher than that of Black Sea water, the freezing point of which is $-1.0°C$.

The urine was markedly hypotonic and all the osmotically active ingredients were present in it in much lower concentrations than in the blood. It is interesting to compare the various findings with those for the freshwater fishes.

There was considerable similarity in quantity of diuresis and urine/plasma concentration indices between these generically and ecologically remote animals which, however, have essentially similar types of osmoregulation (Table 2).

TABLE 1

Object	Diuresis (ml/g/hr)	Freezing temperature		Urea (mg%)		Sodium (meq/l.)		Chlorides (meq/l.)	
		Plasma	Urine	Plasma	Urine	Plasma	Urine	Plasma	Urine
Raja clavata	0·24	− 1·30	− 0·48	17·8	2·1	176	20	212	48
Raja clavata	0·10	− 1·24	− 0·63	14·5	5·5	192	67	236	76
Trigon pastinaca	0·49	− 1·39	− 0·44	13·8	3·7	236	80	280	78
Trigon pastinaca	0·20	− 1·29	− 0·31	14·7	1·9	258	59	258	68
Trigon pastinaca	0·27	− 1·30	− 0·29	13·2	1·2	244	110	248	74
Average	0·26	− 1·30	− 0·43	14·8	2·9	221	67	246	68

TABLE 2

Object	Diuresis (meq/l.)	Urine/Plasma ratio			
		F.P.	Sodium	Chlorides	Urea
Perch	0·43	0·25	0·31	—	—
Pike	0·24	0·30	0·34	—	—
Skate	0·26	0·33	0·30	0·27	0·20

Their reactions to keeping in hypotonic solutions were also similar.

Table 3 shows the results of the experiments on skates examined first in sea water and then transferred to the experimental solution. Despite the small number of animals we had available, the results were found to be quite definite. As in the case of the freshwater fishes, their reaction to increased salinity took the form of restricted diuresis and, consequently,

TABLE 3

Object	F.P. of medium	Percentage of initial value in the natural medium			
		Diuresis	Urea excretion	Sodium excretion	Chloride excretion
Trigon pastinaca	− 1·80	57	67	72	76
Trigon pastinaca	− 1·78	63	69	60	99
Trigon pastinaca	− 0·44	115	181	210	115
Raja clavata	− 0·55	104	96	129	—

reduced discharge of all osmotically active substances. As the natural environment of skates is sea water, we were also able to investigate the effect of transferring them to fresh water. In these experiments diuresis increased slightly and there was increased excretion of osmotically active substances.

The changes observed in the plasma were consistent with the trend in the renal reactions.

After the fishes had been in hypertonic solution the osmotic pressure might be 25 per cent higher, whereas a stay in hypotonic solution tended to reduce the freezing point of the blood slightly. These effects could be linked with corresponding changes in the concentrations of sodium, chlorides and, to a lesser extent, urea (Table 4).

TABLE 4

Object	F.P. of medium	Plasm in percentages of initial values			
		F.P.	Urea	Chlorides	Sodium
Raja clavata	− 0·55	103	100	96	—
Trigon pastinaca	− 0·44	94	96	95	84
Trigon pastinaca	− 1·80	125	95	117	115
Trigon pastinaca	− 1·70	99	105	106	106

Marine Bony Fishes

Urine secretion in marine bony fishes is considerably less than in freshwater fishes. Average diuresis was $0·43 \pm 0·038/100$ g per hr in perch and $0·15 \pm 0·021$ in smarids.

It should be noted that the range of individual variations was much greater in marine than in freshwater fishes. In the case of the perch the maximum diuresis observed in 12 experiments was 2·5 times the minimum diuresis observed. For the smarids, however, the maximum/minimum ratio reached 7·5 in 9 estimations.

The urine secretion of marine fishes living in aquaria tended to increase with the lapse of time when they were increasingly traumatized by handling or laboratory manipulations. The actual cause of this "laboratory diuresis" is unknown (Grafflin, 1935; Forster, 1953). The immediate cause is that the fishes drink excessive quantities of sea water.

Urine secretion increased when the fishes were transferred to hypotonic and even more so, hypertonic solution (Fig. 2).

Placed in hypotonic medium, the marine fish found itself in the same situation as the freshwater fish. Being subjected to hyperhydration it reacted by intensified excretion of the water which entered in excess quantity.

Conversely, in hypertonic water the fish suffered dehydration. Freshwater fish reacted to this by reducing diuresis whereas marine fish reacted by polyuria. The increased salinity of the water acted on them as an intensification of the natural stimulus for osmoregulating processes of the usual type. Exposed to the effect of a high osmotic gradient, the fishes lost more fluid than usual and consequently drank a larger quantity of sea water.

Polyuria in hypertonic water thus developed after the manner of laboratory diuresis, with the sole difference that here the reasons compelling the fish to increase its drinking of water are quite evident.

The effectiveness of the compensatory reactions in marine teleosts is just as inadequate as in the orders already examined. The osmotic pressure of their blood tends towards hypotonicity or hypertonicity exactly in accordance with the experimental effects to which they are exposed (Table 5). Whereas in freshwater fishes and skates the urine is always hypotonic in relation to the blood, when the representatives of the *Teleostei* which we examined were transferred to experimental solutions, the molar concentration of the urine followed the changes in the blood plasma so that the urine/plasma ratio approximated to unity under all conditions.

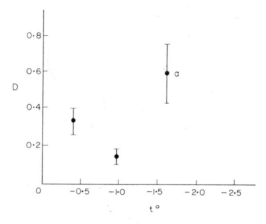

FIG. 2. Diuresis in marine bony fishes in sea water, hypotonic and hypertonic solutions.

a—average and extreme values of diuresis. Ordinate: diuresis (D). Abscissa: freezing point of the solution. The freezing point of sea water is 1·0°C.

The chloride concentrations in both plasma and urine fell in hypotonic and rose in hypertonic solutions. Their concentration ratios did not, however, deviate from unity. The kidney performs no osmotic function affecting the total concentration of osmotically active substances, of which chlorides constitute the main quantity.

Mechanism of the Diuretic Reaction

There is very little reabsorption of water in the renal tubules of fishes. The urine/plasma inulin concentration ratio averages 2·1 in freshwater fish, 2·2 in marine bony fish and 3·8 in skate. This means that total reabsorption of water approximated to 25 per cent in the skate only and that about half the fluid filtered out was removed with the urine in the other

TABLE 5

Object	Medium and its F.P.	Freezing point			Chlorides meq/l.		
		Plasma	Urine	Urine/Plasma	Plasma	Urine	Urine/Plasma
Spicara smaris	Sea-water (−1·0°)	−0·73	−0·70	0·96	173	167	0·96
Odontogadus merlangus		−0·73	−0·70	0·96	173	167	0·96
Spicara smaris	Hypotonic (−0·44°)	−0·64	−0·64	1·0	137	−	−
Odontogadus merlangus		−0·60	−0·61	1·0	141	140	0·99
Spicara smaris	Hypertonic (−1·8°)	−0·86	−0·80	0·93	202	203	1·0
Odontogadus merlangus		−0·83	−0·82	9·99	180	174	0·97

Note: Average values in eight experiments.

TABLE 6

Diuresis (ml/100 g/hr)	Number of estimations		Arithmetic mean with standard error		Reliable limits with $p = 0.05$	
	Freshwater	Marine	Freshwater	Marine	Freshwater	Marine
> 0·2	14	16	3·02 ± 0·23	2·35 ± 0·36	3·52 − 2·52	3·12 − 1·58
0·2 − 0·4	14	13	2·09 ± 0·07	2·28 ± 0·43	2·23 − 1·95	3·23 − 1·35
0·4 − 0·6	8	4	1·96 ± 0·13	2·00 ± 0·31	2·27 − 1·65	2·98 − 1·02
0·6 − 0·9	4	7	2·02 ± 0·09	1·75 ± 0·38	2·31 − 1·73	2·68 − 0·82

fish. For comparison, we would mention that reabsorption in higher vertebrates generally exceeds 98 per cent and that the inulin concentration coefficient is usually above 20 and may exceed 150 in conditions of even moderate dehydration.

Other published reports and the results obtained in this investigation make it clear that all fish are capable of varying the quantity of urine excreted. The main factors determining polyuric and oliguric reactions are always corresponding quantitative changes in filtration. This relationship is seen very distinctly in Fig. 3. Despite the fact that, under natural conditions, diuresis in freshwater fish is almost three times greater than in marine fish, their diuresis/filtration ratios are identical. Freshwater fish, exposed to dehydration, can reduce the formation of urine to values less than the natural diuresis in marine fish. Marine fish, transferred to hypertonic waters, mobilize the potentialities of the renal apparatus and develop diuresis twice as great as the maximum seen in freshwater fish. Figure 3 shows that the urine/plasma inulin concentration ratio ranged between 1·5 and 4·0 for different intensities of diuresis. Although no distinct

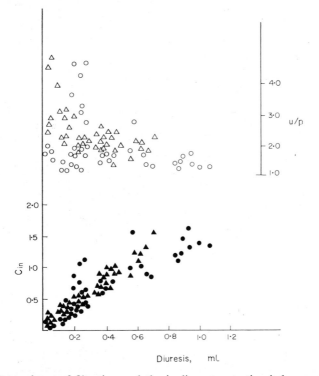

FIG. 3. Dependence of filtration and the inulin concentration index on diuresis.

Ordinate C_{in}—filtration (ml) per 100 g/hr: ▲—freshwater fishes; ●—marine fishes. Ordinate U/P—urine/plasma inulin concentration ratio: △—freshwater fishes; ○—marine fishes. Abscissa—urine excretion (ml/100 g/hr).

relationship between urine excretion and the inulin concentration index can be established, the index had its highest values when diuresis was small (Table 6).

In the case of the freshwater fish (perch) the increase in the index was reliable only when diuresis fell below 0·2 ml. The increase in water reabsorption was then 30 per cent (average), which can hardly be regarded as a manifestation of regulatory activity. It is more probable that the increase in the inulin concentration index was a result and not the cause of the reduction in urine excretion.

The basis of oliguric reactions is reduced filtration with resultant reduction in the loading of the nephron with osmotically active substances. If the rate of reabsorption remains as before, the relative quantity of substances reabsorbed may then be greater than in ordinary diuresis.

There may thus be a slight increase in the inulin concentration index when diuresis is small.

In contrast to freshwater fish, marine bony fish produce a urine which is isotonic with the blood, and not hypotonic. Consequently, the process of reabsorption proceeds in them without the expenditure of work to overcome the osmotic gradient. Because of this the level of the processes in the tubules is more able to follow all the quantitative fluctuations in filtration without change in the relative volume of reabsorption. This would explain why in marine fish, unlike freshwater, no statistically valid relationship between the inulin concentration index and diuresis can be demonstrated.

In all the fishes, therefore, the only target for the reaction was the filtration apparatus, and in all probability the arterioles and capillaries of the glomerulus. The tubular part of the nephron takes no direct part in compensatory reactions.

This would explain the complete absence of renal reaction in fishes to the injection of antidiuretic hormone. This experiment was carried out

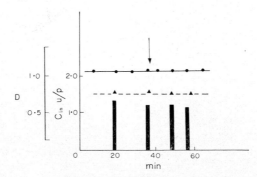

FIG. 4. Absence of any effect on renal function in a carp following the injection of pituitary extract.

▲—diuresis (ordinate D). ●—filtration (ordinate C_{in}). Columns—inulin concentration index (ordinate U/P_{in}). Abscissa—time (min). Arrow—injection of pituitary extract.

on a carp, the convenient size of which made it possible to record urine excretion continuously for several hours. To achieve this, the fish's movements were restricted by a cage immersed in the aquarium and a polyethylene catheter with a pipette was introduced into its urinary bladder. The urine excreted entered the pipette and its quantity was recorded every 15 min. The results of this experiment are shown in Fig. 4.

The injection of pituitary extract produced no change in the quantity of urine in the carp and had no effect on the value of the inulin concentration index.

Extrarenal Osmoregulation

Extrarenal processes connected with the activity of special cells in the gills are known to constitute the main element of osmoregulation in all fishes. In freshwater fish they absorb traces of sodium from the water and in marine fish they excrete sodium to clear excess from the blood (Smith, 1930; Keys, 1933; Krogh, 1939).

The view has recently been expressed that the dehydrogenation of succinic acid is an essential link in the energy process providing for the transport of sodium (Handley and Lavic, 1950; Mustakallio and Telkka, 1953; Caffruni *et al.*, 1955). Thus, the cells in all organs which reabsorb or excrete sodium contain the enzyme succino-dehydrogenase (Sexton and Russell, 1955; Natochin *et al.*, 1960). It is particularly noteworthy that stimulation of the transport of sodium is reflected in intensification of succino-dehydrogenase activity in the cells involved in such stimulation (Natochin *et al.*, 1960). This circumstance enables us to define the location of the effector of the sodium-regulating system by histochemical means.

The greatest succino-dehydrogenase activity was demonstrated in the distal tubules in the kidneys of freshwater fish (*Carassius auratus*), a fact which points to the major importance of this part of the nephron for the reabsorption of sodium (Fig. 5). Succino-dehydrogenase is also present in the gill cells which convey this ion from the environment to the blood.

There is no increase in the activity of this enzyme either in the kidneys or in the gills when fish are kept in distilled water free from all traces of sodium. Nor is reabsorption suppressed when they are placed in waters of increased salinity. It would appear that freshwater fish have no power to regulate the transport of sodium.

The case of marine fish is different. In these the organs richest in succino-dehydrogenase are the gills, the enzyme activity of which is greater than that of the renal tubules. No changes are observed in their renal cells when the fish are transferred to water of increased salinity. But enzyme activity in the gills increases considerably (Fig. 6). Marine fish thus possess a sodium regulating system which is capable of stimulating the excretion of sodium by the gills. This control is basic both in laboratory diuresis and hypertonic polyuria. The entry of excessive quantities of sea water into

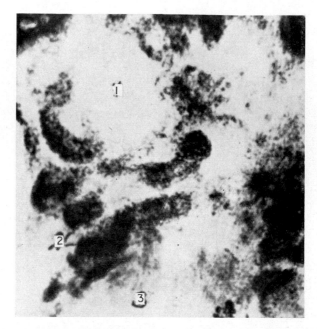

FIG. 5. Succino-dehydrogenase activity in the kidneys of a freshwater fish
(Carassius auratus) ×60.

1—glomerulus (total absence of activity); 2—distal tubule; 3—proximal tubule.

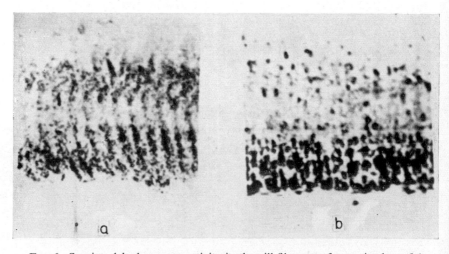

FIG. 6. Succino-dehydrogenase activity in the gill filament of a marine bony fish
(Fracturus mediterraneus) ×60.

a—after living in saline water; b—after living in a hypertonic solution.

the gastro-intestinal tract leads to over-saturation of the blood with univalent and divalent ions. By some mechanism which is not yet understood the excess of sodium drives the gill apparatus to intensify its activity. Freed from excess sodium, sea water is converted to a solution which is iso-osmotic with the blood. This solution is excreted by the kidney with resultant increase in the volume of urine.

DISCUSSION

Compensatory change in diuresis is the only reaction of the kidneys in fish to deviations from the usual degree of salinity in the water. The properties of the urine are unchanged.

In fish the tubular processes proceed with almost complete uniformity. No homeostatic reactions directed to vary the intensity of the reabsorption of water or sodium can be demonstrated in them. The renal element in the osmoregulating process only affects the volume of water contained in the body. Depending on circumstances, freshwater fish and skate can excrete water which is osmotically free to a greater or lesser degree, while marine teleosts can excrete larger or smaller quantities of chloride solution isotonic with the blood.

The osmoregulating process in the kidneys is exclusively quantitative. As tubular reabsorption has very little effect on the volume of filtrate, the level of the latter determines absolutely the quantity of urine excreted and, consequently, the magnitude of the compensatory reaction.

In the case of freshwater fish the only possible change in their natural environment is increase of salinity and their only method of compensation is an oliguric reaction. There is no form of regulation directed to the removal of excess quantities of sodium in the kidney of fish (Table 7). Passing through the glomerular apparatus, the quantity of sodium remains virtually unchanged as an increased concentration in the filtrate is balanced by reduced filtration.

Both the absolute value of sodium excretion and the relative value calculated as a percentage of the filtrate are reduced in a saline water. The task of the kidney is to extract the sodium from the primary urine, and certainly not to excrete this ion, so valuable for freshwater fish. Reabsorption in them is apparently always maximum. It cannot be reduced, even when homeostasis demands this, in fishes finding themselves in unusual environmental conditions.

Marine bony fish are exposed to both reduction and increase of salinity. Their main homeostatic reaction is regulation of the intensity of the gill excretion of sodium in accordance with the quantity of sea water entering the body. The kidney always reacts by polyuria and excretes the excess quantity of water after it has been freed from salts to render it isotonic with the blood.

TABLE 7. Reaction of pike

Medium and F.P.	Diuresis	Filtration	Concentration of Na		Quantity filtered	Na excreted with urine	Percentage Na excreted
	ml/100 g/hr		Plasma	Urine	meq/l./100 g/hr		
			meq/l.				
Fresh	0·28	0·40	90	4·2	36	1·68	4·7
−0·46°	0·31	0·51	96	3·3	49	0·99	2·0
−0·70°	0·14	0·31	116	3·5	36	0·49	1·3
−0·80°	0·08	0·18	130	5·8	23	0·46	2·0

TABLE 8. Sodium concentration (meq/l.)

Object	Sea water			Hypotonic medium			Hypertonic medium		
	Plasma	Urine	Urine/Plasma	Plasma	Urine	Urine/Plasma	Plasma	Urine	Urine/Plasma
Spicara smaris	194	116	0·60	152	94	0·62	221	200	0·90
Odontogadus merlangus	185	79	0·48	147	63	0·43	212	106	0·50

While the urine/plasma chloride ratio in marine bony fishes is always unity, the sodium concentration is invariably less than the concentration in the blood. This circumstance is of special interest in connexion with one of the debatable problems in renal physiology.

Opinion has hitherto been divided on the nature of the process underlying the reabsorption of sodium in the proximal tubules. According to some authors (Wesson and Anslow, 1952; Smith, 1956), the transport of sodium is based on active cell processes in the proximal as well as in the distal tubules. Others (Malvin et al., 1958) assert that no sodium gradient exists between the contents of the tubules and the blood and that reabsorption of sodium in this section is passive and is due to a difference of colloidal osmotic pressure in the protein-free filtrate and the blood plasma flowing through the peritubular capillaries.

The true nature of the mechanism of sodium reabsorption in the proximal tubules is still debatable because the authors taking part base their arguments on indirect findings and not on direct determinations.

The features of the renal structure in marine fish makes them a particularly suitable object for the investigation of this problem. In them sodium is a substance for excretion and is not economically important, as in freshwater fish. Consequently, the distal segment of the nephron, in which intense reabsorption of this ion takes place, has been reduced in marine teleosts. The only section of the nephron remaining in these fish is the proximal tubule which passes directly into the system of excretory channels. The fluid obtained from the bladder under these circumstances is, therefore, merely proximal urine in pure form, uncomplicated by the activity of distal tubules, as it is in all other vertebrate animals.

Table 8 shows that, although the sodium concentration in the urine undergoes changes in different conditions which run parallel with the changes in the concentration of this ion in the blood, it is always less than in the plasma. The urine/plasma ratio is always considerably below unity in both types of fishes examined, although the sodium gradient is more acute in the whiting than in the smarid.

It must be assumed that reduction of the distal segment of the nephron, being a particular form of adaptation in marine bony fishes, has not involved any fundamental changes in the function of the proximal tubules. Our findings indicate that the proximal segment is capable of creating a sodium concentration gradient; consequently, the process of reabsorption of sodium is an active one in this section of the nephron also.

REFERENCES

BROWN, M. E., The Physiology of Fishes, New York 1957.
CAFFRUNI, E., A. FARAH and H. STEFANO, J. Pharm. Expl. Ther. 115, 390 (1955).
FORSTER, R. P., J. Cell. Comp. Physiol. 42, 487 (1953).
GRAFFLIN, A., Biol. Bull. 49, 391 (1935).

HANDLEY, C. A. and P. S. LAVIC, *J. Pharm. Expl. Ther.* **100**, 115 (1950).
KEMPTON, R. T., *Biol. Bull.* **104**, 45 (1953).
KEYS, A. B., *Proc. Roy. Soc.* **112**, 184 (1933).
KORZHUYEV, P. A., Recent Advances in Biology (*Usp. sovrem. biol.*) **9**, 5, 66 (1938).
KOSHTOYANTS, KH. S., *Principles of Comparative Physiology* (Osnovy sravnitel'noi fiziologii), Moscow–Leningrad 1940.
KROGH, A., *Osmotic Regulation in Aquatic Animals*, London 1939.
MALVIN, R. L., W. S. WILDE, A. J. VANDER and L. P. SULLIVAN, *Am. J. Physiol.* **195**, 549 (1958).
MUSTAKALLIO, K. and TELKKA, *Science* **118**, 320 (1935).
NATOCHIN, YU. V., A. A. BRONSHTEIN and T. V. KRESTINSKAYA, Reports of U.S.S.R. Academy of Sciences (*Dokl. Akad. Nauk SSSR*). (In press) (1960).
NATOCHIN, YU. V., T. V. KRESTINSKAYA and P. KHLEBOVICH. (In press) (1960).
PROSSER, L., *Comparative Animal Physiology*. Philadelphia 1950.
SEXTON, A. W. and R. L. RUSSELL, *Science*, **121**, 342 (1955).
SMITH, H. W., *Am. J. Physiol.* **93**, 480 (1930).
SMITH, H. W., *Am. J. Physiol.* **98**, 296 (1931).
SMITH, H. W., *Quart. Rev. Biol.* **7**, 1 (1932).
SMITH, H. W., *Biol. Rev.* **11**, 49 (1938).
SMITH, H. W., *Principles of Renal Physiology* New York 1956.
WESSON, L. G. and W. P. ANSLOW, *Am. J. Physiol.* **170**, 255 (1952).

EVOLUTION OF ELECTROPHYSIOLOGICAL VARIETIES AMONG SENSORY RECEPTOR SYSTEMS*

HARRY GRUNDFEST

Department of Neurology, College of Physicians and Surgeons, Columbia University, New York

INTRODUCTION

Anatomically and to a certain degree also functionally, there is a long-standing distinction between "primary" and "secondary" sensory receptors. The primary type is a neuron exemplified by the crustacean stretch receptor (cf. Eyzaguirre, 1961) or the vertebrate Pacinian corpuscle (cf. Loewenstein, 1961). A receptor portion receives, and analyzes, the intensity of a specific adequate stimulus. The process produces an electrical sign, a depolarizing generator potential graded in proportion to the strength of the stimulus. The sensory message is then encoded into a frequency-number train of all-or-none spikes which is produced in the conductile part of the same cell. In anatomical terminology the sensory element of the primary receptor also has a centripetal or afferent nerve fiber.

In receptors of the secondary type the sensory cell proper does not have an axon, but is directly or indirectly in contact with one or several neurons. The message that is encoded in impulses is initiated in the afferent nerve fiber of the latter. Receptors of the secondary type are said to occur only in vertebrates (cf. Autrum, 1959). However, there is probably at least one invertebrate secondary receptor. The lateral eye of *Limulus* appears to have specialized photochemical receptors ahead of the sensory neuron which is the eccentric cell (cf. Grundfest, 1958b; Fuortes, 1959).

Vertebrate olfaction is mediated by primary sensory cells whose receptor surfaces are dendrites at the olfactory epithelium. All the other special sense systems, vision, hearing, equilibrium and taste are of the secondary type. The chemoreceptive taste buds and the mechanoreceptive hair cells of audition and of equilibrium sense are without axons. They transmit the transduced messages to cranial nerve fibers that are in close association

* This work supported in part by grants from Muscular Dystrophy Associations of America, National Science Foundation, National Institute of Neurological Diseases and Blindness and the United Cerebral Palsy Research and Educational Foundation.

with the sensory cells. Receptor cells in the lateral line organ of fish similarly make contact with neurons having axonal extensions. The sensory system of vertebrate vision is more complicated. The photochemically excited elements, rods and cones, act on horizontal and bipolar cells and the latter in turn react upon neurons (ganglion cells) which send messages to the brain via their axons in the optic nerve.

A considerable body of data has accumulated in recent years which substantiates the views of the present writer (Grundfest, 1956a, 1957c, 1957d, 1957e, 1959b), concerning the specific modes of action of the receptive and transmissional electrogenic membranes and of the functional interrelationships of reception and transmission with the processes of conduction. The basic principle lies in the differentiation of two kinds of electrogenic activity: electrically inexcitable receptive and transmissional activities on the one hand, and electrically excitable conductile processes on the other. From the point of view that the different types of sense organs have common basic properties the present article will seek to raise some questions regarding comparative evolutionary physiology, a subject which occupied Professor Koshtoyants long and fruitfully.

ELECTRICAL INEXCITABILITY OF RECEPTIVE MEMBRANE

The view that electrical inexcitability characterizes certain electrogenic processes derived from a study of transmissional activity in electroplaques of electric fish (Altamirano and Grundfest, 1954; Altamirano et al., 1955; Grundfest, 1957b). It was soon extended, however, to the entire class of receptive membranes (Grundfest, 1956b, 1957e, 1959b)*. This generalization, like most others in biology, has its exceptions. Ephaptic (electrical) transmission between cells occurs in some cases (cf. Watanabe and Grundfest, 1961). In one known case (Furshpan and Potter, 1959) transmission is even polarized, a property which used to be considered as characteristic of synapses (Sherrington, 1906). Polarized (unidirectional) ephaptic transmission, however, is achieved by a different mechanism from that which causes unidirectional transmission at synaptic junctions. The as yet unknown sensory receptors for the electrical guidance systems which occur in certain electric fishes must be electrically excitable from the very nature of the signals which they receive (Grundfest, 1958b). Indeed, these electrical sense organs appear to be adapted to have extraordinarily high sensitivity to an electric gradient as the adequate stimulus, in at least one case detecting a change of about $0.02 \, \mu V/cm$ (Lissmann, 1958; cf. also Hagiwara et al., 1962). All other types of receptive (or input) membranes that have been examined so far appear to be electrically inexcitable. They do not

---

* While the explicit formulation of this classification is only recent, the first observed case of "excitable cells" which do not respond directly to electrical stimuli is probably that of salivary glands (Claude Bernard, 1859).

react to electrical stimuli, but respond specifically to mechanical, photic, thermal or chemical energy as the respective adequate stimuli.

Direct evidence for electrical inexcitability of receptive membrane is now available in at least three different sense organs:

(1) *Chemoreceptors.* In response to chemical stimuli the olfactory epithelium produces a long-lasting potential (Fig. 1), which cannot be evoked by electrical stimuli nor is the chemically evoked potential affected by elec-

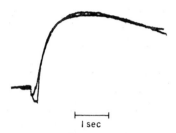

├──────┤
I sec

FIG. 1. Two superimposed extracellularly recorded surface-negative responses of bullfrog olfactory epithelium to stimulation by a jet of air saturated with butyl acetate. Note long-lasting potential and absence of spikes. Initial positivity is artifact during opening of electromechanical valve.
(From: Sigg and Grundfest, 1959.)

trical stimulation (Ottoson, 1956, 1959; cf. Grundfest, 1957d). Long-lasting depolarizing potentials have also been recorded from single taste buds (cf. Kimura and Beidler, 1961). Different cells respond differently (Fig. 2) to each of the four basic taste stimuli: salt, sweet, bitter and acid. Spikes are not produced in these cells and they are very probably electrically inexcitable.

(2) *Mechanoreceptors.* The dendrites of the crayfish stretch receptor do not form an outside-negative "sink" or site of inward flow of current when an antidromic spike is evoked in the cell (C. A. Terzuolo and Y. Washizu, personal communication). Thus the receptor membrane of the stretch receptor neuron appears to be unresponsive to an electrical stimulus as large as the spike of the cell.

According to Loewenstein (1961) the receptive terminal of the Pacinian corpuscle does not support a spike and the spike is not initiated in this sensory region. The generator potential is graded and its size is dependent on the area which is excited by the mechanical stimulus. Responses generated in different areas summate (Fig. 3). The generator potentials of the Pacinian corpuscle have most of the characteristics which have been deduced theoretically for electrically inexcitable membrane (Grundfest, 1957c, 1959a) and which are observed with particular clarity in the large, electrically inexcitable electroplaques of marine electric fishes (Grundfest and Bennett, 1961).

5*

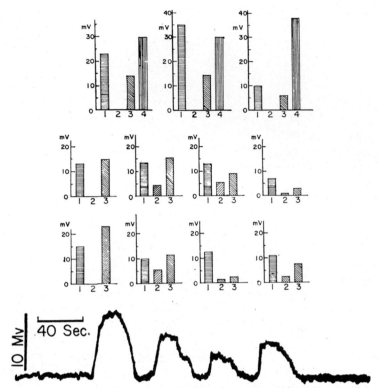

FIG. 2. Electrical activity in single taste buds produced by four standardized stimuli (1) salt, (2) sweet, (3) bitter and (4) acid.

Below: Intracellular records of potential evoked by the four substances acting on a single taste bud. Note long-lasting potential and absence of spikes. *Above:* Different patterns of responses in 11 different cells. (Unpublished data of Beidler and Kimura, courtesy of Dr. Lloyd Beidler.)

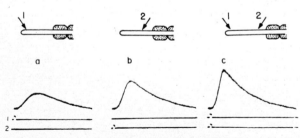

FIG. 3. Spatial summation of generator potentials of Pacinian corpuscle evoked by stimulating two points about 400μ apart on the receptor surface. Diagram shows sites of application of the mechanical stimuli. Stimulation signals are registered on lines 1 and 2 of the records. Simultaneous delivery of both stimuli (c) evoked response which was the sum of the two individual responses (a, b). (From: Loewenstein, 1961.)

Hunt and Takeuchi (1962) and Sato and Ozeki (1963) find, however, that an antidromic impulse can invade the receptor terminal. Hence, the membrane of the latter may have a component of electrically excitable conductile membrane which is interspersed among "patches" of electrically inexcitable receptive elements. It is generally agreed that the generator potential initiates a spike at the first node of the axonal portion. This may indicate that the patches of electrically excitable membrane in the receptive region have a higher threshold (critical firing level) than does the nodal membrane. Such differences in the threshold are well known (cf. Bennett *et. al.*, 1959).

The occurrence of intermingled "patches" of different types of membrane is now a commonplace finding. Two kinds of synaptic, electrically inexcitable membrane, excitatory and inhibitory in function respectively, as well as electrically excitable, spike-generating membrane occur together in various kinds of neurons and muscle fibers. The electrically inexcitable components need not be present only at synapses. Thus, patches of chemically activated membrane capable of depolarizing and repolarizing electrogenesis respectively occur on the cell bodies of neurons in *Aplysia* and *Helix* (cf. references and discussion in Grundfest, 1964a, b). Although these patches have the same pharmacological properties as the synaptic membranes that lie on the axon or axon hillock the two cannot have the same functional relations since the former are not innervated. Since these patches are not innervated and are electrically inexcitable, their presence was undetected by stimulation of the neuron. It was disclosed only by their responses to applications of pharmacological agents. The occurrence of such structures was deduced theoretically and they appear to be fairly common (cf. Grundfest, 1957d, 1958a, 1964b).

It should also be noted that amphibian slow muscle fibers and Rajid electroplaques exhibit forms of electrical excitability (Grundfest, 1961a). While their most prominent response is a depolarizing p.s.p. generated in electrically inexcitable membrane, another membrane component does respond to depolarizing stimuli, with K-activation in the muscle fibers (Belton and Grundfest, 1961), and with Cl-activation in the electroplaques (Cohen *et al.*, 1961). The brief response of the Pacinian corpuscle to a sustained mechanical stimulus may indicate the occurrence of such repolarizing electrically excitable activity. Only a small area of the receptive membrane is excited at one time under the usual experimental conditions. The averaged, electrotonically spread potential may be rather small. In muscle fibers of the mealworm, *Tenebrio molitor* the threshold for K-activation is lower than that for Na-activation (Kusano and Grundfest, unpublished). A similar relation in the electrically excitable component of the receptor region of the Pacinian corpuscle would tend to elicit repolarizing electrogenesis which could act as a type of "inhibitory" activity.

(3) *Eccentric cell of Limulus.* The dendrites and cell body of the eccentric cell of *Limulus* do not generate the spikes which course down the axon

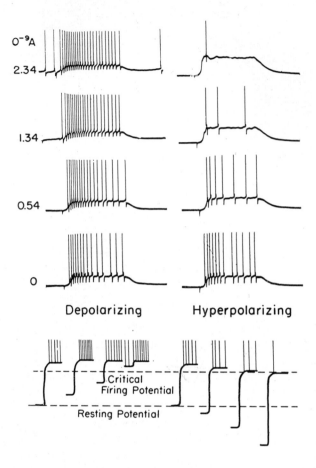

FIG. 4. *A:* Interaction of generator potential and polarizing voltages on electrically excitable (spike-producing) membrane. Eccentric cell of *Limulus* eye was impaled with microelectrode, which was used both for recording and for polarizing the cell. Magnitudes of the applied currents are given on left. During polarization a constant light intensity was also delivered for about 1·5 sec. This stimulus gave rise to a depolarizing generator potential in the electrically inexcitable dendrite (distal process). The potential decreased with increasing depolarization (*left*) while the spike frequency increased. The strongest depolarization itself evoked spikes which recommenced after a silent period following the light stimulus. With increasing hyperpolarization of the cell (*right*) the generator potential increased, but the spike frequency decreased. The diagram indicates how these interactive effects occur. During depolarization the smaller generator potential was carried higher above the critical firing level. For the strongest hyperpolarizing current the generator potential barely attained the critical firing level. The changes in membrane potential from the resting level produced by the polarizing current are drawn proportional to the applied currents, but the amplitudes of the generator potential are exaggerated.

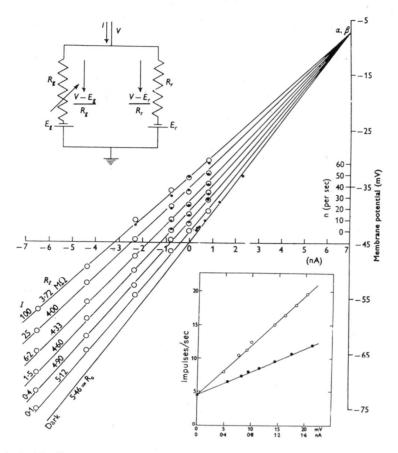

FIG. 4. *B:* Manifestation of electrical inexcitability of eccentric cell of *Limulus.*
The frequency of discharges in the axon was increased by depolarizing the
cell with an intracellularly applied current (dots, lower inset figure; abscissa in
$nA = 10^{-9}$ A) or by lights which produced depolarizing generator potentials of
different amplitudes (circles; abscissa in mV of generator potential). Main graph:
Another experiment. The effects of the applied currents on the spike frequency are
plotted as the dots fitted by the "dark" curve. The circles of the other curves show
the generator potential produced by different intensities of light ($I = 0.1$–100 units)
at various values of polarizing current. The dots show the frequencies of the discharges in the axon under the same condition. The change in the slopes of the
straight lines shows that the membrane resistance of the "dark" cell is decreased
progressively by brighter illuminations. *Upper inset:* Equivalent circuit of the electrically inexcitable *Limulus* eccentric cell. *Er* and *Eg* are the sources of the resting
and generator potentials. One is an unreactive membrane whose resistance (*Rr*) is
unaffected by either illumination or polarization. The other is the generator membrane whose resistance (*Rg*) is diminished by light, but not by applied current (*i*).
The voltage (*V*) resulting from the combined effects of current and illumination is
the effective potential which determines the frequencies of the discharges and may
be calculated from the equivalent circuit. The calculated lines for different illuminations and currents agree quite well with the frequencies (*dots*) and generator
potentials (*circles*) in main graph. (From: Grundfest, 1961 d, after Fuortes, 1959,
and Rushton, 1959.)

of the cell (Tomita, 1956). Intracellularly applied currents do not change
the membrane resistance in that portion of the eccentric cell which produces
a generator potential (Fig. 4). However, photic stimuli do modify the resistance, and thereby lead to the production of generator potentials (Fuortes,
1959; Rushton, 1959).

Indirect evidence for electrical inexcitability of input membrane components derives from data which conform to the theoretically deduced consequences of that condition with respect to certain electrophysiological
and pharmacological properties (Grundfest, 1957c, 1959a). The association
has been verified in a number of cell types, and particularly on the electroplaques of marine electric fishes (cf. Grundfest and Bennett, 1961). The
occurrence of several of these properties in a particular electrogenic system
provides strong evidence that its membrane is electrically inexcitable.

(1) Absence of active propagation is one of these properties, and it is
a characteristic which distinguishes the generator potential from the conductile spike electrogenesis of the electrically excitable axonal membrane.
It has been observed (Figs. 5, 6) in the Pacinian corpuscles (Loewenstein,
1961), crayfish stretch receptors (Eyzaguirre and Kuffler, 1955), muscle
spindles (Katz, 1950; Paintal, 1959), and olfactory receptors (Ottoson, 1956;
Schneider and Hecker, 1956; Schneider and Kaissling, 1957).

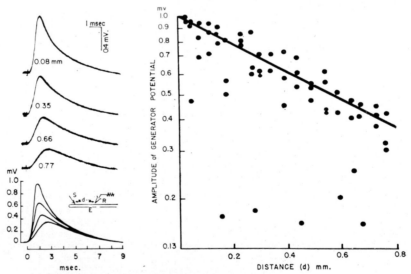

Fig. 5. Absence of active propagation of the generator potential that is evoked
by localized stimulation of Pacinian corpuscle.

Left: Potentials recorded at 4 distances from a fixed site of stimulation. The experimental
arrangement is shown in the diagram. The 4 records are also shown superimposed
(*bottom, left*). Note that the decay of the 4 potentials is nearly the same at the late part
of all the responses. *Right:* Plot of a large number of measurements showing the logar-
ithmic decrease of the peak amplitude of the potential with distance from the site of
the localized stimulus. (Modified: from Loewenstein, 1961.)

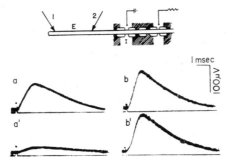

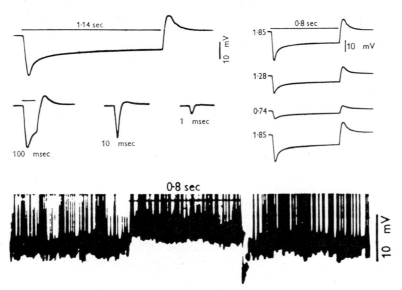

FIG. 6. Independence of membrane events at two regions of receptor membrane of Pacinian corpuscle. Diagram shows experimental arrangement. Mechanical stimuli was delivered independently through styli 1 and 2, about 200 μ apart on the ending (E). Each caused the response in *a* and *b* as recorded from the axon (I). Then a train of stimuli, at 500/sec and 2 sec in duration, was applied through stylus 1. This caused reduction or "inactivation" of testing response at the site (*a'*) but not at the second (*b'*). (From: Loewenstein, 1961.)

FIG. 7. Different kinds of responses of intermediate cells and of a ganglion cell of the cat retina.

Upper left: Hyperpolarization graded in duration and amplitude resulted in the intermediate cell from flashes of constant intensity but varying in duration from 1·0 msec to 1·14 sec. *Upper right:* Gradation of the hyperpolarizing potential by changing the intensity of a light flash of 0·8 sec duration. *Below:* Intracellular recording from a retinal ganglion neuron, showing depolarizing generator potential and augmented spike activity during a light flash of 0·8 sec. Since the depolarizing response of the ganglion cell was evoked in conjunction with hyperpolarization of the preceding elements, electrical activation of the ganglion cells by the intermediate cells is ruled out, and excitation must have occurred by chemical mediators. (From: Grundfest, 1961d, after Brown and Wiesel, 1959.)

The "dendritic" stem connecting the terminal receptor region of insect chemosensory neurons with their cell bodies is capable of generating an impulse (Morita, 1959; Hanson and Wolbarsht, 1962). This finding emphasizes the possibility that "dendrites" may have both receptive and conductile functions (Grundfest, 1957c). Morphological methods cannot at present resolve the presence or the absence of differently excitable membrane components (Grundfest, 1961c). Thus, functional rather than anatomical criteria must be used to classify the components of a neuron (cf. Bodian, 1962). Since the dendritic stem of the chemosensory cells is long and thin, spread of the generator depolarization from the receptor region at the tip of the cell to the cell body would be greatly attenuated. The presence of a conductile, electrically excitable component in the dendritic membrane would ensure impulse generation in the neuron in response to stimulation of the receptive portion by specific chemical agents.

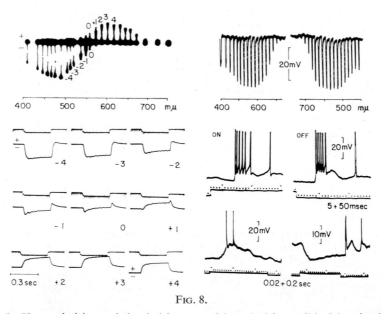

FIG. 8.

Left: Hyperpolarizing and depolarizing potentials evoked in a cell in fish retina by illumination of different wave lengths, but of constant energy. *Above:* Action spectrum by scanning method. *Below:* The responses numbered on the upper traces are individually shown swept out on a time base. Note that the hyperpolarizing and depolarizing potentials appear to counterbalance at the record marked O, except for a brief initial negative deflection and a terminal positive one. Durations of light flashes, monitored on upper traces, were 0·3 sec. (From: Grundfest, 1961d, after MacNichol and Svaetichin, 1958). *Right: (Top):* Hyperpolarizing responses of different magnitudes evoked in a frog retinal cell by light of different wavelengths. *(Middle):* On and off responses in a ganglion cell. Note depolarizations associated with spikes. A brief small hyperpolarization precedes the on-response. *(Bottom):* Records from ganglion cells which respond only "on" (*left*) or "off" (*right*). Note the marked hyperpolarization in the latter cell during the illumination.
(Modified from: Tomita *et al.*, 1961.)

(2) Occurrence of a response of indefinite amplitude and duration*, depending upon the stimulus, sometimes of depolarizing and other times of hyperpolarizing potentials, depending upon the cell and/or the stimulus, represents a group of properties which also provide indirect evidence. These characteristics have been found in the *Limulus* eccentric cell, crayfish stretch receptor, olfactory epithelium, muscle spindle, insect chemoreceptors, vertebrate taste buds and vertebrate visual receptor systems. The long-lasting potentials of the horizontal or bipolar cells in fish, frog and cat retina (MacNichol and Svaetichin, 1958; Brown and Wiesel, 1959; Grüsser, 1957; Motokawa *et al.*, 1957; Tomita *et al.*, 1961) may be hyperpolarizing

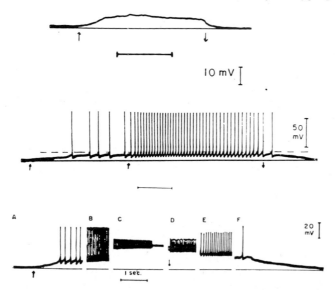

FIG. 9. Depolarizing electrogenesis of crayfish mechanoreceptor sense organ and the effects it evokes in the electrically excitable portion of the cell.

Top: A weak stretch stimulus (↑) caused a depolarization of about 7 mV across the membrane of the cell body. This was maintained until the stretch was released (↓). *Middle:* Records at lower amplification. A weak stimulus produced a low-frequency discharge of spikes. Increased stretch (second arrow) caused a higher frequency discharge which continued with some slowing as long as the stimulus was applied. The spikes generated during the depolarization develop a hyperpolarizing undershoot which is absent when the response is evoked by a single electrical stimulus. *Bottom:* Three increasingly larger stimulations are shown in *A–C.* The spikes produced at a high frequency by the strongest stimulus (*C*) were diminished in amplitude and at the end were no longer evoked while the receptor continued to respond with its sustained depolarization. *D–F:* The return of responsiveness of the electrically excitable membrane after its inactivation. Note that the average level of the depolarization produced by the mechanoreceptor dendrites is graded with the degree of the stimulus.
(From: Grundfest, 1961 d, after Eyzaguirre and Kuffler, 1955.)

---

* The brief response of the Pacinian corpuscle (cf. Figs. 3, 5 and 6), was discussed above. It is also possible that the brief time course of this generator potential may be an artifact created by the presence of covering sheaths over the receptor membrane.

5 a*

(Figs. 7 and 8) or, as in some cells of the fish retina, they may be hyperpolarizing for one range of wavelengths and depolarizing for another
(Fig. 8). In receptors of the primary kind the depolarizing potential is
a generator potential exciting spikes, hyperpolarizing electrogenesis being
inhibitory. In the secondary type of receptors of the retina and the taste
buds, however, there are no spikes. Even in the primary receptor varieties
the generator potential may appear (Fig. 9) without spikes when it is too
small to elicit the latter or when it is so large as to inactivate the spike
generating membrane (Eyzaguirre and Kuffler, 1955; cf. Grundfest, 1957e).
By analogy from the evidence already available, but also on the basis of
functional considerations, it seems likely that other receptors likewise have
electrically inexcitable input membrane.

(3) Differences in reactions to pharmacological agents further help to
characterize the distinction between electrically excitable and electrically
inexcitable membrane components. Receptive membranes which produce
generator potentials react to many pharmacological agents in the same way
as do various synaptic membranes. For example, tetrodotoxin does not
affect the responsiveness of frog neuromuscular synapses to acetylcholine
(Furukawa et al., 1959), but it prevents production of spikes by eliminating
Na-activation in the electrically excitable membrane component (Nakajima
et al., 1962). The toxin also eliminates spike production in receptor neurons,
without affecting their generator potential. This result, predicted on theoretical grounds, has been observed in the crayfish stretch receptor (Loewenstein et al., 1963; Nakajima, Saito and Grundfest, unpublished), in the Pacinian corpuscle (Loewenstein et. al., 1963), in the eccentric cell of *Limulus*
(by R. M. Benolken, personal communication from C. A. Terzuolo), and
in insect chemoreceptors (M. L. Wolbarsht, personal communication).

POSSIBLE COMPLEXITIES IN BEHAVIOR OF ELECTRICALLY
INEXCITABLE MEMBRANE

1. *Overshooting and Undershooting Potentials*

All e.p.s.p.'s that have been analyzed (frog twitch muscle, Takeuchi and
Takeuchi, 1960; frog slow muscle, Belton and Grundfest, 1961; Rajid
electroplaques, Cohen et al., 1961) apparently result from simultaneous
Na- and K-activation by the transmitter agent. There is no reason to suppose, however, that the electrically inexcitable activation processes will
have similar kinetics in all cells. Wherever they differ markedly (with Na-
activation leading) overshoots and undershoots might occur, as in the
activity of electrically excitable membrane (Grundfest, 1957b).

2. *Secondary Changes in Membrane Properties*

The reactivity of the membrane to its normal excitant or to chemical
agents may be modified in either direction during continuous activity or

by experimental procedures (Grundfest, 1957d, 1958a). These "sensitization", "desensitization" and "inactivation" (Fig. 6) phenomena are as yet little understood. One of the most interesting and most thoroughly studied is that of denervation sensitization (cf. Thesleff, 1961). Severing the nerve to a vertebrate muscle results in the muscle fiber membrane away from the endplate becoming responsive to acetylcholine. Apparently "patches" of the fiber membrane change not only their pharmacological but their electrophysiological properties as well to those of synaptic membrane (Grundfest, 1961b, c; Thesleff, 1961). Denervation of crayfish muscle fibers changes their permeability to K^+ and Cl^-, but does not increase their sensitivity to GABA (Girardier et al., 1962). The respective changes develop in frog (Miledi, 1960) as well as in crayfish muscle fibers while stimulation of the severed nerve can still evoke reponses in the muscle. In the cat also, the changes occur after functional denervation is established with botulinum toxin (Thesleff, 1961), which eliminates release of excitatory transmitter while the anatomical connections are still maintained. Thus, it seems that the presence or absence of transmitter agents has long-term effects on some parts of the non-synaptic membrane of muscle fibers.

3. Interplays of Different Excitable Membrane Components

Because of their different modes of excitation the receptive and conductile components operate under different laws. Thus, one may be affected differently from the other under various conditions (Figs. 4, 9, 11), and this difference has given rise to misinterpretations of the observed data (cf. Dudel and Kuffler, 1960; Reuben and Gainer, 1962). Analysis of such interactions is not always easy and it is further complicated by recent findings (Grundfest, 1961a, 1962, 1963) that the electrically excitable membranes respond to stimuli in more varied ways than were envisaged in the Hodgkin–Huxley theory (1952).

It is difficult to decide which, if any, of the above types of complexities play a role in the functioning of sensory systems. However, it has become clear, from data with intracellular recordings, that secondary modifications do occur in the cells. For example, relatively long-lasting terminal potentials of either sign are sometime seen following sustained activity of crayfish stretch receptors (Eyzaguirre and Kuffler, 1955). Potentials reflect only imperfectly the occurrence of changes in membrane properties. It nevertheless seems safe to postulate that such changes do occur when there are changes in potentials. In the specific case of the stretch receptor cell these changes might account for phenomena of adaptation and for excitatory and inhibitory "rebound" effects (cf. Florey, 1957).

Diphasic and still more complicated potentials which have been observed with intracellular recordings from photoreceptor elements (e.g. insects, Naka, 1961; Limulus, Benolken, 1961) may also be due to such factors. When a microelectrode is so positioned that the spikes of a Limulus eccentric cell appear to be less than 1 mV (Fig. 10) the generator potential evoked by strong illumination has a pronounced overshoot to inside-positivity. The response diminishes to inside-negativity when the stimulus is main-

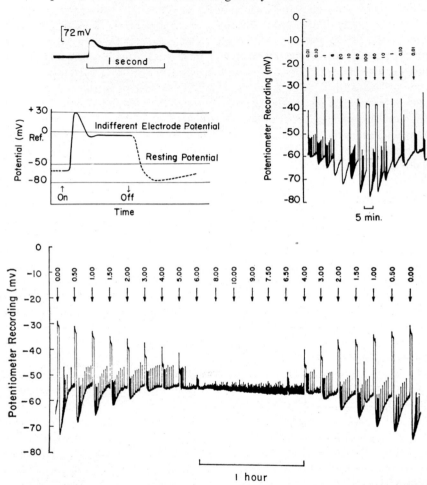

Fig. 10. Overshoots and undershoots in response of *Limulus* eccentric cell dendrite.

Top, left: Response with initial overshoot decreasing to a steady generator potential. Period of illumination (1 sec) shown by bar. *Immediately below* is a diagram showing the potential observed in response to strong illumination. *Below:* Continuous recording on very slow time base of responses to decreasing and then increasing illuminations of constant duration. The relative intensities of illumination are given as negatives of the logarithm of the intensity (strongest stimulus: 0·00). Much of the early overshoot is lost because of the slow response of the recording potentiometer. Intensities lower than about 10^{-5} (relative to maximum) were subthreshold. Between the long pulses, briefer testing illuminations were applied and register as small deflections. *Upper right:* Responses recorded as below, but for flashes of constant intensity and changing duration. Durations ranged between 0·01 and 100 sec. Note gradation of hyperpolarizing "undershoot." (Modified from: Benolken, 1961.)

tained. When the latter is terminated the potential may swing into long-lasting hyperpolarization. This phase is particularly dependent upon the intensity and duration of the light.

Benolken (1961) believes that the microelectrode recording these changes is located in the most distal part of the eccentric cell dendrite. Thus, it seems that the membrane of this region has an inside-positive action generator, which may be due (Grundfest, 1957b) to relative prominence of Na-activation over K-activation. Since the dendrite proximal to the cell body does not develop an overshooting generator potential, it follows that there is a marked regional difference in the electrophysiological properties of the membrane (Grundfest, 1961c). The nature of the plateau and the hyperpolarizing potentials of Fig. 10 cannot be specified with the available data, since they might be caused by one or several of the complexities enumerated above*.

THE INTERACTION OF TWO KINDS OF ELECTROGENIC ACTIVITY IN RECEPTOR NEURONS

The functional problem confronting receptor neurons is the transformation of a specific local stimulus to a coded message capable of propagating information rapidly over relatively long distances which is then amenable to decoding at the terminus of the message line. In theory this is a formidable problem. The biological solution, however, is remarkably simple in principle. Two electrogenic systems, an electrically inexcitable specific receptive input component and an electrically excitable conductile element which eventually evokes specific secretory activity cooperate to achieve the desired goals (Grundfest, 1959b).

It is now clear from data with intracellular recording (cf. Eyzaguirre and Kuffler, 1955; Fuortes, 1959; Hartline et al., 1952; Tomita, 1956) that earlier surmises about the mode of action of receptor neurons (cf. Adrian, 1928; Granit, 1955; Katz, 1950), though based on less direct evidence, were essentially correct. The adequate stimulus produces a generator potential which is always depolarizing; its amplitude is proportional in some degree to the stimulus intensity; and it lasts approximately as long as does the stimulus. The depolarizing generator potential acts as an excitant to the electrically excitable component of the same cell. Secondary factors, as noted above, may change the amplitude of the generator potential itself. These perturbing factors may include electrically excitable conductance changes which induce repolarizing or hyperpolarizing electrogenesis (Grundfest, 1961a, 1962, 1963).

---

* Another possibility is that a local region of the dendrite might have electrically excitable membrane, as appears to be the case in some hippocampal dendrites (Kandel and Spencer, 1961).

Another type is the modification caused by inhibitory postsynaptic potentials (i.p.s.p.'s) evoked in the neuron. Intracellular recordings of this activity have been obtained (Fig. 11) from the crayfish stretch receptor (Kuffler and Eyzaguirre, 1955) and the eccentric cell of *Limulus* (cf. Hartline *et al.*, 1961). Inhibitory interactions have also been observed in the cat retina (Kuffler, 1953; Brown and Wiesel, 1959) and probably are of general importance in localization of stimuli and in "sharpening" of local sign (cf. Granit, 1961; Hartline *et al.*, 1961).*

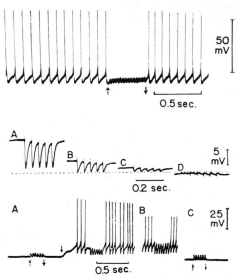

FIG. 11. Synaptic inhibition in crayfish stretch receptor.

Top: Slowly adapting cell. Train of spikes evoked by maintained stretch was eliminated by stimulating the inhibitory axon (between arrows). The i.p.s.p.'s are seen as small deflections in tempo with the stimuli to the axon. *Middle:* Rapidly adapting cell. *A:* Stretch caused depolarization of 16·5 mV. The i.p.s.p.'s evoked at this time were large hyperpolarizations. *B–D:* During progressive relaxation of the stretch the i.p.s.p.'s declined in size and inverted. The broken line indicates the reversal potential which was about 5 mV positive to the resting potential of the completely relaxed cell. *Lower:* Another rapidly adapting cell initially nearly fully relaxed. *A:* At beginning of record i.p.s.p.'s were depolarizing. Stimulation of axon indicated between arrows. Stretch was applied at 3rd arrow, causing depolarization of about 20 mV and evoking spikes. The train was stopped by an intercurrent inhibitory stimulation. I.p.s.p.'s were now inverted. Increasing stretch following this stimulation and in *B* evoked spikes at higher frequencies. Note that the spikes decreased in amplitude while the generator potential increased. The i.p.s.p.'s evoked by stimulating the axon were still larger hyperpolarizations. They became depolarizing and small when the stretch was terminated (*C*). Note that the i.p.s.p.'s of crayfish stretch receptors show no facilitation. (Modified from: Kuffler and Eyzaguirre, 1955.)

* The properties of the inhibitory synaptic system may play a role in the degree of this "sharpness." For example, there is almost no gradation in the i.p.s.p.'s of crayfish stretch receptors (Fig. 11). The i.p.s.p.'s therefore condition the responsiveness of the receptor cell in an all-or-none manner. It is conceivable that gradation of the i.p.s.p. could help to modulate the afferent impulses more subtly in other systems.

However, the main determinant of frequency-number coding of the impulses probably lies in the properties of the electrically excitable membrane itself (Hodgkin, 1948). The critical firing level, the rate of impulse production, and factors such as accommodation and refractoriness enter into the determination of the message. So do spike duration, after-potentials and post-spike conductance changes. In large measure, at least, these are in turn dependent upon the kinetics of the electrically excitable and potential-determined ionic processes (Hodgkin and Huxley, 1952) which differ in

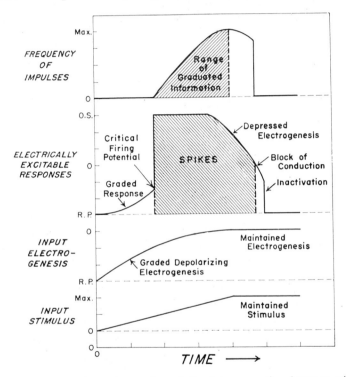

FIG. 12. Diagrammatic representation of the interconnection between stimulus at input and impulses conducted to the output of a receptor neuron. The stimulus is increased linearly with time and then maintained at its maximal effective value. The depolarizing electrogenesis of the input (generator potential) reproduces the momentary amplitude of the stimulus, although with some distortion. The changes in electrically excitable responses caused by the input activity are shown in the next level of the diagram and the frequency of the impulses at the uppermost. Amplitudes of the spikes decrease during continued activity at high frequency. Loss of all-or-none responsiveness followed by refractoriness and inactivation causes block of propagation and the end of spike production. Thus, the output receives no information within a range of weak stimulation of the input; then the information is roughly proportional to the stimulus, designated in the upper level as the range of graduated information; proportionality may be lost at the extreme upper range of information transmission. Finally, when propagation is lost, no information is transmitted. (From: Grundfest, 1959 b.)

various ways in different membranes or in regions of the cell surface (Grundfest, 1961a, c, 1962, 1963).

Message transmission begins (Fig. 12) when the generator potential reaches a critical firing level, but it may cease because the generator potential becomes so large that it causes inactivation of the electrically excitable membrane (Grundfest, 1957d, 1959b). Thus arises the elimination of spike activity by "overstimulation" of the crayfish stretch receptor while the generator potential of the mechano-sensory dendrites continues at a high level (Fig. 10). It is analogous to the depolarizing synaptic blockade which causes Vedensky inhibition (Grundfest, 1957d, 1957e) and to depolarizing "curarization" by drugs which activate depolarizing synapses (Grundfest, 1957d, 1958a, 1959a). However, even before its electrogenic capacity is inactivated, electrically excitable membrane may lose the ability to conduct impulses, because the activity becomes graded and incapable of conducting decrementlessly (Grundfest, 1959b).

THE MODE OF ACTION OF RECEPTOR CELLS

The cell which generates centripetal impulses in secondary receptor systems is a "final common path" for preceding sensory elements and acts essentially like a primary receptor neuron. It must be capable of developing a graded depolarizing generator potential which is produced by an electrically inexcitable membrane and which acts upon an electrically excitable spike generating component. The eccentric cell of *Limulus* and the ganglion cells of frog and cat retina are examples that have been studied with intracellular recording (Hartline *et al.*, 1952, 1961; Tomita, 1956; Fuortes, 1959; Brown and Wiesel, 1959; Tomita *et al.*, 1961). However, the preceding sensing and transducing elements may act entirely differently (Grundfest, 1958b, 1961d). Thus far, no one has succeeded in recording potentials associated with the photochemical activity of the rhabdomes in a *Limulus* ommatidium or of the rods and cones of the vertebrate eye (cf. Naka, 1961, for data on insect eyes). Assuming that the retinal cells were not seriously damaged by penetration, it is therefore possible that they do not generate a potential during activity.

In the vertebrate retina the interposition of another electrically inexcitable component in the form of horizontal and bipolar cells complicates the picture still further (Figs. 7 and 8). Some of these elements generate hyperpolarizing potentials during illumination. Nevertheless, hyperpolarization in these intermediate cells is associated with excitation of the subsequent neurons and generation of centripetal impulses.

The retinal ganglionic neurons generate both depolarizing and hyperpolarizing p.s.p.'s (Brown and Wiesel, 1959; Tomita *et al.*, 1961). Accordingly, the potentials that are generated by the preceding receptor components or whether they are generated at all are matters of no consequence for the functioning of the neurons as message formulating centers. The intermediate cel!s therefore must function in the capacity of secretory elements transmitting excitation by chemical agents. Whether a cell is depolarized or hyperpolarized during its secretory activity or whether it has no potential at all is immaterial. The appearance or absence of potentials of either type will depend upon the types of ionic processes involved and on the electro-chemical conditions that may prevail during the cell's primary function, the secretion of one or more agents capable of initiating generator activity at the electrically inexcitable input of the final path receptor neuron.

It is only because of the traditional emphasis on electrically excitable membranes and the consequent association between depolarization and spike generation that the concept of excitable systems which generate hyperpolarizing potentials seems strange. For example, Granit (1955) re-jected Svaetichin's report (cf. 1956) of hyperpolarizing retinal cells. He did so on the basis that hyperpolarization is known to be associated with in-hibition, while excitation is caused by depolarization. This is true for a generator potential which is integrally linked with the electrically excitable membrane, but it is not true when the excitatory activity is transcellular, involving a secretory link.

If an electrogenesis is associated with this secretory activity it cannot *sensu strictu* be called a "generator potential", since the latter implies a functional intracellular linkage with spike-producing membrane and must always be depolarizing. Davis (1961) has suggested that the term "receptor potential" be reserved for the electrogenesis of those sensory receptor cells that are here classified as electrically inexcitable and non-conductile. This usage is adopted in the present paper (Table 1). It should not be forgotten,

TABLE 1. Classification of Electrogenic Systems

Electrogenesis	Depolarizing	Polarizing
Transducer action for:	Na + K and/or Cl	K and/or Cl
Electrically inexcitable activity	Depolarizing receptor potentials Generator potentials Excitatory p.s.p.'s Depolarizing secretory potentials	Hyperpolarizing receptor potentials Inhibitory p.s.p.'s Hyperpolarizing secretory potentials
Electrically excitable activity	Graded responses Spikes Negative afterpotentials	Rectifying conductance increase (May develop small de- or hyper-polarizations) Positive afterpotentials

(For definitions see Grundfest, 1961 a)

however, that the potential need have no function and, indeed, that activity of the receptor cell need have no electrical sign.

The receptor potential may, however, be functionally important for auditory sensation (cf. Davis, 1957). A battery situated in the stria vascularis of the inner ear maintains the endolymphatic space of the scala media about 80 mV positive to the perilymph in the scala tympani. The hair cells of the organ of Corti, changing resistance during activation, might act as a resistance microphone. During auditory stimuli, the nerve fibers of the auditory nerve then might be subjected to a variable electric current. As noted above, sensory receptors to electrical current must exist in the electric fishes which have an electrical guidance system. It is therefore possible that a similar mechanism developed in the eighth nerve of the land vertebrates as in the lateral line system of the electric fishes.

However, there is no evidence at present that the sensory cells of the organ of Corti act through this electrical mechanism. It is equally possible that the hair cells are secretory in nature, mechanoreceptors which release transmitter agents to act upon the nerve terminals. At first glance, the frequencies involved appear to be too high for the capabilities of chemical transmission. However, this is not the case (Grundfest, 1961d). Synaptic transmission involving electrically inexcitable processes and therefore depending obligatorily upon release of chemical agents, occurs at two sites in the repetitively discharging Gymnotid electric fish. One-to-one production

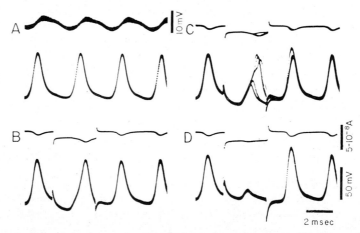

FIG. 13. Postsynaptic potentials and spikes in spinal cord electromotor neuron of *Sternarchus albifrons.*

A: Activity of single neuron (*lower trace*) is synchronous with organ discharge at about 620/sec (*upper trace*). B–D: Upper trace is monitor for hyperpolarizing current applied to the neuron. Current of organ discharges also appears in this trace. B: Weak hyperpolarization delayed the spike somewhat. C: Superimposed traces show variation in response with stronger hyperpolarization. D: Still stronger hyperpolarization eliminated spikes, leaving p.s.p. behind as evidence that each neuronal spike arises by activation through a descending bulbo-spinal tract system. (From: Grundfest, 1961d.)

of post-synaptic potentials in both neurons and electroplaques of *Sternarchus* has been recorded in fish discharging continuously at about 600–800/sec (Fig. 13). It probably also occurs in forms which discharge at even higher frequencies (the highest frequency recorded is about 1600/sec; Lissmann, 1958). It is unlikely that the auditory nerve fibers conduct at higher frequencies than 1000 impulses per second. Thus it is theoretically possible for the cells of the organ of Corti to transmit their message to the nerve by chemical means.

Vestibular receptors also may act by transmitting electrically, but in this case there is no known potential generator outside that of the cells themselves. Thus, the hair cells of the macular structures presumably would themselves have to be the generators causing electrical excitation of the vestibular nerves. If the vestibular nerve fibers have specialized electrical receptors as sensitive as are those in some electric fish, then excitation by ephaptic means (cf. Grundfest, 1959a) would be entirely possible. The potential generated by the cells would have to be depolarizing and might then be entitled to be termed a generator potential. However, chemical transmission in this case, too, is not ruled out.*

EVOLUTION OF ELECTROGENESIS

Existence of two classes of excitable membrane, each manifesting two fundamentally different types of phenomena (Fig. 14) sharpens questions on the nature and evolutionary history of electrogenesis. Viewed in terms of the ionic theory (Hodgkin, 1957) both classes of membrane develop repolarizing or hyperpolarizing electrogenesis, in which Na-activation is absent, as well as the depolarizing variety in which Na-activation predominates. Thus, a given type of ionic activation process can exist independently of the stimulus modalities which distinguish the different classes of membrane. Furthermore, the channels involved in K- and Cl-activation appear to have independent existence and different excitabilities in both classes of membrane. Na-activation and K-activation also assort independently or may be independently affected by experimental procedures in electrically excitable membrane. However, a similar separation has not yet been clearly observed in depolarizing electrically inexcitable membrane.

Differentiation of the various ion-specific channels and of their excitabilities permits an evaluation of the resting potential in an evolutionary context. The inside negativity is determined by predominance of anionic charge among the intracellular macromolecules. It thus appears to be a manifestation of ancient "protoplasmic" factors that are essentially independent of the cell membrane. The result, an inside-negative Donnan potential, does not

* A similar view has recently been expressed independently by Vinnikov and Titova (1961).

require that the semipermeable cell boundary be reactive in any way. Thus, the membrane may be electrogenically inert, as contrasted with electro-genically reactive membranes of excitable cells (Grundfest, 1961 a, 1962, 1963).

While a Donnan system can deliver current, connections between the two phases are needed which probably do not exist across the electrogenic

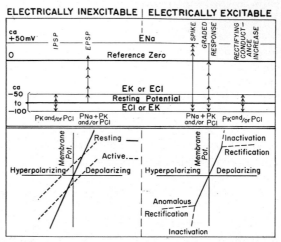

FIG. 14. Diagrammatic summary of the components of activity of electrogenic membranes.

Upper part: The different varieties of electrogenesis and their probable ionic mechanisms. The resting potential is represented as lying between E_K and E_{Cl} (the electrode potentials for K and Cl respectively). The electrode potential for Na (E_{Na}) is about 50 mV positive to the reference zero. The membrane reaction (transducer action) to an appropriate stimulus can change its permeability to one or to several ionic species. In electrically excitable as well as electrically inexcitable membrane, increase in permeability toward K or Cl, or both ions, leads to a small electrical effect, its sign depending on the relation of the resting potential to the electrode potential(s) of the relevant ion(s). The graded nature of the electrogenic processes is indicated by the multiple arrowheads. The ex-citatory synaptic membrane also produces a graded response, but depolarizing by virtue of a component for increased Na-conductance. The e.p.s.p. conceivably may overshoot the reference zero. Depolarizing graded responses can also be produced by electrically excitable membrane and, if P_K and/or P_{Cl} outlast P_{Na} and stand in appro-priate electrochemical relation to the resting potential, the activity may also develop an" undershoot ". Membrane capable of all-or-none responses may also develop an undershoot after the depolarizing conductance component has subsided. *Lower part:* Current–voltage relations of the membranes disclose further features. *Left:* The electric-ally inexcitable membrane has a linear I–E curve (solid line). When the membrane is excited by an appropriate stimulus the slope decreases, reflecting the increased con-ductance described above. The e.p.s.p. displaces the I–E curve (*broken line*) in a positive direction. The i.p.s.p. is shown as hyperpolarizing. The values at which each active line crosses the resting is the reversal point of the p.s.p.; on depolarization for the e.p.s.p. and on hyperpolarization for the hyperpolarizing i.p.s.p. *Right:* The I–E relations of electrically excitable membrane show various nonlinearities. Changes causing in-creased conductance to depolarizing and hyperpolarizing currents are termed recti-fication and "anomalous" rectification respectively. Membrane reactions that result in increased resistance are termed depolarizing and hyperpolarizing inactivation. Generation of spikes nor diagrammed. (From: Grundfest, 1961 a.)

membrane. However, other sources of potential energy are established in the living system as the diffusion potentials that result from unequal distribution of K^+ and Na^+. To minimize expenditure of energy it would be appropriate to have the diffusion potential of the resting cell of the same sign as the Donnan potential. Since Na^+ is the predominant cation of body fluids (as of sea water) the intracellular Na^+ would have to be very high to establish the appropriate inside-negativity. Accordingly, intracellular concentration of K^+ is the more feasible solution, particularly since the extracellular levels of this ion are usually very low. The opposite (though not necessarily equal) concentration gradients for K^+ and Na^+ are established by metabolically driven (active) transport or "pumps" in which the efflux of Na^+ is perhaps coupled to some degree with the influx of K^+. Active Cl-transport may also be involved in some cells. Another adaptation is the predominance of the diffusion potential for K^+ in the resting cell over the inside-positive Na-diffusion potential. The mechanisms responsible for both active transport and for the "electrode properties" of the resting membrane as well as for changes in the latter (activation and inactivation phenomena) are still unknown.

Given inside-negativity under the electrochemical and electrophysiological conditions described above, the predominance of depolarization as the stimulus for electrically excitable electrogenic membrane is also made evident. Increased membrane permeability for K^+ or Cl^- can lead to relatively little change in the membrane potential, whereas Na-activation can shift the potential to inside-positivity determined by the diffusion potential for Na^+. The regenerative requirements of all-or-none spikes thus determine that depolarization is the stimulus for, as well as the product of, Na-activation.

However, inactivation and activation processes specific for any of the 3 dominant extracellular inorganic ions may be produced in electrically excitable membranes by hyperpolarizing as well as by depolarizing stimuli. Under experimental conditions the electrochemical conditions may be so set that regenerative activity is produced without the need for Na-activation. These can give rise to various types of "spikes" and "anomalous responses". The latter have bemused opponents of the ionic theory and some have regarded them as throwing into doubt the validity of the ionic mechanisms themselves. In fact, however, the ionic theory is very much strengthened by its ability to account for and to predict phenomena other than that of "normal" spike electrogenesis (Grundfest, 1961a, 1962, 1963).

The spikes of regenerative electrical excitability are obligatory only for axons, the specialized conductile tissue. They do occur also in some kinds of muscle fibers, electroplaques, and neuron somata and dendrites. However, their absence in other neuron somata and dendrites betokens the primary function of these structures, to receive and integrate information. The function of generalizing and spreading excitation in muscle fibers and

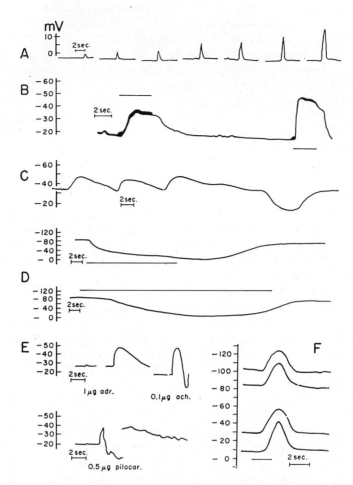

FIG. 15. Different types of electrical activity in cat salivary gland cells. Depolarization shown as downward deflection in these records.

A: Type I cells produce hyperpolarizing p.s.p.'s which are graded with strength of the stimulus. Single shocks to chorda tympani evoke p.s.p.'s which last about 1 sec. *B:* Type I cells produce only hyperpolarizing p.s.p.'s to excitation of the sympathetic (*upper signal*) or parasympathetic (*lower signal*) nerves. However, the latencies and magnitudes of the p.s.p.'s differ somewhat. *C:* Type II cells develop hyperpolarizing p.s.p.'s on stimulating the chorda tympani and depolarizing p.s.p.'s through their sympathetic innervation. *D:* Type III cells (which may be myoepithelial elements of the ducts) respond only with depolarizing p.s.p.'s to parasympathetic (*above*) or sympathetic (*below*) stimulation. The resting potential, about −80 mV, is large in comparison with that of Type I or II cells and resembles that of muscle fibers. *E:* Type I cells respond with hyperpolarization to epinephrine, acetylcholine and pilocarpine. (From: Lundberg, 1955.) *F:* The hyperpolarizing p.s.p. of the gland cell is remarkably insensitive to changes of the membrane potential. The resting potential was 30 mV.
(From: Lundberg, 1956.)

electroplaques may likewise be removed from the cells themselves, and assigned to their innervation. Thus diffuse, widespread innervation in electroplaques of marine electric fishes and in various kinds of muscle fibers makes possible the functioning of these electrically inexcitable cells. Graded though electrically excitable depolarizing electrogenesis is also functionally useful in diffusely innervated muscle fibers and does occur in various invertebrate forms. Graded electrically excitable responsiveness probably also occurs in some parts of vertebrate cardiac muscle, in which various regeneratively excitable specialized muscular conductile pathways spread activation throughout the muscle mass.

Repolarizing or hyperpolarizing electrogenesis which results from activation either for K^+ or Cl^- is inhibitory only in the context of an effect on depolarizing electrically excitable electrogenesis. Thus, in gland cells (Fig. 15) as in receptor cells (Figs. 2, 7, and 8) the electrical activity is a secondary phenomenon and the hyperpolarizing electrogenesis has the same functional significance as depolarization; both are signs of activity. The electrically excitable Cl-activation of Rajid electroplaques is "excitatory" in the sense that the activation decreases the membrane resistance and thereby permits a large current to be delivered extracellularly from the depolarizing electrically inexcitable response, which is a postsynaptic potential (cf. Bennett, 1961). In contrast, the electrically excitable K-activation of frog slow muscle fibers would appear to be "inhibitory" since the repolarizing electrogenesis decreases and cuts short the action of the depolarizing p.s.p.'s on the excitation-contraction coupling of the muscle fibers.*

The electrically excitable fresh water algae present a rather different problem from animal cells (except fresh water protozoa). The high extracellular Na^+ of body fluids is lacking in the fresh water environment and the electrogenesis of the algae is presumably achieved by a different ion mechanism. However, the nature of the process is still in question (Gaffey and Mullins, 1958; Hope, 1961; Spyropoulos et al., 1961).

EVOLUTION OF SENSE ORGANS

According to Parker (1919) the nervous system grew out of a parcellation of functions of primitive receptor cells. At one point there arose sense organs; at another effectors developed, the two components being tied together by neurons. In the process of this displacement and correlation, a conductile function became elaborated that had not been necessary in the primitive receptor-effectors. It has seemed useful to consider this conductile element as an evolutionary addition to ancestral components

---

* Under appropriate electrochemical conditions the response of "inhibitory" synaptic membrane is a large depolarization which can evoke spikes in cat motoneurons, crayfish stretch receptors or molluscan neurons (Grundfest, 1959a. 1961b, 1964b).

(cf. Bishop, 1956), but all three incorporated in the same cell (Grundfest, 1957c, 1959b). According to this view, therefore, receptor and effector activity of glands or of electrically inexcitable muscle fibers are paradigms of the primitive nervous system.

An examination of sense organs in terms of their functional components emphasizes, however, the important discrepancy which has already been mentioned. The known invertebrate sense organs are usually of the "primary type" in which the supposedly later conductile components of electrically excitable membrane have already been incorporated. The presumably more primitive type of sensory receptors in which the conductile component is lacking occurs in four special senses of vertebrates, only olfaction (which is usually considered to be the most primitive!) being served by primary receptors. Do the secondary receptors then present a regressive feature, loss of an electrically excitable component? And if so, is the electrically excitable conductile property perhaps as primitive an evolutionary component as is the electrically inexcitable receptive function? Once these questions are formulated, however, the deficiences in our data and concepts on sense organs become apparent.*

As in the study of nerve and muscle (cf. Grundfest, 1957a) so perhaps in the study of sense organs also, methodological conveniences may have tended to obscure important data. It is almost always easier to record impulses from nerve than to get at the stimulus-specific activities of receptors where activity, it should be stressed, may or may not involve electrogenesis. Thus receptors have been studied chiefly by manifestations of impulses recorded from nerve fibers. Indeed, today we still know about auditory and vestibular reception in vertebrates and chemoreception in the invertebrates only from the study of the nerve fibers.

The eccentric cell of *Limulus* is an important example. Only recently has it come to be recognized as a secondary receptor neuron excited through the pigment-containing photochemically-activated rhabdome of the retinular cells. Are there other types of invertebrate receptors in which concentration of interest on the neuronal activity has obscured the existence of a secondary receptor? Many arthropod receptors of complex anatomy and which produce generator potentials (cf. Schneider and Hecker, 1956; Schneider and Kaissling, 1957) well might give clues to this question.

Another methodological factor may have also obscured evolutionary data on sense organs. Electrophysiological studies on invertebrate sense organs

---

* Recent studies on muscle fibers are relevant to this point. Data on fetal and denervated muscle fibers support a suggestion made in 1942 by Ginetsinskii and Shamarina (cf. Thesleff, 1961) that in their primitive state the fibers have widespread chemosensitivity, which becomes restricted to sites of synaptic contact by innervation. Since these chemosensitive patches both diffuse and restricted, are electrically inexcitable (Grundfest, 1961a, 1961c; Werman, 1963) the muscle fiber membrane originally may have lacked an electrically excitable component.

are done chiefly in arthropods which are advanced and specialized forms. However, the nervous system with its complex synaptic interactions and wealth of organization already appears to have been laid down in forms as low as the worms (Grundfest, 1959 b) and probably even at the level of coelenterates (cf. Horridge, 1961). Many special adaptations were developed by higher forms, and particularly in arthropods, for economizing on the number of cells and on the volume of components in the nervous system and the neuromuscular apparatus. It seems possible, therefore, that arthropod sense organs also may have undergone considerable evolutionary specialization.

A third aspect of the deficiencies relates to our conceptual framework. Neurosecretory cells which emphasize the basic similarity between neurons and gland cells are found in lower forms as well as higher (cf. Scharrer and Scharrer, 1954; Ortmann, 1960). Some respond to external stimuli such as changes in luminous or thermal energy, others to changes in various chemical components, osmotic pressure and temperature of body fluids. Still others are probably activated only by specific excitatory innervation. Distinctions between sense organs, neurons and the neurosecretory cells therefore are also tenuous.

Cells of the fish urohypophysis generate both p.s.p.'s and spikes (Bennett, and Fox, 1962). Thus, unlike gland cells, neurosecretory cells may have electrically excitable as well as electrically inexcitable membrane. Neurosecretory cells may be classified into various structural-functional types, not only with respect to their input characteristics, i.e. their sensitivity to excitants, but also on the basis of their mechanisms for releasing their own products (Fig. 16). Some neurosecretory cells are probably small, like gland cells, releasing their secretions to the immediate environment. Others appear to have extensions down which the secretory products travel. These extensions may be merely tubes for conveying substances that are formed

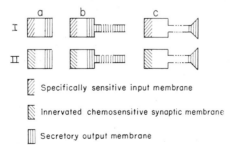

Specifically sensitive input membrane

Innervated chemosensitive synaptic membrane

Secretory output membrane

FIG. 16. Diagrammatic representation of six possible types of related cells: secretory, neurosecretory, receptor and neuron.

Group I: Cells which receive excitation from external or internal specific stimuli. *Group II:* Cells that are excited by innervation. (*a*) Simple columnar cells which might oq glands, neurosecretory cells, or receptor cells. (*b*) Receptor or neurosecretory cells. (*c*) Receptor, neurosecretory and correlational neurons. (From: Grundfest, 1961 d.)

in the cell body. In some cases these extensions might be electrogenic, as they are in urohypophyseal cells (Bennett and Fox, 1962) and probably also in the hypophyseal stalk (Potter and Loewenstein, 1955; Bennett and Fox, 1962). A further development, the concentration of the transmissional secretory activity at the end of the extension would result in a neuron, electrically inexcitable at the receptor surface, conductile in its extension and secretory at the terminus of the latter.

Thus, three conditions of electrophysiological interest would have had to be satisfied if the extended cells were to become neurons. (1) The transducer action of their receptor surfaces had to become electrogenic. (2) The electrogenesis had to be depolarizing, or predominantly so. (3) The extension had to develop electrically excitable membrane capable of generating all-or-none spikes. Since all three conditions are essential for neuronal activity it is obviously useless to expect to find neurons entirely lacking one of these features. However, spatially distinctive parts of various neurons do seem to reflect these different evolutionary stages.

The methodology of electrophysiology usually precludes detection of transducer actions that are not electrogenic. Transducer processes that lead to hyperpolarizing electrogenesis do occur in gland cells, in sensory receptors and even in neurons and muscle fibers. As noted above, graded responsiveness of electrically excitable membrane is a normally functional type of activity in muscle fibers, and it can be converted to all-or-none responsiveness by appropriate experimental procedures. Similarly, the all-or-none responsiveness of axons, neurons, muscle fibers and electroplaques may be changed to graded responsiveness. These changes, and the numerous kinds of "anomalous" responses reflect the independent assortment of the different processes of electrogenic membranes. Thus, every aspect of electrogenesis indicates the various evolutionary steps that must have taken place in the development of complex functional entities out of the primitive receptor–effector cell.

Recapitulation

Briefly summarizing the view proposed here, it is suggested that the sensory receptor cells which do not have a conductile component are probably the more primitive type. According to this view sensory receptors and neurons developed out of ancestral secretory cells. The "secondary" receptors developed specialization chiefly at their receptive surfaces and in the form of high sensitivity to various specific stimuli. Extension of the primitive cells by long processes terminating in the blood vessels or perhaps also on other cells led to differentiation of neurosecretory cells, and eventually to neurons, in which the secretory activity is concentrated at the terminals. The present day ectodermal endocrine and neurosecretory systems and the nervous system with its sensory receptor adjuncts probably derive from common ancestral elements and continue to be the control mechanisms of the animal organisms.

Electrical excitability must have developed as early as the appearance of functional nervous interconnections, probably in the coelenterates. It may therefore, perhaps, be necessary to investigate the still lower Poriphera in order to examine still more primitive nervous elements. However, the difficulties of studying the lower metazoan forms are augmented by the small size of their cells. For this reason the study of sense organs and neuro-secretory elements in these various lower forms should not be neglected. Here, again, Professor Koshtoyants was one of the pioneers.

REFERENCES

ADRIAN, E. D., *The Basis of Sensation.* London, Christopher Press 1928.

ALTAMIRANO, M., C. W. COATES and H. GRUNDFEST, Mechanisms of direct and neural excitability in electroplaques of electric eel. *J. Gen. Physiol.* **38**, 319 (1955).

ALTAMIRANO, M. and H. GRUNDFEST, Three excitable systems of the synaptic unit in the innervated electroplaque preparation. *Trans. A.N.A.* **79**, 79 (1954).

AUTRUM H., Nonphotic receptors in lower forms. Chapt. XVI in: *Handbook of Physiology. Neurophysiology I.* Washington, D.C., American Physiological Society 1959.

BELTON, P. and H. GRUNDFEST, The ionic factors in the electrogenesis of the electrically excitable membrane components of frog slow muscle fibers. *Biol. Bull.* **121**, 382 (1961).

BENNETT, M. V. L., Modes of operation of electric organs. *Ann. N. Y. Acad. Sci.* **94**, 458 (1961).

BENNETT, M. V. L., S. M. CRAIN and H. GRUNDFEST, Electrophysiology of supramedullary neurons in *Spheroides maculatus. J. Gen. Physiol.* **43**, 159 (1959).

BENNETT, M. V. L. and S. FOX, Electrophysiology of caudal neurosecretory cells in the skate and fluke. *J. Comp. Endocrin.*, **2**, 77 (1962).

BENOLKEN, R. M., Reversal of photoreceptor polarity recorded during the graded receptor potential response to light in the eye of *Limulus. Biophys. J.* **1**, 551 (1961).

BERNARD, C., *Leçons sur les Propriétés Physiologiques et les Altérations Pathologiques des Liquides de l'Organisme.* Vol. 2, Paris, Baillière 1859.

BISHOP, G. H., Natural history of the nerve impulse. *Physiol. Revs.* **36**, 376 (1956).

BODIAN, D., The generalized vertabrate neuron. *Science* **137**, 323 (1962).

BROWN, K. T. and T. N. WIESEL, Intraretinal recording with micropipette electrodes in the intact cat eye. *J. Physiol.* **149**, 537 (1959).

COHEN, B., M. V. L. BENNETT and H. GRUNDFEST, Electrically excitable responses in *Raia erinacea* electroplaques. *Fed. Proc.* **20**, 339 (1961).

DAVIS, H., Biophysics and physiology of the inner ear. *Physiol. Revs.* **37**, 1 (1957).

DAVIS, H., Some principles of sensory receptor action. *Physiol. Revs.* **41**, 391 (1961).

DUDEL, J. and S. W. KUFFLER, Excitation at the crayfish neuromuscular junction with decreased membrane conductance. *Nature* **187**, 246 (1960).

EYZAGUIRRE, C., Excitatory and inhibitory processes in crustacean sensory nerve cells. Pp. 285–317 in: *Nervous Inhibition*, London, Pergamon Press 1961.

EYZAGUIRRE, C. and S. W. KUFFLER, Process of excitation in the dendrites and in the soma of single isolated nerve cells of the lobster and crayfish. *J. Gen. Physiol.* **39**, 87 (1955).

FLOREY, E., Chemical transmission and adaptation. *J. Gen. Physiol.* **40**, 533 (1957).

FUORTES, M. G. F., Initiation of impulses in visual cells of *Limulus. J. Physiol., London* **148**, 14 (1959).

FURSHPAN, E. J. and D. D. POTTER, Transmission at the giant motor synapse of the crayfish. *J. Physiol., London* **145**, 289 (1959).

FURUKAWA, J., T. SASMOKA and Y. HOSOYA, Effects of tetrodotoxin on the neuromuscular junction. *Jap. J. Physiol.* **9**, 143 (1959).

GAFFEY, C. T. and L. J. MULLINS, Ion fluxes during the action potential in *Chara*. *J. Physiol., London* **144**, 505 (1958).

GIRARDIER, L., J. P. REUBEN and H. GRUNDFEST. Changes in membrane properties of crayfish muscle fibers caused by denervation. *Fed. Proc.* 21, 357 (1962).

GRANIT, R., *Receptors and Sensory Perception.* New Haven, Yale University Press 1955.

GRANIT, R., Regulation of discharge rate by inhibition, especially by recurrent inhibition. Pp. 61–70 in: *Nervous Inhibition.* London, Pergamon Press 1961.

GRUNDFEST, H., Some properties of excitable tissue. Pp. 177–218 in: *Fifth Conference on Nerve Impulse.* New York, Josiah Macy, Jr. Foundation 1956a.

GRUNDFEST, H., Electric field effects and synaptic potentials in the functioning of the nervous system. Pp. 81–97 in: *Problems of Modern Physiology of the Nerve and Muscle Systems.* Tbilisi, Izdat. Akad. Nauk, Georgian SSR 1956b.

GRUNDFEST, H., Excitation at synapses. *J. Neurophysiol.* **20**, 316 (1957a).

GRUNDFEST, H., The mechanisms of discharge of the electric organ in relation to general and comparative electrophysiology. Chapt. I in: *Progress in Biophysics*, Vol. 7, London, Pergamon Press 1957b.

GRUNDFEST, H., Electrical inexcitability of synapses and some of its consequences in the central nervous system. *Physiol. Revs.* **37**, 337 (1957c).

GRUNDFEST, H., General problems of drug action on bioelectric phenomena. *Ann. N. Y. Acad. Sci.* **66**, 537 (1957d).

GRUNDFEST, H., Excitation triggers in post-junctional cells. Pp. 119–151 in: *Physiological Triggers.* Washington, D.C., American Physiological Society 1957e.

GRUNDFEST, H., An electrophysiological basis for neuropharmacology. *Fed. Proc.* **17**, 1006 (1958a).

GRUNDFEST, H., An electrophysiological basis for cone vision in fish. *Arch. ital. Biol.* **96**, 135 (1958b).

GRUNDFEST, H., Synaptic and ephaptic transmission. Chapt. V in: *Handbook of Physiology. Neurophysiology I.* Washington, D.C., American Physiological Society 1959a.

GRUNDFEST, H., Evolution and conduction in the nervous system. Pp. 43–86 in: *Evolution of Nervous Control.* Washington, D.C. Publ. No. 52, American Association for the Advancement of Science 1959b.

GRUNDFEST, H., Ionic mechanisms in electrogenesis. *Ann. N. Y. Acad. Sci.* **94**, 405 (1961a).

GRUNDFEST, H., General physiology and pharmacology of junctional transmission. Pp. 329–389 in: *Biophysics of Physiological and Pharmacological Actions.* Washington, D.C., Publ. No. 69, American Association for the Advancement of Science 1961b.

GRUNDFEST, H., Functional specifications for membranes in excitable cells. Pp. 378–402 in: *Regional Neurochemistry.* London, Pergamon Press 1961c.

GRUNDFEST, H., Excitation by hyperpolarizing potentials. A general theory of receptor activities. Pp. 326–341 in: *Nervous Inhibition.* London, Pergamon Press 1961d.

GRUNDFEST, H., Ionic transport across neural and non-neural membranes Pp. 71–99 in: *Properties of Membranes and Diseases of the Nervous System.* New York, Springer 1962.

GRUNDFEST, H., Impulse-conducting properties of cells. Pp. 277–322 in: *The General Physiology of Cell Specialization*, New York, McGraw-Hill 1963.

GRUNDFEST, H., The theoretical basis of the central action of drugs. In: *Proc. III Colleg. Internat. Neuropsychopharmacol.* (in press) Amsterdam, Elsevier 1964a.

GRUNDFEST, H., The chemical mediators. In: *Unfinished Tasks in the Behavioral Sciences* (in press) Baltimore, Williams & Wilkins 1964b.

GRUNDFEST, H. and M. V. L. BENNETT, Studies on morphology and electrophysiology of electric organs. I. Electrophysiology of marine electric fishes. Pp. 57–101 in: *Bioelectrogenesis.* Amsterdam, Elsevier 1961.

GRÜSSER, O.-J., Rezeptorpotentiale einzelner retinaler Zapfen der Katze. *Naturwiss.* **19**, 44 (1957).

HAGIWARA, S., K. KUSANO and K. NEGISHI, Physiological properties of electroreceptors in some Gymnotids. *J. Neurophysiol.*, **25**, 430 (1962).

HANSON, F. E. and M. L. WOLBARSHT, Dendritic action potentials in insect chemoreceptors. *Amer. Zool.* **2**, 528 (1962).

HARTLINE, H. K., F. RATLIFF and W. H. MILLER, Inhibitory interaction in the retina and its significance in vision. Pp. 241–284 in: *Nervous Inhibition.* London, Pergamon Press 1961.

HARTLINE, H. K., H. G. WAGNER and E. F. MACNICHOL, JR.. The peripheral origin of nervous activity in the visual system. *Cold Spring Harbor Symp.* **27**, 125 (1952).

HODGKIN, A. L., The local electric changes associated with repetitive action in a non-medullated axon. *J. Physiol., London* **107**, 165 (1948).

HODGKIN, A. L., The Croonian Lecture: Ionic movements and electrical activity in giant nerve fibres. *Proc. Roy. Soc. Lond.* (B), **148**, 1 (1957).

HODGKIN, A. L. and A. F. HUXLEY, A quantitative description of membrane current and its applications to conduction and excitation in nerve. *J. Physiol., London* **117**, 500 (1952).

HOPE, A. B., The action potential in cells of *Chara. Nature* **191**, 811 (1961).

HORRIDGE, G. A., The organization of the primitive central nervous system as suggested by examples of inhibition and the structure of neuropile. Pp. 395–409 in: *Nervous Inhibition.* London, Pergamon Press 1961.

HUNT, C. C. and A. TAKEUCHI, Responses of the nerve terminal of the Pacinian corpuscle. *J. Physiol., London* **160**, 1 (1962).

KANDEL, E. R. and W. A. SPENCER, Electrophysiological properties of an archicortical neuron. *Ann. N. Y. Acad. Sci.* **94**, 570 (1961).

KATZ, B., Depolarization of sensory terminals and the initation of impulses in the muscle spindle. *J. Physiol., London* **11**, 261 (1950).

KIMURA, K. and L. M. BEIDLER, Microelectrode study of taste receptors of rat and hamster. *J. Cell. Comp. Physiol.* **58**, 131 (1961).

KUFFLER, S. W., Discharge patterns and functional organization of mammalian retina. *J. Neurophysiol.* **16**, 37 (1953).

KUFFLER, S. W. and C. EYZAGUIRRE, Synaptic inhibitions in an isolated nerve cell. *J. Gen. Physiol.* **39**, 155 (1955).

LISSMANN, H. W., On the function and evolution of electric organs in fish. *J. exp. Biol.* **35**, 156 (1958).

LOEWENSTEIN, W. R., Excitation and inactivation in a receptor membrane. *Ann. N. Y. Acad. Sci.* **94**, 510 (1961).

LOEWENSTEIN, W. R., C. A. TERZUOLO and Y. WASHIZU, Separation of transducer and impulse generating processes. *Science* **142**, 1180 (1963).

LUNDBERG, A., The electrophysiology of the submaxillary gland of the cat. *Acta Physiol. Scand.* **35** 1 (1955).

LUNDBERG, A., Secretory potentials and secretion in the sublingual gland of the cat. *Nature* **177**, 1080 (1956).

MACNICHOL, E. J., JR. and G. SVAETICHIN, Electric responses from the isolated retinas of fishes. *Am. J. Ophthal.* **46**, 26 (1958).

MILEDI, R., The acetylcholine sensitivity of frog muscle fibres after complete or partial denervation. *J. Physiol., London* **151**, 1 (1960).

MORITA, H., Initiation of spike potentials in contact chemosensory hairs of insect. *J. Cell. Comp. Physiol.* **54**, 189 (1959).

MOTOKAWA, K., T. OIKAWA and K. TASAKI, Receptor potential of vertebrate retina. *J. Neurophysiol.* **20**, 186 (1957).

NAKA, K.-I., Recording of retinal action potentials from single cells in the insect compound eye. *J. Gen. Physiol.* **44**, 571 (1961).

NAKAJIMA, S., S. IWASAKI and K. OBATA, Delayed rectification and anomalous rectification in frog's skeletal muscle membrane. *J. Gen. Physiol.* **46**, 97 (1962).

ORTMANN, R., Neurosecretion. Chapt. XL in: *Handbook of Physiology. Neurophysiology II.* Washington, D.C., American Physiological Society 1960.

OTTOSON, D., Analysis of the electric activity of the olfactory epithelium. *Acta physiol. scand.* **35**, Suppl. 122 (1956).

OTTOSON, D., Olfactory bulb potentials induced by electrical stimulation of the nasal mucosa in the frog. *Acta physiol. scand.* **47**, 160 (1959).

PAINTAL, A. S., Intramuscular propagation of sensory impulses. *J. Physiol.*, *London* **148**, 240 (1959).

PARKER, G. H., *The Elementary Nervous System.* Philadelphia, Lippincott 1919.

POTTER, D. D. and W. R. LOEWENSTEIN, Electrical activity of neurosecretory cells. *Am. J. Physiol.* **182**, 652 (1955).

REUBEN, J. P. and H. GAINER, Membrane conductance during depolarizing postsynaptic potentials of crayfish muscle fibre. *Nature* **193**, 142 (1962).

RUSHTON, W. A. H., A theoretical treatment of Fuortes' observations upon eccentric cell activity in *Limulus. J. Physiol.*, *London* **148**, 29 (1959).

SATO, M. and M. OZEKI, Response of the non-myelinated nerve terminal in Pacinian corpuscles to mechanical and antidromic stimulation and the effect of procaine, choline and cooling. *Jap. J. Physiol.* **13**, 564 (1963).

SCHARRER, E. and B. SCHARRER, Neurosekretion. In: *Handbuch der mikroskopischen Anatomie des Menschen.* Berlin, Springer-Verlag 1954.

SCHNEIDER, D. and E. HECKER, Zur Elektrophysiologie der Antenne des Seidenspinners *Bombyx mori* bei Reizung mit angereicherten Extrakten des Sexuallockstoffes. *Z. Naturforsch.* **11 b**, 121 (1956).

SCHNEIDER, D. and K.-E. KAISSLING, Der Bau der Antenne des Seidenspinners *Bombyx mori* L. II. Sensillen, cuticulare Bildungen und innerer Bau. *Zool. Jahrb. (Anat.)* **76**, 223 (1957).

SHERRINGTON, C. S., *The Integrative Action of the Nervous System.* (1906). Reprinted by Cambridge University Press 1947.

SIGG, E. B. and H. GRUNDFEST, Pharmacological differences of similarly electrogenic neuraxial sites of bullfrog. *Am. J. Physiol.* **197**, 539 (1959).

SPYROPOULOS, C. S., I. TASAKI and G. HAYWARD, Fractionation of tracer effluxes during action potential. *Science* **133**, 2064 (1961).

SVAETICHIN, G., Spectral response curves from single cones. *Acta physiol. scand.* **39**, Suppl. 34 (1956).

TAKEUCHI, A. and N. TAKEUCHI, On the permeability of end-plate membrane during the action of transmitter. *J. Physiol.*, *London* **154**, 52 (1960).

THESLEFF, S., Nervous control of chemosensitivity in muscle. *Ann. N. Y. Acad. Sci.* **94**, 535 (1961).

TOMITA, T., The nature of action potentials in the lateral eye of the horseshoe crab as revealed by simultaneous intra- and extracellular recording. *Jap. J. Physiol.* **6**, 327 (1956).

TOMITA, T., M. MURAKAMI, Y. HASHIMOTO and Y. SASAKI, Electrical activity of single neurons in frog's retina. Pp. 23–40 in: *The Visual System: Neuropharmacology and Psychophysics.* Berlin, Springer 1961.

VINNIKOV, YA. A. and L. I. TITOVA, *The Organ of Corti.* (Kortiyev organ). Izdat. Akad. Nauk. SSSR Moscow 1961. English translation in preparation by Pergamon Press.

WATANABE, A. and H. GRUNDFEST, Impulse propagation at the septal and commisural junctions of crayfish lateral giant axons. *J. Gen. Physiol.* **45**, 267 (1961).

WERMAN, R., Electrical inexcitability of the frog neuromuscular synapse. *J. Gen. Physiol.* **46**, 517 (1963).

GENESIS OF EXCITATORY TRANSMITTER IN THE BRAIN OF DOGS

Takashi Hayashi

Department of Physiology, School of Medicine
Keio University, Tokyo, Japan

The distribution of cholinacetylase indicates that not all central neurons transmit their effects by the liberation of acetylcholine. In the past few years many attempts have been made to identify the non-cholinergic transmitter substance or substances (Crossland, 1960).

As my earlier paper showed, there is evidence that γ-aminobutyric acid (GABA) is the parent substance of both inhibitory and excitatory transmitter. In relation to the inhibitory transmitter, vitamin B_6 has an important role and in relation to the excitatory transmitter, vitamin B_1 together with vitamin B_{12} are of importance (Hayashi, 1958, 1960).

The experimental method was to introduce into the cerebrospinal fluid of dogs via the ventricle the substrate to be converted into the effective substance, the energy-liberating substrate and the coenzyme required for the liberation of energy, etc.

These substances were introduced by themselves or in combination. After a certain time interval some cerebrospinal fluid was removed and assayed for the substance which was supposedly formed. In the simplest case, the expected substance would have some effect *in situ*. For example, when we expected the formation of excitatory transmitter, its overproduction should necessarily produce some motor effect. Thus the most convenient indicator for this overproduction was seizure, especially generalized seizure.

When metrazol and sodium glutamate were introduced into the ventricle of dogs, they produced generalized seizures as shown in Table 1 with latent periods of 15–30 sec. In contrast, isonicotinic acid hydrazide (INH), oxy-methylpyrimidine (OMP) as well as D-tubocurarine produced seizures with latencies of 600–2400 sec (10–40 min), that is about 30–200 times longer than those of the former substances.

To our surprise, vitamin B_1 as well as folic acid produced seizure if given in appropriate concentration and the latency belongs to the second group. To our further surprise, all convulsants were found to fall into these two categories.

The most simple interpretation of this phenomenon would be that convulsants of shorter latent periods acted by direct action of their own, while

TABLE 1. The critical dosage to produce seizure in dogs

Substances	Introduced into c.s.f.		Latent period	Seizure
Metrazol	0·0377 M	1·0 ml	10–15 sec	+
Sodium glutamate	0·1 M	1·0 ml	15–30 sec	+
INH	0·1 M	1·0 ml	40·3 min	+
OMP	0·1 M	1·0 ml	15·5 min	+
D-Tubocurarine	0·04 M	1·0 ml	11·5 min	+
Vitamin B$_1$	0·1 M	1·0 ml	15·0 min	+
Folic acid	0·0003 M	1·0 ml	24·0 min	+

convulsants with longer latent periods acted not directly but by secondary and indirect actions which could be, for example, as follows:

(1) the substance undergoes some change in its chemical structure to become the real excitatory transmitter, or

(2) the substance accelerates the production of the real excitatory transmitter, or

(3) it inhibits the production of the anti-substance of the excitatory transmitter in the brain.

The substances INH, OMP and curarine, as well as semicarbazide and hydroxylamine, were found to belong to the last category mentioned above (3). We found the convulsants which belonged to the above category (2) to be guanidine or methylene blue, while GABA was found to belong to category (1). As shown in Table 2, when GABA was introduced into the ventricle of dogs, it produced a seizure in one case out of twenty experiments. But we found that when vitamin B$_{12}$ and B$_1$ accompanied GABA it

TABLE 2. The critical dosage to produce seizure in dogs

Substances	Introduced into c.s.f.		Seizure	Remarks
GABA	0·002 M	1·0 ml	–	
Vitamin B$_{12}$	0·0002%	1·0 ml	–	
ATP	0·002%	1·0 ml	–	
GABA + Vitamin B$_{12}$	0·002 M + 0·0002%	1·0 ml 1·0 ml	–	
ATP + Vitamin B$_{12}$	0·002% + 0·0002%	1·0 ml 1·0 ml	–	
GABA + Vitamin B$_{12}$ + ATP	0·002 M + 0·0002% + 0·002%	1·0 ml 1·0 ml 1·0 ml	+	Latent period 22 min

produced seizures in twenty cases out of twenty. Here GABA was changed into some unknown factor which acted to produce generalized seizure. The normal brain contains GABA in the concentration of 0·031 per cent and it has been argued that GABA might be the mother substance of both the excitatory and the inhibitory transmitter in higher animals (Hayashi, 1959).

As a control experiment γ-aminocrotonic acid was used, but this substance did not produce any motor action when introduced into c.s.f. of dogs, either alone or with B_{12} and B_1.

NEW METHOD FOR DEMONSTRATING THE GENESIS OF AN EXCITATORY TRANSMITTER

The method we used was to introduce a substance into the cerebrospinal fluid of a dog and, at the same time, to introduce a coenzyme in order to transform the substance into the excitatory transmitter. As in the experiment described in Table 2, we took folic acid instead of vitamin B_{12} in a concentration which by itself caused no motor effects. When combined with GABA and ATP it produced strong seizures. Vitamin B_1 could be used instead of ATP in this case and the result indicated that it acts as energy liberator in the reaction (Hayashi, 1960).

The method hitherto used to detect enzymatic actions in tissues consisted in the artificial addition of substrate to homogenates or slices of brain *in vitro* and either estimation of the expected substances in the incubation fluid or measurement of the output of CO_2 as an indicator. This was essentially the procedure in biochemistry. But here we found a method of neurochemistry whereby the substrate is introduced *in vivo* into the cerebrospinal fluid of a dog so that it can contact the cells of the brain that contain the enzymatic systems whose substrate was increased by the artificial addition. It was assumed that if this excess of substrate drives the reaction in the direction of synthesis of a new substance at a rate which is greater than that of the normal state, this resulting substance should be detectable by any indicator, in our case, the production of a seizure. From the experiments just mentioned we could formulate the reaction that produces the excitatory chemical transmitter in the central nervous system (at least in the motor system).

$$\text{GABA plus vitamin } B_{12} \text{ plus } B_1 \rightarrow cc^* \qquad (1)$$
$$\text{GABA plus folic acid plus } B_1 \rightarrow cc^*$$

Instead of vitamin B_{12} we tested vitamin B_2, biotin, lipoic acid and vitamin C, but these substances did not accelerate the reaction. Pantothenic acid was, however, found to produce clonic convulsions according to the following reaction:

$$\text{GABA plus panthothenic acid plus } B_1 \rightarrow cc \qquad (2)$$

* cc = clonic convulsions.

6*

It was now a question whether the reaction of formulae (1) and (2) represented the same sequence (that is, whether pantothenic acid had the same action as B_{12} or folic acid), or if there were quite different reactions leading to two different substances.

When GABA, vitamin B_{12}, pantothenic acid and vitamin B_1 were combined, the seizure was delayed or the concentration of each substance needed to be increased in order to produce a seizure. In other words, the reactions of vitamin B_{12} on the one hand and the reaction of pantothenic acid on the other are quite different and it is likely that they both represent stages in the same direction so that reaction (1) produced reaction (2) or vice versa. At any rate, the excitatory transmitter substance was produced from GABA with the aid of a coenzyme and energy in that certain sequence of reactions (1) and (2).

A tentative structure is put forward for the excitatory chemical transmitter substance of the motor system. The reaction (1) suggests that a methylation process is involved in the course of reconversion of GABA into the chemical transmitter. We therefore tried the action of several methylated derivatives of GABA on the motor system, for example:

(1) dimethylaminoethanol

(2) γ-aminobutyrobetaine

(3) acetyl-γ-aminobutyrobetaine

All these compounds did not produce any seizure when they were introduced into the cerebrospinal fluid of dogs.

From the reaction (2) we might expect that GABA was at first combined with coenzyme A and that GABA-coenzyme A was converted into GABA-choline. Accordingly, one would expect that GABA-choline should cause seizures, but it was found to have no such action as indicated in Table 3. We then tried to give the methylated compounds together with vitamins B_{12}

TABLE 3. Derivatives of GABA and their action on the motor system of dogs

Substances	Dose administered into c.s.f.		Seizure
Dimethylaminoethanol	0·01–1·0 M	1 ml	None
γ-aminobutyrobetaine	0·01–1·0 M	1 ml	None
γ-acetoaminobutyric acid ethyl ester	0·01–1·0 M	1 ml	None
γ-aminobutyrylcholine	0·01–1·0 M	1 ml	None
γ-aminobutyrylcholine + Folic acid + Vitamin B_1	0·02 M 0·0002 M 0·02 M		Seizure

and B_1. We found the first three did not produce seizures but γ-amino-butyrylcholine with vitamins B_{12} and B_1 produced seizures with a latent period of 15–60 min. This suggests that the methylation of γ-amino-butyrylcholine, that is, dimethyl-γ-butyrylcholine, might not yet be the real transmitter for excitation in the central motor system.

REFERENCES

CROSSLAND, J., Chemical transmission in the central nervous system. *J. Pharmacy and Pharmacol.* **12**, pp. 1–36 (1960).

HAYASHI, T., Inhibition and Excitation due to γ-aminobutyric acid in the central nervous system. *Nature* **182**, 1076 (1958).

HAYASHI, T., *Neurophysiology and Neurochemistry of Convulsion.* Dainihon-Tosho, Tokyo 1959.

HAYASHI, T., Gamma-aminobutyric acid as the parent substance for an inhibitory and an excitatory transmitter. In: *Inhibition in Nervous System and γ-aminobutyric Acid,* edited by Roberts E. pp. 515–522, Pergamon Press 1960.

HAYASHI, T., Physiological mechanism of producing excitatory transmitter in the brain of dogs. In: *Nervous Inhibition,* edited by Florey E., pp. 378–384 Pergamon Press 1961.

CHANGES IN MUSCLE PROTEINS IN SOME PATHOLOGICAL STATES

I. I. IVANOV

Department of Biochemistry, Paediatric Medical Institute,
and the Biochemical Laboratory of the Institute of Obstetrics
and Gynaecology, U.S.S.R. Academy of Medical Sciences, Leningrad

Translated by Dr. R. Crawford

STUDY of the biochemical changes occurring in the various forms of muscle pathology is very important for an understanding of the nature of certain muscle diseases and in the search for methods of treatment. Changes in muscle proteins and, more particularly, in their fractional composition in diseases involving prolonged disturbance of the motor functions of skeletal and smooth muscle have attracted special attention.

The changes in muscle chemistry about which most is known at the present time are those associated with denervation, sympathectomy, tenotomy, progressive muscular atrophy, poliomyelitis, contractures, osteo-articular affections, certain avitaminoses and endocrine disturbances, the application of tourniquets, hypertensive disease and some other forms of pathological change in muscle. The most characteristic changes in a number of these conditions are reduction in the total protein content of muscle tissue, marked reduction in its myosin content, increase in the quantity of collagen and stroma proteins, increase of myo-albumin, change in the ratios of other protein fractions, reduced ATP-ase activity, etc.

The changes noted in the fractional composition of muscle proteins in the presence of atrophic processes of widely varying origin have been established by the classical methods of examination now accepted in the biochemistry of muscle.

A marked change in the relationship between proteins of the actomyosin complex and the readily soluble sarcoplasmic proteins, particularly myo-albumin, has, for example, been demonstrated in our laboratory in the sequelae of poliomyelitis in children (Fig. 1). We tried to arrive at a method for the biochemical evaluation of the functional state of the affected muscles in poliomyelitis by correlation of the results of biochemical examination with the clinical features of the disease. The results led us to express the view that the biochemical assessment of the functional state of muscles constituted an accurate and objective method which might be of considerable importance in surgical practice for the resolution of doubts connected with the indications for operations such as muscle and tendon transplantation, etc.

The fractional composition of skeletal muscle proteins in atrophic states requires further investigation, however, as a result of recent findings on the presence of proteins, soluble in salt solutions of low ion strength but bound with actomyosin into a single complex, in the myofibrils of both skeletal and smooth tonic muscles, but particularly the latter, these proteins having been isolated and described by a number of authors (Szent-Gyorgyi *et al.*, 1955; Perry and Zydomo, 1959; Tsao *et al.*, 1956, 1958; Hanson and Huxley, 1953; Ivanov *et al.*, 1959; and others).

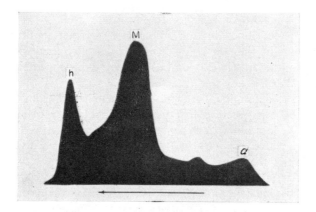

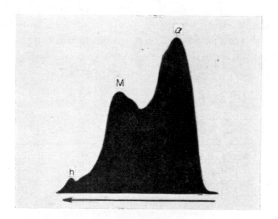

Fig. 1. Proteinogram of skeletal muscle proteins in man (on paper).

α—actomyosin + myosin. *M*—myogen fraction. *h*—myo-albumin. Extract with high ion strength −0·5. Conditions of electrophoresis: tension 6–8 V/cm; current strength 0·9 mA per cm cross section; duration of electrophoresis 18 hr. 1 a—normal muscle. 1 b—muscle atrophy after paralysis (sequela of poliomyelitis).

I. I. Ivanov and his co-workers linked the tonic (sphincter) function—the capacity of muscle for prolonged, fatigueless resistance to stretching—with this protein fraction, which they termed fraction T. The capacity of muscle (skeletal, smooth or cardiac) for contractile reactions of any type has, on the other hand, always been linked with the presence of actomyosin in muscle, the quantity of which is higher in proportion to the intensity of the contractile function of the muscular organ. The ratio of actomyosin complex proteins to readily soluble myofibril proteins in normal rabbit skeletal muscle ranges around 80/20. It is 60/40 in cardiac muscle and 40/60 in the smooth muscle of the stomach.

Our results indicate that the fraction T proteins in skeletal, cardiac and smooth muscle are the water-soluble myofibril proteins of Tsao, tropomyosin and a certain quantity of extremely unstable globulins of the type of Beber's globulin-X (unpublished findings).

The method developed in our laboratory for fractionation of the myofibrillar proteins in different types of muscle was also used for examination of changes in the fractional composition of muscle proteins in various pathological states.

We decided to determine, first of all, whether there was any change in the ratio of actomyosin fraction to fraction T in atrophy of skeletal muscle associated with loss of capacity for typical tetanic reaction to stimulation.

In our work with Mirovich (1960) muscle atrophy was produced in rabbits by transection of the spinal cord at the level of the 4th or 5th lumbar vertebra. Examined 28–32 days after the operation, the denervated muscles revealed a sharp increase in the quantity of stroma proteins and a reduction by half in total myofibrillar proteins extracted from muscle with 0·6 M KCl after complete extraction of the readily soluble sarcoplasmic proteins.

Another characteristic change in protein composition was seen within the fraction of myofibrillar proteins itself: the actomyosin fraction/fraction T ratio was reduced from a normal value of 80/20 to 60/40 (Tables 1 and 2).

TABLE 1. Fractional composition of rabbit skeletal muscle protein after spinal cord transection (Ivanov and Mirovich) (mg nitrogen per g fresh tissue and fraction nitrogen as a percentage of total tissue nitrogen)

Total nitrogen		Non-protein nitrogen		Sarcoplasmic proteins		Myofibrillar proteins		Stroma proteins	
mg/g	%	mg/g	%	mg/g	%	mg/g	%	mg/g	%
Normal (average of three experiments)									
35·5	100	4·3	12·1	10·59	29·8	16·92	47·7	3·77	10·6
28–32 days after spinal cord transection (average of six experiments)									
30·0	100	4·4	14·6	7·80	26·1	10·20	33·8	7·70	25·5

TABLE 2. Fractional composition of myofibrillar proteins in rabbit skeletal muscle after spinal cord transection (Ivanov and Mirovich) (mg nitrogen per g fresh tissue and fraction nitrogen as percentage of total tissue nitrogen)

Total content		Soluble in salt solutions with high ion strength—actomyosin fraction		Soluble in salt solutions with low ion strength—fraction T	
mg/g	%	mg/g	%	mg/g	%
Normal (average of three experiments)					
16·92	100	13·64	81	3·28	19
28–32 days after spinal cord transection (average of six experiments)					
10·20	100	6·50	63	3·70	37

The muscle denervation produced by spinal cord transection was also associated with certain changes in the properties of contractile proteins: the power of actinomyosin gel to reduce its viscosity in the presence of ATP and the percentage of muscle fibres contracting when macerated in glycerol were diminished.

Working in our laboratory, Yur'yev (1960) obtained some interesting results by fractionation of the myofibrillar proteins in the course of an investigation on changes in the proteins of the smooth musculature of the vessel walls in hypertensive disease. The material studied was not muscle tissue of vessels as such, but the muscular layer as a definite anatomical structure. These cannot be regarded as equivalent, as the media of the vessels contains a certain, sometimes quite considerable, quantity of elastic fibres in addition to the muscle elements. A high content of stroma proteins in the muscular walls of vessels is undoubtedly closely connected with this feature in their histological structure. At the same time this circumstance cannot have any material effect on quantitative ratios between the fractions of myofibrillar proteins (actomyosin fraction and fraction T).

Fraction T proteins constitute most of the myofibrillar proteins in normal vessels; only about 25 per cent can be regarded as belonging to the proteins of what we have provisionally termed the "actomyosin fraction." In hypertensive patients, on the other hand, the actomyosin fraction constitutes the major part of all the myofibrillar proteins in the vessels (Table 3).

Another interesting point was that the ATP-ase activity of the myofibrillar proteins isolated from pathological vessels (vessels from cadavers of individuals with chronic forms of hypertension) was much greater than the activity of the proteins from the muscle layer of normal vessels. This too may point to higher myosin and actomyosin contents in the vessel wall in such cases.

These changes in the protein composition of the smooth muscle of vessels undoubtedly reflect the unusual nature of the vascular reaction to some

TABLE 3. Fractional composition of proteins in the muscle of the vessel wall (V. A. Yur'yev)
(Fraction nitrogen as a percentage of total nitrogen)

Nonprotein nitrogen	Sarcoplasmic protein	Myofibrillar proteins				Stroma
		Total	Actomyosin (AM)	T	AM/T	
Normal (average of four experiments)						
1·95	10·81	9·94	1·9	7·87	1/4	75·7
Hypertensive disease (average of six experiments)						
2·79	13·05	9·13	5·18	3·52	1·5/1	73·88

stimuli or other, physiological or pathological. They may be regarded as the result of hypertrophy connected with intensification of the contractile reaction throughout the entire cardiovascular system—with changes of opposite nature to atrophic processes.

Electrophoretic and immunochemical investigations are now proceeding in our laboratory on quantitative and qualitative changes in the proteins of both skeletal and smooth muscle of various organs in various pathological states.

REFERENCES

HANSON, J. and H. HUXLEY, *Symp. Soc. Expl. Biol.* **9**, 228 (1953).
HUXLEY, H. and J. HANSON, *Biochim. Biophys. Acta* **23**, 229 (1957).
IVANOV, I. I., V. A. YUR'YEV, D. A. NOVOZHILOV, L. A. MIKHAILOVSKAYA and B. M. KRYMSKAYA, Problems of Medical Chemistry (*Vopr. med. khim.*) **5**, 243 (1959).
IVANOV, I. I., Z. N. ZHAKHOVA, I. P. ZINOV'YEVA, N. I. MIROVICH, V. P. MOISEYEVA, E. A. PARSHINA, S. YE. TUKACHINSKII and V. A. YUR'YEV, Biochemistry (*Biokhimiya*) **24**, 51 (1959).
IVANOV, I. I., N. I. MIROVICH, V. P. MOISEYEVA, E. A. PARSHINA, S. E. TUKACHINSKY, V. A. YUR'YEV, Z. N. KHAKHOVA and I. P. ZINOV'YEVA, *Acta Physiol. Hung.* **16**, 7 (1959).
IVANOV, I. I. and N. I. MIROVICH, Problems of Medical Chemistry (*Vopr. med. khim.*) **6**, 403 (1960).
IVANOV, I. I., N. I. MIROVICH, Z. N. ZHAKOVA and S. YE. TUKACHINSKII, Biochemistry (*Biokhimiya*) **27**, 94 (1962).
MIKHAILOVSKAYA, L. A., D. A. NOVOZHILOV and I. I. IVANOV, Traumatology and Prosthesis (*Travmatologiya i protezirovaniye*) **3**, 28 (1958).
PERRY, S. and M. ZYDOMO, *Biochem. J.* **23** (2), 220 (1959).
SZENT-GYORGYI, A., D. MAZIA and A. SZENT-GYORGYO, *Biochim. Biophys. Acta* **16**, 336 (1955).
TSAO, T., HSU-KAI, *Acta Physiol. Sinica* **20**, 189 (1956).
TSAO, T., HSU-KAI, M. N. JEN, C. H. PAN, P. H. TAN, T. C. TAO, N. Y. WEN and C. I. NIN, *Scientia Sinica* **11**, 6 (1958).

EVOLUTION OF FUNCTIONS IN THE HIGHER DIVISIONS OF THE CENTRAL NERVOUS SYSTEM AND OF THEIR REGULATING MECHANISMS

A. I. KARAMYAN

Institute of Evolutionary Physiology, U.S.S.R. Academy
of Sciences, Leningrad

Translated by Dr. R. Crawford

THE concept of morphophysiological transformation in the evolutionary process of the individual and of the species has been clearly formulated by biologists in the form of the principles of "balance of organs", "correlation", "differentiation", "co-ordination", "interpretation" and so on.

These ideas could not, however, be developed because of the lack of special experimental methods of investigation. The cardinal problem, which had already been enunciated by Severtsov—in what manner and in what ways "individual capacity for behavioural adaptation is grafted on to inherited adaptability"*—could only be decided by physiological, biochemical and neurohistological investigations. Such investigations should, however, be carried out in accordance with the generally accepted biological principles that the evolutionary process is based on progressive and regressive development, as revealed by the development of new morphophysiological systems providing for more perfect forms of adaptation and the disappearance or transformation of old forms of nervous activity and nervous regulation which have become superfluous or which interfere with further progress.

The wide use of the historical method in physiological and biochemical research (Orbeli, 1923, 1938, 1958; Koshtoyants, 1934, 1957; Kreps, 1925; Verzhbinskaya and Kreps, 1959; Ginetsinskii, 1960; Volkhov, 1951,1959; Biryukov, 1948, 1959; Voronin, 1957; Karamyan, 1956, 1958, 1959; and others) promoted the development of evolutionary physiology into an independent branch of science. This new subject, which was based on the evolutionary physiological views of Sechenov and Pavlov, has, in the view

---

* A. N. Severtsov, *Collected Works*. Vol. 3. Izdat. Akad. Nauk SSSR, p. 311 (1945).

of Orbeli (1958), its own specific investigational methods and its own specific tasks, which include "not only explanation of the course of development, the actual features of development and the sequence of events, but also establishment of their interrelationships and of the environmental factors acting on 'living substance', and factors originating from the animal itself in the form of interaction between its individual parts standing in causal relationship to all transformations and changes".*

It is known that the principle of replacement of functions or of staged development of nervous activity is one of the most important in questions of functional evolution. It has been established, for example, that organisms in the nerveless stage of development reacted directly to environmental changes. As nerve elements arose and central structures took shape, there commenced a stage in which there were two forms of functioning, local and central, and later, this stage of development was replaced by a period of complete suppression or complete disappearance of all automatism in the activity of contractile and secretory systems.

The question arises—is this course of evolution characteristic only for primitive forms of co-ordination or is the principle of replacement of functions of universal validity, and applicable therefore to the central nervous system?

We describe in this paper certain facts of a general nature which indicate that the superimposition of acquired on inborn forms of nervous activity also proceeds on the principle of replacement of functions in the ascending series of development of the central nervous system, wherein evolutionary transformations are known to proceed much more rapidly than in other systems.

Morphological investigations have shown that, in the early stages of vertebrate development, connexions can be demonstrated between the primary visual and auditory centres and the cerebellum in teleostome and bony fishes (Franz, 1912; Zelikin, 1957). These systems of connexions are reduced in amphibians. A new system of connexions, the tectocerebral tract, is present in these animals, and also in reptiles and birds. Finally, in mammals, as a result of the development of the cortex, these connexions are replaced by the thalamocortical tract, the importance of which increases progressively in the process of mammalian evolution.

The results of investigations in comparative physiology are in complete accord with these conclusions arrived at by morphologists. It has been shown that the midbrain constitutes the main system for the closure of temporary connexions for motor activity in cyclostomes (Baru, 1951; Fanardzhyan, 1954; Karamyan, 1956). In teleostomes and bony fishes the main system for closure of temporary connexions (visual and auditory) for

---

* L. A. Orbeli. The basic methods and tasks of evolutionary physiology. In: *Evolution of nervous system functions*, p. 7, Medgiz (1958).

motor, compensatory and trophic activities is formed by nerve formations in
the midbrain and cerebellum. The hemispheres of the forebrain have no
part in these functions (Karamyan, 1956; Baru, 1955; Malyukina, 1955).
Furthermore, it has been shown that, with the development in the vertebrate evolutionary series of the palaeocortex and archicortex (in amphibians, reptiles and birds) and, later, the powerful development of the neo-
cortex (in mammals), all the functions mentioned gradually became concentrated, first in the strial system of the hemispheres and later, depending
on the level of mammalian development, in the cerebral cortex (Karamyan,
1959).

This general trend of the evolutionary process has been observed also
in electrophysiological investigations. Those of Zagorul'ko (1959) and
Karamyan (1956) have shown that, in fishes, there are no electrical reactions to photic and acoustic stimuli in the hemispheres of the forebrain,
but that definite electrical responses are recorded from the surface of the
optic lobes of the midbrain and in the cerebellum. These results have since
been confirmed by Gusel'nikov (1958) and Schade and Weiler (1959).
Furthermore, Zagorul'ko has shown that electrical responses to photic
stimulation can be recorded from the entire surface of the hemispheres
of the brain without any definite localization in amphibians, as distinct
from fish. On the other hand, Bremer et al. (1939), Zagorul'ko (1959),
Gusel'nikov (1958) and Bagryanskii (1958, 1959) have established that, in
the case of tortoises, pigeons and rabbits, these reactions are recorded in
certain definite regions of the hemispheres, which means that these animals
are already showing definite localization of electrical responses (Fig. 1).

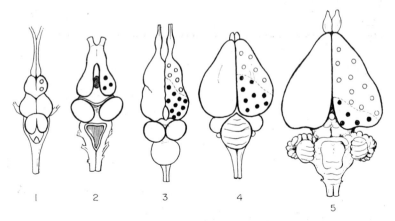

FIG. 1. Distribution of electrical reactions to photic stimulation of the eyes in the
hemispheres of various vertebrates
(from the work of Zagorul'ko and Bagryanskii, 1959).

1—fish (carp). 2—amphibian (frog). 3—reptile (tortoise). 4—bird (pigeon). 5—mammal
(rabbit). The black circles indicate regions where electrical responses developed and
the white circles, zones in which no responses were recorded.

The morphological, comparative physiological and electrophysiological investigations discussed, indicate that the encephalization and corticalization of the closing of temporary connexions has proceeded parallel with the regressive and progressive morphological evolution of the brain, with the result that the properties of the acquired forms of reflex reactions have become perfected, but not narrowly specialized forms of reaction to limited groups of stimuli; more universal and varied forms of analysis and synthesis have thus emerged and have undergone development stage by stage.

One of the typical examples of staged development in the central nervous system is the evolution of the functions of the central connexions of the cerebellum. Early classical neurophysiology regarded the cerebellum as the central organ for involuntary motor acts and the cortex as the organ for voluntary movements. The investigations of Luciani (1893) and, more particularly, the comprehensive experimental research carried out over many years by Orbeli and his school put an end to this one-sided conception. The result was that the following basic positions were established. The cerebellum is the stabilizer of the functions of efferent and afferent systems and the highest adaptation-trophic organ, controlling the functional state of centres of both somatic and autonomic systems. Between the cerebellum and the cortex there has been developed the closest functional connexion, whereby antagonistic relationships between inborn and acquired forms of nervous activity are removed. These views have been completely confirmed by subsequent physiological investigations.

Our evolutionary physiological investigations have established that the functional relationships between cerebellum and forebrain hemispheres differ in structure in animals at different levels of evolutionary development. In teleostome and bony fishes all afferent and efferent connexions are concentrated in the optic lobes of the midbrain and in the cerebellum and play the leading part in motor, sensory and conditioned reflex activity.

Veselkin's investigations have established that, with local illumination of the lamprey retina, quite definite electrical reactions could be demonstrated in the optic lobes of the midbrain, in the octavovestibular complex, i.e. in the region of the primitive cerebellum and in the region of the rhomboid fossa of the medulla. There were no reactions in the region of the forebrain hemispheres in response to the photic stimulations (Fig. 2). This indicates that although functions in cyclostomes are concentrated in certain regions of the brain, signs of diffuseness are still present.

The concentration of exteroceptive afferent impulses in certain definite systems of the brain is seen more clearly in teleostome and bony fishes. Investigations carried out on two species of teleostome fishes, the deep-water skate (*Raia clavata*) and the sting-ray (*Trygon pastinaca*), have shown that, when the optic nerve was stimulated electrically, definite electrical reactions were observed in the optic lobes of the midbrain and the anterior parts of the body of the cerebellum; as for electrical reactions in the hemispheres of the forebrain, the visual system is not represented in the forebrain of these fishes (Fig. 3).

In amphibians and reptiles, with the development of the pallium and archicortex and the development of connexions between them and the

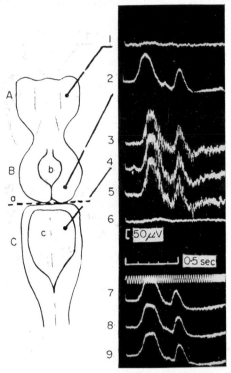

FIG. 2. Responses in the brain to stimulation of the right eye of a curarized lamprey with single light flashes.

1—forebrain. 2—midbrain. 3–5—medulla. 6—medulla after division along the line *a*. 7—midbrain after division along the line *a*. Positive deflection upwards. The moment of the commencement of the stimulation coincided with the commencement of the beam.

neothalamus, the role of the cerebellum has become restricted to participation in motor activity only. Although the motor and trophic functions of the cerebellum are greater in birds, complete removal of the cerebellum does not lead to any particular changes in autonomic positive and negative conditioned reflexes (Yavorskaya, 1959). Cortico-cerebellar relationships are quite differently constituted in mammals. Yavorskaya (1958) has shown that cerebellectomy in these animals leads to distinct changes in positive and negative conditioned reflexes and changes in the electrical activity of the cortex.

We have now been able to show that these effects are produced in their different ways through two phylogenetically different parts of the cerebellum,

the palaeocerebellar and the neocerebellar systems. Investigations have
shown that removal of the neocerebellum, which means exclusion of the
neocerebellocortical system which, in the evolutionary vertebrate series,
emerges and develops parallel with the appearance and development of
the cortex, is followed by marked reduction in the excitability of the cortex.

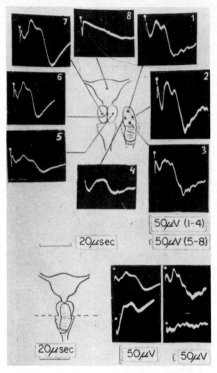

FIG. 3. Electrical responses in the brain of the curarized skate to electrical stimulation of the right optic nerve (rectangular pulses 0·5 msec, 2 V). The upper
diagram shows the responses in the midbrain (5–7) and in the cerebellum (1–4).
There were no responses in the forebrain (8). The control experiment is shown
in the lower diagram. The upper two curves on the left are for the response in the
midbrain and the upper two on the right, the response in the cerebellum. Lower
two curves—after division of the brain-stem at the junction of the midbrain and
hindbrain; responses persisted in the midbrain (*left*) and disappeared in the
cerebellum (*right*). Polarity of the responses: positivity—upwards. The moment
of delivery of the stimulus coincided with the commencement of the travel of the
beam.

For example, removal of the neocerebellum in cats with well elaborated
autonomic (respiratory and cardiac) conditioned reflexes resulted in acute
enfeeblement or complete disappearance of positive conditioned reflexes,
weakening of orientation reactions and the development of drowsy states
during the experiments.

Similar results, i.e. results indicating reduced excitability of the cortex, were obtained in the experiments of Malyukina (in print) on dogs and in those of Antonova (1960) on rats in relation to the elaboration of motor alimentary conditioned reflexes. These experiments showed that positive conditioned reflexes were absent at first after damage to the neocerebellum but were restored later, although disturbances in the form of irregularity of the reflexes and marked prolongation of the latent periods persisted for 3–7 months. These various facts thus indicate that the most characteristic disturbance in rats, cats and dogs was reduction of cortical excitability.

Opposite results were obtained after removal of the palaeocerebellum. The characteristic and very constant effect of this operation was increased cortical excitability, as shown by marked exaggeration of the autonomic components of orientation reactions, more intense positive conditioned reflexes and disinhibition of differential inhibition. Disinhibition of differential inhibition when excitability was high was generally of widely generalized type. Animals well trained to the experimental conditions became restless after removal of the palaeocerebellum, there was acute lowering of the threshold of electrical stimulation used as unconditioned reinforcement, cardiac activity and respiratory movements became very labile and accesses of motor excitement were frequently observed during the experiments. But compared with the disturbances caused by removal of the neocerebellum, these changes were transient and were corrected much more rapidly.

Electrophysiological investigation of the parts played by the palaeocerebellar and neocerebellar divisions of the cat cerebellum in the regulation of electrical activity in the spinal cord and cortex revealed that monosynaptic reactions in the spinal cord were inhibited more effectively by the palaeocerebellar than the neocerebellar division of the cerebellum. As for ascending cerebellar effects, the voltage of spontaneous cortical discharges in the controlateral sensorimotor region of the forebrain was increased during anodal polarization of the neocerebellum, whereas polarization of the palaeocerebellum generally led to desynchronization in the electrocorticogram (Fig. 4).

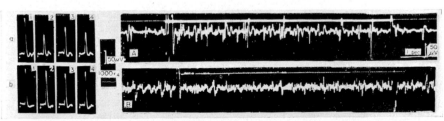

FIG. 4. Monosynaptic reactions in the spinal cord in the normal state (a, 1, b, 1) and during anodal polarization of the palaeocerebellum (a, 2, 3, 4) and neocerebellum (b, 2, 3, 4). Spontaneous electrical activity in the sensorimotor region of the cortex during anodal polarization of the neocerebellum (A) and palaeocerebellum (B). Thick white line—time of cerebellar polarization.

All these facts thus lead to the conclusion that the system of connexions between cerebellum and cortex, which has been formed by grafting on to phylogenetically old nerve formations, operates over two routes—a palaeo-cerebello-reticular and a neocerebello-thalamic.

The facts described will have made it evident that qualitatively different forms of disturbance result from the exclusion of these paths: exclusion of the palaeocerebello-reticular system leads to transient intensification of cortical excitation and disinhibition of differential inhibition, while exclusion of the neocerebello-thalamic system is associated with profound and prolonged disturbances of conditioned reflex activity.

A possible assumption is that these two qualitatively different effects are connected with two different forms of cerebellar activity—tonic activity, mediated through centres in the reticular formation, and phasic activity effected through the neuronal connexions between the neocerebellum and cortex. These conclusions are based, not only on the facts we have described, but also on the results of an enormous number of neurohistological and electrophysiological investigations affording evidence that the palaeo-cerebellar system is represented in the reticular formation by direct afferent and efferent fibres (Brodal, 1957) and may exercise inhibitory and excitatory influences on the electrical discharges of individual cells in the reticular formation (Baumgarten et al., 1954).

On the other hand, it has been established that the neocerebellar system has afferent and efferent connexions with nuclear formations in the thalamus, hypothalamus, globus pallidus, caudate nucleus, corpus striatum, limbic system and with all regions of the cortex (Whiteside and Snider, 1953; Rand, 1954; Carrea and Mettler, 1954; Iwata and Snider, 1959; Anand et al., 1959; and others).

Numerous electrophysiological investigations on monkeys, cats and rats have revealed that almost all forms of sensation—proprioceptive, interoceptive and exteroceptive (including vision and hearing) are represented in various zones of the cerebellum (Dow and Anderson, 1942; Adrian, 1943; Snider, 1950; Lam and Ogura, 1952; Withlock, 1952; Widen, 1955; Firsov, 1957; Dow and Moruzzi, 1958; Chernigovskii, 1959; and others). Somato-tonic central connexions between cerebellum and cortex have been established for all these receptor systems (Adrian, 1943; Snider, 1950; Snider and Eldred, 1952; and others). Some authors regard these cortico-cerebellar connexions as "point to point" projections.

All this neuromorphological, comparative physiological and electrophysiological evidence thus indicates that a general tendency to shifting of the closing function in the central nervous system in the course of phylogenetic development can be observed in the ascending evolutionary series. And any system capable of effecting temporary connexions is always phylogenetically younger and is always highly dynamic because of the absence of specialization. There are reasons for thinking that, in the process of vertebrate development, the system for the closure of temporary connexions, or the grafting of individual on to inherited forms of behaviour, has proceeded through all stages in the morphological development of the central nervous system, from the spinal cord to the cerebral cortex.

All the facts described and the theoretical conclusions following therefrom refer to the evolution of co-ordinating systems. Questions of great importance for an understanding of the evolution of nervous activity as a whole are those connected with the development of regulating mechanisms. Emphasizing the urgent importance of this, Koshtoyants wrote that "the trophic influence of the nervous system plays an important part in the complex processes of progressive and regressive change in the course of ontogenetic and phylogenetic development".*

Pavlov (1920) and Gaskell (1920) formulated the theory of the initiating and trophic functions of the nervous system on the basis of the extensive research carried out in the course of the nineteenth century and their own experimental investigations. These concepts of Pavlov and Gaskell formed the basis of the brilliant investigations carried out over many years by Orbeli (1938, 1958), who created the doctrine of the adaptation-trophic role of the sympathetic nervous system.

The fundamental content of this doctrine is that all contractile and secretory systems have dual innervation—functional, leading to some nervous, muscular or secretory act, and adaptation-trophic, controlling the functional capacity of the system.

It is very important to emphasize that the sympathetic nervous system also exerts an adaptation-trophic influence on the central nervous system. It has been established that stimulation of the cervical sympathetic nerves may have either inhibitory or excitatory effects on the functioning of the vasomotor and respiratory centres (Krestovnikov and Savich, 1928; Krestovnikov, 1928), on the hypothalamus (Strel'tsov, 1931; Moiseyev and Tonkikh, 1939; Tonkikh, 1956; and others) and the cerebellum (Saprokhin, 1945; and others). Investigations by Asratyan (1935), Skipin (1947), Maiorov et al. (1949), Airapet'yants (1949), Alekseyeva (1952), Pavlov (1955), Maiorov et al. (1956) and Sollertinskaya (1957) have demonstrated definite disturbances of higher nervous activity in dogs and rabbits after removal or irradiation of the cervical sympathetic ganglia. These disturbances took the form of prolonged reduction of unconditioned and conditioned excitation, intensification of internal inhibition or disturbance of the balance between the basic nervous processes in the cerebral cortex.

That the sympathetic nervous system also has efferent influences on the functioning of the higher divisions of the central nervous system has also been established in electro-physiological research. Investigations by Popov (1934), Zagorul'ko (1960), Bodenko (1955), Boiko (1958), Aleksanyan and

* Kh. S. Koshtoyants, *Principles of comparative physiology*. Vol. 2, p. 21, 1957.

Arutyunyan (1958) and Aladzhalova (1960) have demonstrated various forms of disturbance of the electrical activity in the cortex and hypothalamus after division and stimulation of cervical sympathetic nerves or removal of the ganglia. Some authors observed enfeeblement of the slow EEG waves and absence of any reaction of desynchronization in response to exteroceptive stimulation while, conversely, others noted increase of slow wave amplitude and intensified reactions of desynchronization.

We have shown in more systematic investigations (Sollertinskaya, 1956, 1957, 1960; Karamyan, 1959; Veselkin, 1959) that removal of the superior cervical sympathetic ganglia in rabbits and pigeons was followed by prolonged reduction in the amplitude of the slow waves or their complete suppression, with some increase in the size and number of fast waves in the electroencephalogram and, conversely, the development of slow rhythms in the cerebellogram.

In an attempt to explain the reasons for these contradictions Van Tai-An' (1960) carried out some fresh investigations in our laboratory. After the

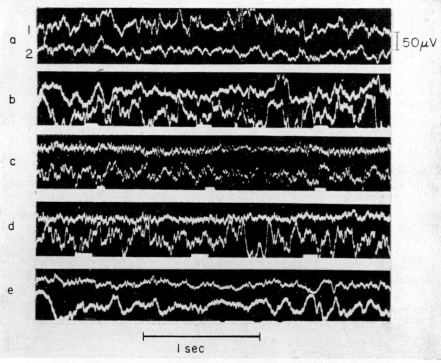

FIG. 5. Changes in the electrical activities of rabbit cortex and hypothalamus after bilateral removal of the superior and inferior cervical sympathic ganglia.

a—before sympathectomy. b—3 days after sympathectomy. c—10 days after. d—21 days after. e—45 days after sympathectomy. 1—electrogram of the parietal cortex. 2—electrogram of the hypothalamus.

rabbits had been given a prolonged training to accustom them to the experimental conditions and the background electrical activities of the cortex and hypothalamus had been established, the rabbits were subjected to sympathectomies extending from the superior cervical to the stellate ganglia, inclusive. These investigations revealed that the slow waves in the EEG of the parietal region of the cortex were suppressed and the amplitude of the slow waves in the hypothalamus was increased 4 to 10 days after this almost complete interruption of all sympathetic innervation to the higher divisions of the central nervous system (Fig. 5). Reduction or disappearance of the slow and fast EEG waves in pigeons was observed in the experiments of Belekhova (1962) after destruction by electrolysis of various parts of the diencephalon in the region where the higher autonomic centres are situated (Fig. 6).

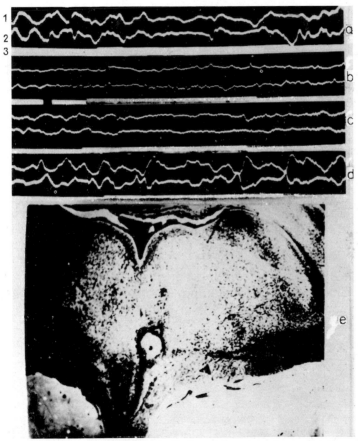

FIG. 6. Changes in the background EEG and in orientation reactions to light in a pigeon after the production of a lesion of the diencephalon on the left side. a—before destruction. b—on the 1st day after destruction. c—on the 3rd day. d—on the 10th day. 1—left EEG. 2—right EEG. 3—time (0·02 sec) and also stimulation. e—photomicrograph of the lesion in the diencephalon on the left side (Nissl staining).

The identical nature of the effects produced by peripheral and central formations of the sympathetic nervous system on electrical activity in the cerebral hemispheres made it essential that the relationships of the sympathetic nervous system and the nonspecific thalamic nuclei, with the functions of which many authors link the development of slow rhythms in the cortex, should be examined. Investigations were therefore carried out to demonstrate the effects of the cervical sympathetic ganglia and adrenaline on the "recruitment reaction" produced by direct stimulation of the non-specific thalamic nuclei (n. centralis medialis, centrum medianum, n. ventralis anterior), effected with the assistance of a stereotaxic apparatus.

These investigations of Van Tai-An' and Belekhova (1961) and of Belekhova (1962) in acute experiments on cats revealed that electrical stimulation of the cervical sympathetic nerves or the intravenous injection of adrenaline 60–180 μg/kg suppressed the recruitment reaction. In a number of instances it was possible to observe a second phase in their action—a considerable increase in the amplitude of the response reactions—immediately after the reduction in the amplitude of the cortical reactions. Stimulation of the cervical sympathetic nerve had also a mainly depressing effect, sometimes with subsequent facilitation, on the convulsive discharges produced in the cortex by the local application of 0·1 per cent strychnine solution (Fig. 7).

With a view to explaining the relationship between the sympathetic nervous system and the specific systems, we carried out a series of experiments on the effect of stimulation of the cervical sympathetic nerves and the injection of adrenaline on primary responses in the auditory projection area of the cortex produced by local stimulation of the medial geniculate body. These experiments showed that stimulation of a cervical sympathetic nerve and the injection of adrenaline either had no effect whatever on the functioning of the specific system or merely led to slight increase in the size of the primary responses.

All these facts indicate that there are close interrelationships, indicative of a common genetic connexion, between the sympathetic nervous system and the nonspecific systems in the thalamus. It can at least be stated definitely that the sympathetic nervous system can exercise its toning influence on higher nervous functions through the tonic (Dell, 1958) and phasic (Jasper, 1958) systems in the reticular formation.

These various points are in complete accord with the results of experimental investigations by Palenov (1901) and Gellhorn (1948) and with our own experimental investigations showing that the effect of sympathectomy is greater in animals lower on the phylogenetic scale (Fig. 8).

All these facts, arrived at by study of evolutionary physiology, indicate, first, that there are definite functional connexions between the sympathetic nervous system and nonspecific structures in rostral and caudal parts of the reticular formation and that these connexions are apparently more in evidence in the early stages of phylogenetic development; secondly, that

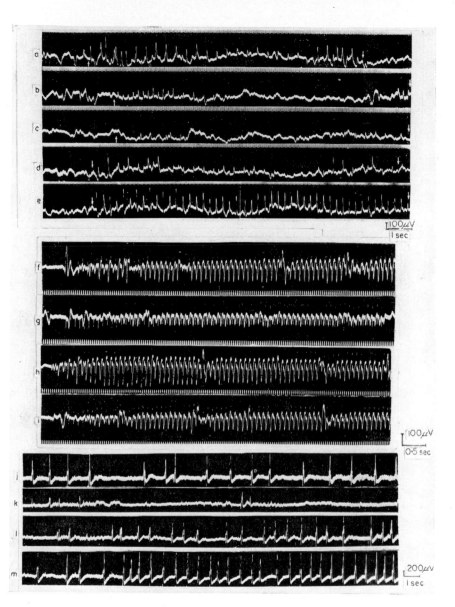

FIG. 7. Effects of stimulation of the left cervical sympathetic nerve and injection of adrenaline 65 µg/kg on the recruitment reaction and on strychnine discharges in the gyrus suprasylvius of the ipselateral hemisphere.

a—recruitment reaction in response to stimulation of the nucleus centralis medialis before stimulation of the sympathetic nerve. b—after 1 min of sympathetic stimulation. c—after 1·5 min of sympathetic stimulation. d—8 min after the end of stimulation. e—10 min after stimulation. f—recruitment reaction in response to stimulation of the nucleus ventralis anterior before injection of adrenaline. g—30 sec after injection of adrenaline. h—11 min after. i—13 min after injection of adrenaline. j—strychnine discharges before stimulation of the sympathetic nerve. k—after 1 min of stimulation. 1—1 min after stimulation. m—3 min after stimulation.

nonspecific systems also develop and undergo modification as differentiation and specialization of the structures and functions of the higher divisions of the central nervous system advance and the development of specific co-ordination systems progresses. There is now definite morphological evidence (Bishop, 1958) that the nonspecific system has, like the specific, been built up on old nerve structures in the evolutionary vertebrate series and reaches the cortex in highly organized animals.

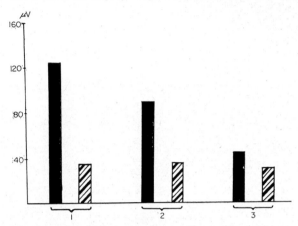

FIG. 8. Changes in the amplitude of the slow EEG waves in various vertebrates after removal of the superior cervical sympathetic ganglia.

1—pigeon, 2—rabbit. 3—cat. Left-hand columns—voltage (μV) of slow waves before operation. Right-hand columns—voltage after operation.

REFERENCES

ADRIAN, E. D., *Brain* **66**, 289 (1943).
AIRAPET'YANTS, E. SH., Physiol. J. U.S.S.R. (*Fiziol. zh. SSSR*) **35**, 481 (1949).
ALADZHALOVA, N. A., *Slow Electrical Processes in the Brain* (Medlennyye elektricheskiye protsessy v golovnom mozge), Moscow 1960.
ALEKSANYAN, A. M. and R. S. ARUTYUNYAN, Reports of the U.S.S.R. Academy of Sciences (*Dokl. Akad. Nauk SSSR*) **125**, 1 (1958).
ALEKSEYEVA, N. S., Physiol. J. U.S.S.R. (*Fiziol. zh. SSSR*) **38**, 5 (1952).
ANAND, B. K., C. H. MALHOTRA, BALDEY, SINGH and S. DUA, *J. Neurophysiol.* **22**, 451 (1959).
ANTONOVA, A. A., *Scientific papers of the Institute of Experimental Medicine, U.S.S.R. Academy of Medial Sciences* (Trudy In-ta eksp. med. Akad. Med. Nauk SSSR), Leningrad 1960.
ASRATYAN, E. A., Physiol. J. U.S.S.R. (*Fiziol. zh. SSSR*) **18**, 5 (1935).
BAGRYANSKII, V. I., *Scientific papers of the Institute of Experimental Medicine, U.S.S.R. Academy of Medial Sciences* (Trudy In-ta eksp. med. Akad. Med. Nauk SSSR), Leningrad 1958.
BAGRYANSKII, V. I., *Research on the Evolution of Nervous Activity. A collection of the works of the Institute of Experimental Medicine, U.S.S.R. Academy of Medical Sciences* (V sb. issledovanii po evolvutsii nervnoi deyatel'nosti. Trudy In-ta eksp. med. Akad. Med. Nauk SSSR), Leningrad 1959.

BARU, A. V., *Comparative Physiology of Conditioned Reflexes* (K sravnitel'noi fiziologii uslovnykh refleksov). Leningrad.

BARU, A. V., In the collection *Problems of the Comparative Physiology and Pythology of Higher Nervous Activity* (Voprosy sravnit. fiziol. i patol. vyssh. nerv. deyat.). Medgiz (1955).

BAUMGARTEN, R., A. MOLLICA and G. MORUZZI, *Pflüg. Arch.* **259**, 56 (1954).

BELEKHOVA, M. G., Bull. of Experimental Biology and Medicine (*Byull. eksp. biol. i med.*) **2** (1962).

BELEKHOVA, M. G., Physiol. J. U.S.S.R. (*Fiziol. zh. SSSR*) **48**, 2 (1962).

BIANKI, V. L., Bull. of Leningrad University, biological series (*Vestnik LGU, seriya biol.*) **3**, 1 (1960).

BIRYUKOV, D. A., *Comparative Physiology of Conditioned Reflexes. Papers of Voronezh. Med. Inst., Voronezh.* (K sravnitel'noi fiziologii uslovnykh refleksov. Trud. Voronezhskogo med. in-ta, Voronezh) (1948).

BIRYUKOV, D. A., *Ninth Congress of All-Union Society of Physiologists, Biochemists and Pharmacologists* (IX s"ezd Vses. ob-va fiziol., biokhim. i farmakol.), Minsk 1959.

BISHOP, G. H., *Reticular formation of the brain*, Boston 1958.

BODENKO, L. V., *Annotation of the research work of the U.S.S.R. Academy of Medical Sciences for the year 1955* (Annotatsiya nauchnykh rabot Akad. Med. Nauk SSSR za 1955 g), Rostov-on-Don 1955.

BOIKO, A. N., Theses and resumés submitted to the annual scientific meeting for 1955 (Sb. "Tezisov i referatov k otchetnoi nauchnoi sessii za 1955 g."), Rostov-on-Don 1958.

BREMER, F., P. S. DOW and G. MORUZZI, *J. Neurophysiol.* **2** (1939).

BRODAL, A., *The Reticular Formation of the Brain Stem. Anatomical Aspects and Functional Correlations*, Edinburgh 1957.

CARREA, R. M. E. and F. A. METTLER, *J. Comp. Neurol.* **101**, 565 (1954).

CHERNIGOVSKII, V. N., *Ninth Congress of the All-Union Soc. of Physiologists, Biochemists and Pharmacologists* (IX s"ezd Vses. ob-va fiziol., biokhim. i farmakol.), Moscow and Minsk 1959.

DELL, P., *Reticular Formation of the Brain*, Boston 1958.

DOW, R. S. and R. ANDERSON, *J. Neurophysiol.* **5**, 363 (1942).

DOW, R. S. and G. MORUZZI, *The Physiology and Pathology of the Cerebellum*, Minneapolis 1958.

FANARDZHYAN, V. V., *Comparative Physiology of Trace Conditioned Reflexes* (K sravnitel'noi fiziologii sledovykh uslovnykh refleksov), Leningrad 1954.

FIRSOV, L. A., Physiol. J. U.S.S.R. (*Fiziol. zh. SSSR*) **43**, 9 (1957).

FRANZ, V., *Zool. Jb.* **32** (1912).

GASKELL, W., *The Involuntary Nervous System*, London 1920.

GELLHORN, E., *Regulating Functions of the Autonomic Nervous System* (Regulyatornyye functsii avtonomnoi nervnoi sistemy), Moscow 1948.

GINETSINSKII, A. G., *On the Evolution of Functions and Functional Evolution* (Ob evolyutsii funktsii i funktsional'noi evolyutsii). Izdat. Akad. Nauk SSSR (1960).

GUSEL'NIKOV, V. A., *Orienting Reflex and Orienting-investigatory Activity* (Orientirovochnyi refleks i oriyentirovochno-issledovatel'skaya deyatel'nost'). Izd. Akad. Ped. Nauk RSFSR, Moscow 1958.

IWATA, K. and R. S. SNIDER, *EEG Clin. Neurophysiol.* **11**, 3, 439 (1959).

JASPER, H., *Reticular Formation of the Brain*, p. 319, Boston 1958.

KARAMYAN, A. I., *Evolution of Cerebellar and Cerebral Functions* (Evolyutsiya funktsii mozzhechka i bol'shikh polusharii golovnogo mozga), Leningrad 1956.

KARAMYAN, A. I., Collection: *Evolution of Nervous System Function* (V sb. "Evolyutsiya funktsii nervnoi sistemy") Medgiz (1953).

*KARAMYAN, A. I., J. Higher Nervous Activity (*Zh. vyssh. nervn. deyat.*) **9**, 3 (1959).

Koshtoyants, Kh. S., *Some Problems of Comparative Physiology* (V. sb. "Nekotoryye voprosy sravnitel'noi fiziologii), Moscow 1934.

Koshtoyants, Kh. S., *Principles of Comparative Physiology. Comparative Physiology of the Nervous System* (Osnovy sravnitel'noi fiziologii. Sravnitel'naya fiziologiya nervnoi sistemy) (1957).

Kreps, Ye. M., The reaction of ascidians to stimulation. (*Arkh. biol. nauk*) 25, 4 (1925).

Krestovnikov, A. N., Medical Biological J. (*Med. biol. zh.*) 1, 17 (1928).

Krestovnikov, A. N. and V. V. Savich, Medical Biological J. (*Med. biol. zh.*) 1, 3 (1929).

Lam, R. L. and J. H. Ogura, *Laryngoscopa* 62, 486 (1952).

Luciani, L., *Das Kleinhirn*, Leipzig 1893.

Maiorov, F. P., I. N. Nemenov and L. S. Vasil'yev, *Proceedings of Scientific Meeting commemorating the centenary of Pavlov's birth* (Tez. dokl. nauchn. sessii, posvyashch. 100-letiyu so dnya rozhdeniya akad. I. P. Pavlova), p. 85, Moscow 1949.

Maiorov, F. P., B. V. Pavlov and N. Ya. Lipatova, Papers of the Institute of Physiology, U.S.S.R. Academy of Sciences (*Trudy In-ta fiziol. Akad. Nauk SSSR*) 5, 79 (1956).

Malyukina, G. A., J. Higher Nervous Activity (*Zh. vyssh. nervn. deyat.*) 5, 3 (1955).

Malyukova, I. V., J. Higher Nervous Activity (*Zh. vyssh. nervn. deyat.*) in press.

Moiseyev, Ye. A. and A. V. Tomkikh, Physiol. J. U.S.S.R. (*Fiziol. zh. SSSR*) 26, 394 (1939).

Orbeli, L. A., *Bull. of the Leningrad Science Institute* (Izv. Leningr. nauchnogo in-ta im. P. F. Lesgafta) 6 (1923).

Orbeli, L. A., *Lectures on Nervous System Physiology. Principal Methods and Objecttives of Comparative Physiology.* (Lektsii po fiziologii nervnoi sistemy. Osnovnyye metody i zadachi evolyutsionnoi fiziologii) (1938).

Orbeli, L. A., J. Higher Nervous Activity (*Zh. vyssh. nervn. deyat*) (1949).

Orbeli, L. A., *Evolution of Nervous System Functions* (Evolyutsiya funktsii nervnoi sistemy), p. 7, Medgiz (1958).

Palenov, A. L., Medical Supplement to Naval Collection of Papers No. 1–5 (1901).

Pavlov, B. V., Papers at a scientific meeting of Leningrad University (*Tez. dokl. nauchn. sessii LGU*) 25 (1955).

Pavlov, I. P., *Selected Works* (Izbr. proizv.) (1920).

Popov, N. F., Modern Neuropathology, Psychiatry and Mental Hygiene (*Sovrem. nevropatol. psikhiatr. i psikhogigiena*) 3, 11–12 (1934).

Rand, R. W., *J. Comp. Neurol.* 101, 167 (1957).

Saprokhin, M. I., *Effects of Stimulation of the Peripheral (cephalic) Section of a Cervical Sympathetic Nerve and of the Cerebellum* (Ob effektakh razdrazheniya perifericheskogo (golovnogo) otrezka sheinogo simpaticheskogo nerva i mozzhechka), Leningrad 1945.

Skipin, G. V., *Proceedings of 1st All-Union Congress of Physiologists, Biochemists and Pharmacologists* (Dokl. VII Vses. s"ezda fiziol., biokhim. i farmakol.). Medgiz (1947).

Schade, J. P. and I. J. Weiler, *J. Expl. Biol.* 36, 435 (1959).

Snider, R. S., *Arch. Neur. Psych.* 64, 196 (1950).

Snider, R. S. and E. Eldred, *Neurophysiol.* 27 (1952).

Sollertinskaya, T. N., Papers of the U.S.S.R. Academy of Sciences (*Dokl. Akad. Nauk SSSR*) 3, 6 (1956).

Sollertinskaya, T. N., Papers of the U.S.S.R. Academy of Sciences (*Dokl. Akad. Nauk SSSR*) 112, 1 (1957).

Sollertinskaya, T. N., *Problems of Electrophysiology and Electroencephalography* (Voprosy elektrofiziologii i elektroentsefalografii), Moscow and Leningrad 1960.

Strel'tsov, M. I., Archives of Biological Sciences (*Arkh. biol. nauk*) 31, 263 (1931).

Tonkikh, A. V., On evolutionary physiology (*K sravnitel'noi fiziologii*) 1, 317 (1956).

TONKIKH, A. V., On evolutionary physiology (*K sravnitel'noi fiziologii*) **1**, 317 (1956).

VAN TAI-AN', Physiol. J. U.S.S.R. (*Fiziol. zh. SSSR*) **46**, 8 (1960).

VAN TAI-AN' and M. G. BELEKHOVA, Physiol. J. U.S.S.R. (*Fiziol. zh. SSSR*) **47**, 1 (1961).

VERZHBINSKAYA, N. A. and YE. M. KREPS, *Ninth Congress of the All-Union Society of Physiologists, Biochemists and Pharmacologists*, 3, Moscow and Minsk 1959.

VESELKIN, N. P., Papers of the U.S.S.R. Academy of Sciences (*Dokl. Akad. Nauk SSSR*) **124**, 3, 723 (1959).

VESELKIN, N. P., Physiol. J. U.S.S.R. (*Fiziol. zh. SSSR*) in press.

VOLOKHOV, A. A., *Patterns in the Ontogenesis of Nervous Activity* (Zakonomernosti ontogeneza nervnoi deyatel'nosti), Moscow and Leningrad 1951.

VOLOKHOV, A. A., *Ninth Congress of the All-Union Society of Physiologists, Biochemists and Pharmacologists* (IX s"ezd Vses. ob-va fiziol., biokhim i farmakol), Moscow and Minsk 1959.

VORONIN, L. G., *Lectures on the Comparative Physiology of Higher Nervous Activity* (Lektsiyi po sravnitel'noi fiziologiyi vysshei nervnoi deyatel'nosti), Moscow, University Press 1957.

WHITESIDE, J. and R. S. SNIDER, *J. Neurophysiol.* **16**, 397 (1953).

WIDEN, L., *Acta Physiol. Scand.* **33**, 117 (1955).

WITHLOCK, D. G., *J. Comp. Neurol.* **97**, 567 (1952).

YAVORSKAYA, K. YA., *Problems in the Comparative Physiology of Nervous Activity*. Inst. exp. med., Akad. med. nauk S.S.S.R. 180 (1958).

YAVORSKAYA, K. YA., On the question of the influence of the cerebellum on conditioned reflexes in birds and mammals. Author's abstract, Leningrad (1959).

ZAGORUL'KO, T. M., *Problems of Comparative Physiology and Pathology of Higher Nervous Activity* (V sb. Voprosy sravnit. fiziol. i patol. vysshei nervnoi deyatel'nosti). Medgiz (1955).

ZAGORUL'KO, T. M., *Papers of the Institute of Experimental Medicine, U.S.S.R. Academy of Med. Sciences* (Trudy In-ta eksp. med. Akad. Med. Nauk SSSR), Leningrad 1959.

ZAGORUL'KO, T. M., Collection: *Problems of Electrophysiology and Electroencephalography* (Voprosy elektrofiziologii i elektroentsefalografii), Moscow and Leningrad 1960.

CHANGES IN THE K⁺ ION CONCENTRATION IN THE EXTRACELLULAR SPACE OF THE RAT CORTEX IN RELATION TO VARIOUS FORMS OF ELECTRICAL ACTIVITY

O. KH. KOSHTOYANTS

Institute of Physiology, Czechoslovakian Academy of Sciences, Prague,
and Institute of Biophysics, U.S.S.R. Academy of Sciences, Moscow

Translated by Dr. R. Crawford

EVIDENCE has recently been accumulating that the discharge of intracellular potassium into the extracellular space and increase in the potassium concentration in this space play an important part in relation to the functional state of cortical neurons and in the nature of their electrical activity. This conclusion is illustrated with particular clarity by the fact that increase in the potassium ion concentration in the extracellular space plays an important part in the production of spreading depression (Leão, 1944) and asphytic depolarization (Van Harreveld and Schade, 1959) of the cortex (Marshall, 1959; Brinley *et al.*, 1960; Křivánek and Bureš, 1960; Bureš and Křivánek, 1958).

On the other hand, it is unknown what shifts in potassium ions in the extracellular space are associated with other typical forms of electrical activity in the cortex, whether produced by pharmacological agents or by electrical stimulation. This investigation was an attempt to determine this.*

METHOD

Rats aged 2–3 months, narcotized with dial (40 mg/kg) or immobilized with D-tubocurarine (1·5 mg/kg) were used in the experiments. Changes in the extracellular potassium ion concentration were studied by washing the surface of the rat cortex through an epidural cannula (Bureš and Křivánek, 1958, 1960). The washing was with normal saline (0·9 per cent NaCl) or isotonic saccharose solution (0·25 M), to which cardiazol or strychnine was always added. The rate of washing was 130 ml/min and the area

---

* The author expresses his gratitude to Dr. J. Bureš and Dr. J. Křivánek for their valuable advice and help in the work and discussion of the results.

washed was 12·5 mm². The potassium and sodium concentrations in the sample were determined with a Zeiss flame photometer.

In the experiments for investigation of the discharge of potassium ions on direct stimulation of the cortex, a surface-negative response was produced by bipolar silver electrodes housed within the Plexiglas cannula used for washing. Stimulation was effected with rectangular impulses 0·05–0·2 msec in length, which were delivered to the electrodes through a radio frequency

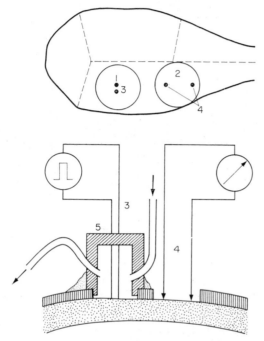

FIG. 1. Diagram of the position of the cannula for irrigation of the surface of the rat cortex.

1—trephine opening for cannula. 2—trephine opening for recording. 3—stimulating electrodes. 4—recording electrodes. 5—cannula.

output. The response was recorded in the neighbouring zone, alongside the cannula (distance 4–6 mm, Fig. 1) and was observed on the oscillograph screen; both primary responses to stimulation of the sciatic nerve and convulsive discharges produced by the local action of cardiazol were observed by this method. Electrical activity was recorded with an ink-writing electroencephalograph in occasional experiments.

Ion Shifts in a Focus of Convulsive Activity

Convulsive activity was produced in 18 rats by the addition of 10 per cent cardiazol to the saccharose irrigating solution (10 experiments) or the sodium chloride solution (8 experiments). The irrigated fluid was first passed through the cannula for three periods of 20 min, after which irrigation was carried out with the 10 per cent cardiazol solution for 20 min. Return of the electrical activity to normal was then studied for 1 hr. Table 1 gives the results of these experiments—the potassium and sodium ion concentrations in the last sample before, during, and in the first sample after irrigation with cardiazol. The concentrations of these ions in the irrigation fluid 1 hr after the cardiazol irrigation are also given. The corresponding electrical activities are shown in Fig. 2.

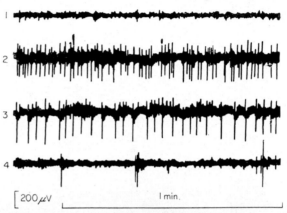

FIG. 2. Typical changes in the electrical activity of the rat cortex in the cardiazol experiments.

1—before cardiazol (normal). 2—during cardiazol irrigation. 3—immediately after cardiazol irrigation. 4—1 hr after cardiazol irrigation.

Table 1 shows clearly that, when the cortex was irrigated with cardiazol, the potassium ion concentration was increased three times and the sodium ion concentration 2·5 times. It is difficult to ascribe this considerable discharge of potassium solely to the nerve elements. The simultaneous increase in the discharge of sodium ions led us to assume that this reaction was connected to some extent with discharge of intracellular potassium ions, but mainly with change in the permeability of the blood–brain barrier.

Ion Shifts in the Projection Region of the Cortex on Peripheral Stimulation

As the experiment in which convulsive substances were applied locally did not give any clear indication as to the place of origin of the potassium ions, an attempt was made to increase cortical activity by means of afferent stimulation. In order to increase synchronized activity in the neurons of the projection region, it was at the same time irrigated with a strychnine solution of a strength (0·5 per cent) which gave only infrequent spontaneous discharges. After irrigation with strychnine for 20–40 min the sciatic nerve

TABLE 1. Changes in the concentrations of K⁺ and Na⁺ in the irrigating fluid on irrigation of the surface of the cortex in the area of the focus of convulsive activity (meq/l.)

Ion estimated	Irrigating fluid	Number of experiments	Normal (A)	Cardiazol irrigation (B)	First sample after cardiazol irrigation	Sample taken 1 hr after cardiazol irrigation	Statistical validity (A–B)
K⁺	NaCl	8	0·019 ± 0·002	0·057 ± 0·006	0·049 ± 0·006	0·028 ± 0·003*	p 0·01
K⁺	Saccharose	10	0·027 ± 0·002	0·089 ± 0·020	0·054 ± 0·005	0·031 ± 0·003*	p 0·01
Na⁺	Saccharose	8	0·301 ± 0·047	0·838 ± 0·074	0·759 ± 0·071	0·426 ± 0·070*	p 0·01

* Average of five experiments

TABLE 2. Changes in the potassium and sodium ion concentrations in the irrigating fluid on direct electrical stimulation with the production of a surface-negative response (meq/l.)

| | K ion contents in relation to stimulation frequencies of — | | | | | | | | Na ion content | |
| | 2 c/s 13 expts | | 4 c/s 22 expts | | 7 c/s 15 expts | | 15 c/s 8 expts | | 4 c/s 15 expts | |
	Norm	Stimulation	Norm	Stimulation	Norm	Stimulation	Norm	Stimulation	Norm	Stimulation
	0·016	0·016	0·014	0·016	0·014	0·016	0·013	0·013	0·300	0·296
Difference	—		0·002 ± 0·0009		0·002 ± 0·0008		—		0·004 ± 0·002	
Percentage difference	—		14		14		—		1	
Statistical reliability	—		p < 0·05		p < 0·05		—		—	

was stimulated for 20 min at frequency 2–3 c/s. The results of 9 experiments showed that irrigation of the cortical surface with 0·5 per cent strychnine solution alone increased the discharge of potassium ions into the irrigation fluid by about twice (0·050 ± 0·004). With such a high initial level, the slight increase in the potassium ion concentration (0·059 ± 0·014) at the time of the primary responses was not statistically valid.

The increase might also have been due to the fact that the stimulation frequency employed was small and that activation of the superficial layers of the cortex by the afferent impulses was insufficient.

Ion Shifts in the Area of Direct Cortical Stimulation

A series of experiments in which surface-negative responses with frequencies of 2, 4, 7 and 17 c/s were produced was carried out to determine whether discharge of potassium ions into the irrigated fluid could be recorded when the surface of the cortex was periodically excited by direct electrical stimulation. We sought to determine whether there was any relationship between the discharge of potassium ions into the irrigated fluid and the frequency of the surface-negative response.

Samples were taken every 5 min. After 2–4 control samples had been taken stimulation was delivered and then two or three more control samples were taken. The results of these experiments are shown in Table 2.

No discharge of potassium ions was observed with a frequency 2 c/s. When the frequency of the responses was increased (with frequencies of 4 and 7 c/s), an increase in the potassium ion concentration, which was statistically reliable, was noted in the irrigated fluid during the period of stimulation. With a frequency of 15 c/s the amplitude of stimulation (the maximum for single responses was selected) was insufficient to produce regular responses, so that no change in the potassium concentration was recorded in relation to this stimulation.

As no increased discharge of sodium was observed when effective frequencies were used, it can be assumed that the increase in the potassium ion concentration in the irrigation fluid was connected with discharge of potassium from the intracellular space.

DISCUSSION

The most definite results were obtained in the experiments in which the cortex was stimulated directly. The slight increase in the concentration of potassium in the extracellular space with a stimulation frequency of 7 c/s (in comparison with low frequencies—2 c/s) can be explained by the temporary accumulation of potassium ions in this space as a result of the predominance of potassium discharge over its reabsorption. It can be assumed that, with a stimulation frequency of 7 c/s, not all the potassium which was discharged into the extracellular space during a single excitation was "returned" to the cell, as a fresh stimulation again produced depolarization with fresh discharge of intracellular potassium. Consequently, the concentration gradient between cortex and irrigating fluid increased slightly.

The electrical manifestation of the accumulation of potassium ions in the extracellular space consisted of slow potentials which accompanied stimulation of the cortex and continued for some time after it had stopped (Rhoton et al., 1960). Intensified stimulation with considerable accumulation of potassium ions in the extracellular space can, of course, cause depression.

Essentially similar results can be expected in the case of convulsive activity, which is also accompanied by slow potentials and corresponding ion shifts. The discharge of intracellular potassium during convulsive activity was observed by Colfer and Essex (1947). But convulsants produce great changes in the permeability of the blood–brain barrier (Fregni and De Poli, 1954). With convulsive substances, the irrigation method does not, unfortunately, enable us to differentiate these two effects (discharge of potassium into the extracellular space from the cell and discharge of potassium and sodium from the vascular system), effects which can only be examined separately with radioactive potassium (^{42}K) (Bureš et al., 1960).

REFERENCES

BRINLEY, F. J., E. R. KANDEL and W. H. MARSHALL, J. Neurophysiol. 23, 246 (1960).
BUREŠ, J., O. BUREŠOVÁ and J. KŘIVÁNEK, In this collection, p. 58 (1961).
BUREŠ, J. and J. KŘIVÁNEK, Internat. Symp. über den Mechanismus der Erregung, Berlin 1958.
BUREŠ, J. and J. KŘIVÁNEK, Physiol. Bohemosl. 9, 488 (1960).
COLFER, H. F. and H. E. ESSEX, Am. J. Physiol. 150, 27 (1947).
FREGNI, R. and A. DE POLI, A.M.A. Arch. Otolaryngol. 60, 149 (1954).
KŘIVÁNEK, J. and J. BUREŠ, Physiol. Bohemosl. 9, 494 (1960).
LEÃO, A. A. P., J. Neurophysiol. 7, 359 (1944).
MARSHALL, W. H., Physiol. Rev. 39, 239 (1959).
RHOTON, A., S. GOLDRING and J. L. O'LEARY, Am. J. Physiol. 199, 677 (1960).
VAN HARREVELD, A. and J. P. SCHADE, J. Cell. Comp. Physiol. 54, 65 (1959).

FURTHER INVESTIGATIONS
ON AN INHIBITORY SUBSTANCE
EXTRACTED FROM BRAIN

K. LISSÁK, E. ENDRÖCZI and E. VINCZE

Physiological Institute, University of Pécs, Hungary

Translated by Dr. R. Crawford

REPORTS published in the last few years and investigations carried out by the authors of this paper have shown that brain tissue contains a substance which may possibly be responsible for processes of inhibition in the central nervous system. The authors established in earlier investigations that this substance could suppress the sensitivity of receptors in peripheral muscles to acetylcholine, the transmission of excitation in nerve ganglia and, when applied locally, could reduce the excitability of the spinal cord and cerebral cortex (Lissák and Endröczi, 1949, 1955, 1956a, b, c, 1957).

Hayashi and Nagai (1956) and Bazemore *et al.* (1956) have stated that extract of brain tissue contains a considerable quantity of γ-aminobutyric acid (GABA). On the evidence afforded by certain biological reactions, they assume that the naturally occurring inhibitory substance and GABA are identical. Later, McLennan (1957, 1959) concluded from the results of paper chromatography investigations that GABA was only responsible for part of the inhibitory effect of brain tissue extract. At about the same time Hayashi (1959) directed attention to γ-amino-β-oxybutyric acid (GABOBA), which was quantitatively more effective than GABA.

The present paper is a short report of investigations of the properties and distribution in brain tissue of inhibitory substance and the above-mentioned derivatives of γ-aminobutyric acid in the normal state and in relation to different functional states of the brain.

Extracts of dog, rat and mouse brain were used in the investigations. In some experiments the animals were frozen in liquid air and the brain then extracted while in the others the brain was extracted immediately after the animal had been killed. It should be emphasized that no particular differences were observed in the properties of extracts obtained by these respective methods. The method described in the author's earlier detailed communications was also used to determine the effect of naturally occurring

172

inhibitory substance and those of GABA and GABOBA. The essential features of the method are the removal of protein from brain tissue by means of aluminium hydroxide or three volumes of alcohol, and subsequent purification by repeated precipitation with alcohol, and adsorption on activated charcoal. Further purification was attained by paper chromatography.

This investigation was carried out with two different systems of solvents: (1) ascending chromatography in a mixture of butyl alcohol, acetic acid and water (4:1:1); (2) descending chromatography in a mixture of phenol and water (80:20). In both cases GABA and GABOBA were chromatographed simultaneously in quantities of 10, 20, 30 and 50 μg. Thereafter the paper strips were dried and the corresponding segments were cut out and extracted with Tyrode solution for subsequent biological examination; alternatively, they were treated with ninhydrin.

The ninhydrin reaction affords a method for the quantitative estimation of GABA and GABOBA. These substances were eluted with a mixture of ethyl alcohol and 0·1 M NaOH (4:1). The error in the estimation of unknown quantities by this method should not exceed 5 per cent.

The results obtained can be summarized in the following manner:

(1) The experiments with extract of dog brain tissue established that the local action of approximately a third of the volume of this extract on the exposed motor region of the cat cortex led to reduced cortical excitability.

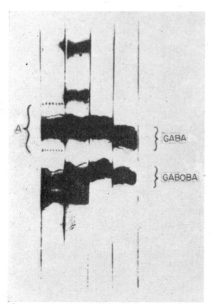

Fig. 1. Paper chromatographic analysis of GABA (R_F: 0·43), GABOBA (R_F: 0·31) and natural inhibitory factor obtained from an extract of dog brain.

A—zone giving a positive picrate reaction.

7*

It is, however, impossible to regard this effect as being produced by the concentration of GABA present in the extract, as determined by paper chromatography. It was noted that the local application of GABA in a concentration 5 or 6 times greater did not produce this effect.

(2) Unlike brain extract, which the former experiments of the authors had shown to suppress acetylcholine-induced contractions, GABA and GABOBA in quantities of up to 100 $\mu g/cm^3$ did not produce this effect on the isolated ileum of the cat.

(3) Examination by the method of paper chromatography (Fig. 1) established that the positions of the natural inhibitory substance and GABA were almost identical in respect of the value of R_F. The eluate prepared with Tyrode solution from the segment of the chromatogram corresponding to GABA (length 3–4 cm) had effective inhibitory actions on both the intestine and the cerebral cortex of the cat, effects not shown by eluate from the other segments of the chromatogram. This indicates that GABA and inhibitory factor may have some common structural element.

(4) The distribution of GABA in different parts of the central nervous system was also investigated. As other investigators have shown, the greatest concentration of GABA was found in the tissues of the grey substance. The following concentrations of GABA were found in an examination of the dog brain (Fig. 2).

(5) The observations on rats and mice established that the content of GABA was usually increased by about 30 per cent in strychnine convulsions

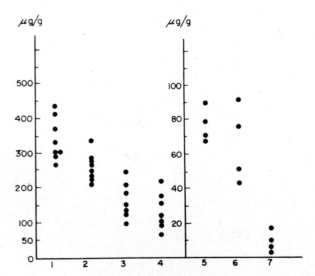

FIG. 2. Distribution of GABA ($\mu g/g$ tissue) in different regions of the nervous system in the dog.

1—cortex. 2—brain stem. 3—hypothalamus. 4—palaeocortex. 5—spinal cord. 6—sympathetic nervous system. 7—motor and sensory nerves.

(30 μg/100 g). In some cases of metrazol (10 mg/100 g) convulsions the GABA content was unchanged. The GABA content was reduced in brain tissue during dial narcosis (for 1 hr). In later experiments a marked reduction of the GABA content was seen to be produced by semicarbazide (80 mg/kg), which would appear to suppress GABA synthesis (Fig. 3).

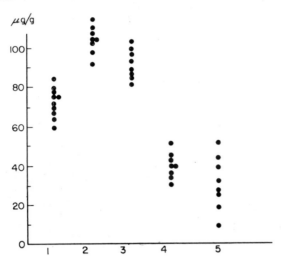

FIG. 3. GABA concentration in the tissue of the rat brain after the injection of strychnine (2), optikor (3), dial (4) and semicarbazide (5). 1—control.

(6) Although GABA is not regarded as identical with natural inhibitory substance, study of its quantitative distribution is of interest as the quantities contained in different parts of the brain are subject to changes similar to the changes in the content of inhibitory substance during convulsions and in narcosis. These observations suggest that strychnine and metrazol probably abolish the effect of inhibitory factor on the synaptic membrane and that semicarbazide produces convulsions by suppressing synthesis of the inhibitory substance and thus reducing its content (Fig. 3).

To sum up, it may be stated that inhibitory substance is similar to GABA in its quantitative distribution in brain tissue and in its behaviour in paper chromatography. The effect of inhibitory substance may, however, be more powerful and qualitatively different. It may be considered that natural inhibitory substance is formed as a result of similar metabolism and is relatively close to GABA in structure.

REFERENCES

BAZEMORE, A., K. A. C. ELLIOTT and E. FLOREY, Nature, **178**, 1052 (1956).
HAYASHI, T., J. Physiol. **145**, 570 (1959).
HAYASHI, T. and K. NAGAI, XX Congress International de Physiologie, Bruxelles 1956.

LISSÁK, K. and E. ENDRÖCZI, *Kiserletes Orvostudomany* 1, 205 (1949).
LISSÁK, K. and E. ENDRÖCZI, *Naturwissenschaften* 42, 630 (1955).
LISSÁK, K. and E. ENDRÖCZI, *Acta Physiol. Hung.* 9, 111 (1956a).
LISSÁK, K. and E. ENDRÖCZI, XX Congrès International de Physiologie, Bruxelles 1956.
LISSÁK, K. and E. ENDRÖCZI, *Phisiologia Bohemoslovenica* 5, 129 (1956c).
LISSÁK, K. and E. ENDRÖCZI, *Acta Physiol. Hung.* 11, 377 (1957).
MCLENNAN, H., *J. Physiol.* 139, 179 (1957).
MCLENNAN, H., *J. Physiol.* 146, 358 (1959).

EVOLUTIONARY CONCEPTS OF BRAIN FUNCTION FOLLOWING DARWIN AND SPENCER

H. W. MAGOUN

School of Medicine, University of California, Los Angeles, California

IT IS a privilege indeed to be able to contribute to a volume honoring the sixtieth birthday of Professor Kh. S. Koshtoyants. As Director of the Laboratory of Comparative Physiology at the University of Moscow, his accomplishments in the study of the evolutionary development of physiological processes extend to an appreciation of the history of science generally and to an interest in the broad relations of science with society. All of these interests of Professor Koshtoyants are represented strongly in the program of research and training which he so ably directs. Anyone visiting his laboratory is impressed both by the number of talented and enthusiastic young associates and by the variety and excellence of the work in progress.

Because the centennial of the publication of Charles Darwin's classic work[3], *Origin of Species by Natural Selection, or The Preservation of Favoured Races in the Struggle for Life* (1859), has just been celebrated, it may be of interest as a contribution in Professor Koshtoyants' honor to explore the development of evolutionary concepts concerning the brain in the century following 1859. Briefly, it may be pointed out that the *Scala naturae*, in which living beings were arranged in a spectrum of increasing complexity, was familiar both to early naturalists and to the biologists of the eighteenth century, by whom its order was generally conceived as the immutable product of divine creation. A hundred years ago, Darwin's revolutionary conception proposed instead that natural selection working on the range of normal variations led to survival of the fittest and so accounted, in a materialistic way, both for evolution and for the adaptation of existing forms to their environments.

Darwin's later writings[4,5] on *The Descent of Man* (1871) and *The Expression of Emotion in Man and Animals* (1872), called more particular attention to the phylogenetic development of the brain. In keeping with these contributions, and related to the interest in evolution created by them, views were subsequently developed by Hughlings Jackson in clinical neurology, by Pavlov in neurophysiology and by Freud in psychiatry, each of

177

whom accounted for the phylogenetic elaboration of the central nervous system in terms of a series of superimposed levels, added successively as the evolutionary scale was ascended (Fig. 1).

In each of these conceptual systems, the management of primitive, innate, stereotyped behavior, having to do with the preservation of the

Synthesis	Psycho-analytic psychiatry S. Freud	Comparative neuro-anatomy Edinger, Kappers, Herrick	Russian neurology Pavlov	English neurology Jackson
Abstraction Analysis Symbolization Generalization	Superego		Second signal system	Upper level
Evoked adaptive behaviour	Ego		Conditioned reflex	Middle level
Inborn stereotypic response	Id	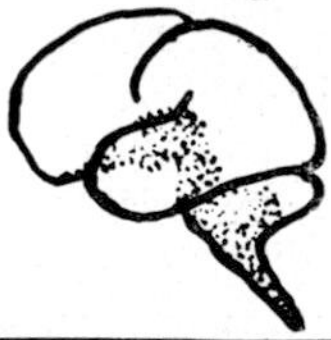	Uncondit-ioned reflex	Lower level

FIG. 1. Chart comparing the evolutionary concepts of the organization and function of the brain which developed after Darwin and Spencer.

individual and the race, was attributed to older, subcortical, neuraxial portions of the central nervous system, which formed Jackson's lowest level and subserved the Pavlovian unconditioned reflexes and the Freudian id.

Next, the more mutable, adaptive, learned behavior of Pavlov's conditional reflexes, together with the capacity of the Freudian ego for perception and the initiation of movements were ascribed to higher neural structures, including the sensori-motor cortex of Jackson's middle level, which developed above or upon the older subjacent parts.

Finally, in the brain of man, hypertrophy of the associational cortices of the frontal and parieto-occipital-temporal lobes, forming Jackson's highest level, was correlated with the capacities of Freud's superego and, in the dominant hemisphere, with the capabilities of Pavlov's second signal system for symbolization and communication by means of spoken and written language.

Further testimony for the evolution of neurological function in these terms was provided by Jackson's view of dissolution, or regression by reversal of the phylogenetic process, when clinical impairment proceeded from highest through middle to lowest levels during neurological disease in man[13]. Jackson specified that the resulting deficit was usually accompanied by some release of lower activity, normally subjugated to higher control. This latter feature was elaborated also in the Freudian system, in which conflicting interests of the different levels were emphasized as a potential source of psychic disturbance.

In much the same way that increased complexity and specialization appeared as the ladder of nature was ascended by the earlier classificationists, more and more elaborate functions came to view as one climbed cephalically up the successive levels of the central nervous system. In its progressive encephalization, the brain came to resemble the earth itself, not simply in its globular form, but in consisting as well of a series of strata laid down like those of geology, one upon the other, in evolutionary time. Each neural accretion was associated with a characteristic increment of function and, following Jackson, a dissolutionary school of neurophysiology developed, in which encephalization was reversed by operative transection, and evolution traced backward by observing residual capacities diminish in the increasingly truncated decorticate, decerebrate and spinal preparations. Probably because such views are still so contemporary, little attention has been given to exploring the role of Darwin, and the interest in evolution excited by his work, in establishing these concepts of neural organization and function.

Hughlings Jackson

The views of Hughlings Jackson[13], which might be presumed to be the most directly Darwinian, were, on the contrary, derived chiefly from Thomas Laycock, with whom Jackson began his career in York, and from Herbert Spencer, whom he admired greatly. In 1851, Herbert Spencer, from whom Darwin later borrowed the term "survival of the fittest" formulated the basic principles that were to be elaborated in his later work. Spencer had been asked to write a notice of a new edition of Carpenter's *Principles of Physiology* and "in the course," he noted [21], "of such perusal as was needed to give an account of its contents," came across the theory of von Baer—that the development of all plants and animals was from homogeneity to heterogeneity. This concept of progressive differentiation, added to that of Lamarckian adaptation, became his distinctive evolutionary view. Having just turned forty, Spencer devoted the remainder of his career to the systematic application of this concept to the whole field of knowledge. Flagging a dilatatory cerebral circulation, with which he was hypochondriacally preoccupied, he embarked on the exposition of a *System of Synthetic Philosophy*, the successive parts of which appeared at intervals through the balance of the nineteenth century.

In the first edition of this *Principles of Psychology*, published in 1855, and thus four years before the *Origin of Species*, Spencer[20] pointed out that his arguments "imply a tacit adhesion to the development hypothesis, that Life in its multitudinous and infinitely varied embodiments has risen out of the lowest and simplest beginnings, by steps as gradual as those

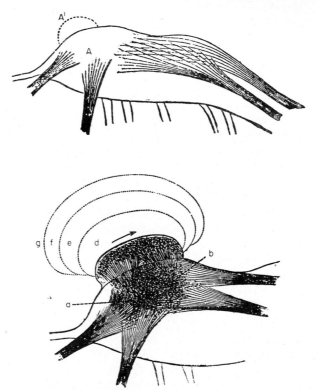

Fig. 2. Diagrams of a ganglion, prepared by Spencer[20], showing the development of superimposed levels of neural coordination.

which evolve a homogeneous, microscopic germ into a complex organism, by progressive unbroken evolution, and through the instrumentality of what we call natural causes. Save for those who still adhere to the Hebrew myth or to the doctrine of special creation derived from it, there is no alternative but this hypothesis or no hypothesis."

Applying this "development hypothesis" to psychology, Spencer reasoned: "If the doctrine of Evolution is true, the inevitable implication is that Mind can be understood only by observing how Mind is evolved. If creatures of the most elevated kinds have reached those highly integrated, very definite and extremely heterogeneous organizations they possess, through modification upon modification accumulated during an immeasurable past, if the developed nervous systems of such creatures have gained their complex structure and functions little by little: then, necessarily, the involved forms of consciousness, which are the correlates of these complex structures and functions, must also have arisen by degrees."

As to the problem "of how such higher coordinations are evolved out of lower ones and how the structure of the nervous system becomes progressively complicated," Spencer proposed the interpolation of new plexuses of fibers and cells between those originally existing. In diagrammatic sketches, apparently of an invertebrate ganglion, Spencer distinguished (Fig. 2, above) "a nervous center to which afferent fibers bring all order of peripheral feelings, and from which efferent fibers carry to muscle the stimuli producing their appropriately combined contractions." If a part of the coordinating plexus (A) "takes on a relatively greater development in answer to new adjustments which environing conditions furnish, we may expect one part of this region (A) to become protruberant, as at A^1." Because space within the plexus was already pre-empted, "the interpolated plexus, which effects indirect coordination, must be superimposed (Fig. 2, A^1, above; d, below), and the coordinating discharges must take roundabout courses as shown by the arrow. Little by little, there is an enlargement of the superior coordinating center by the interpolation of new coordinating plexuses at its periphery (Fig. 2, e, f, g, below)."

Ivan P. Pavlov

Though Pavlov's work in the physiology of the central nervous system did not commence until his fifties, its conceptualization was influenced strongly by the ideas of Darwin and of Spencer, encountered in his youth through the writings of Pisarev and Sechenov. In his *Autobiography*, Pavlov[16] wrote: "I was born in the town of Ryazan in 1849 and received my secondary education at the local theological seminary. Influenced by the literature of the sixties, and particularly by Pisarev, our intellectual interests turned to natural science and many, myself included, decided to take the subject at the university." There seems little doubt that Pavlov first became captivated by Darwin and the theory of evolution from reading Pisarev's lengthy, systematic, popular exposition of the *Origin of Species* entitled, *Progress in the Animal and Vegetable Worlds*[17]. The ecstatic attitude toward Darwin, which Pavlov preserved to the end of his days, can easily be identified with Pisarev's lofty expression.

"For us ordinary and unenlightened people," Pisarev wrote, Darwin's discoveries are precious and important just because they are so fascinating in their simplicity, so easy to understand; they not only enrich us with new knowledge, they give fresh life to all the system of our ideas and widen our mental horizon in all dimensions. In nearly all branches of natural science, Darwin's ideas bring about a complete revolution. Even experimental psychology finds in his discoveries the guiding principle that will link up the numerous observations already made and put investigators on the way to new fruitful discoveries.

A second early influence upon Pavlov was provided by the writings of Sechenov[19]. Later in his career, Pavlov referred[16] to beginning the study of higher nervous activity with the objective techniques of conditional reflex physiology. "The most important motive for my decision, even though an unconscious one, arose out of the impression made upon me during my youth by the monograph of I. M. Sechenov, the Father of Russian physiology, entitled *Reflexes of the Brain* and published in 1863. The influence of thoughts which are strong by virtue of their novelty and truth, especially when they act during youth, remains deep and permanent, even though concealed. In this book, a brilliant attempt was made, altogether extraordinary for that time, to represent our subjective world from the standpoint of neurophysiology."

Though not appearing in time to influence *Reflexes of the Brain* (1863), both Darwin's and Spencer's works were early translated into Russian, the *Origin of Species* in 1864 by Professor S. A. Rachinskii, of whose efforts Pisarev was highly critical, and a year later by K. A. Timiryazev, the leading Darwinist in Russia (Platonov[18]). Spencer[21] learned of a Russian translation of his *First Principles* in 1866, and a decade later heard from the University of Kiev that all of his works had then been translated into Russian, excepting his *Sociology*, which was soon to be added to the list.

In his *Elements of Thought* (1883), Sechenov[19] wrote: "Darwin's great theory of the evolution of species has placed the idea of evolution on such a firm basis that it is at present accepted by the vast majority of naturalists. This logically necessitates the recognition of the principle of evolution of psychical activities. Spencer's hypothesis may actually be called the application of Darwinism to the sphere of psychical phenomena."

And later: "Another and no less important success in the study of the mental development of man in general we owe to the famous English scientist, Herbert Spencer. It is only on the ground of Spencer's hypothesis, concerning the sequence of stages of neuropsychical development from age to age, that we can solve the ancient philosophical problem of the development of mature thought from initial infantile forms. To Spencer we owe the establishment, on the basis of very wide analogies, of the general type of mental development in man, as well as the proofs of the fact that the type of evolution of mental processes remains unchanged through all stages of the development of thought. The present essay is based on the theories of Spencer; therefore, our first task will be to expound the main principles of his theory. It even appeared at the same time as Darwin's theory and is practically a part of the general theory of organic evolution."

In a report on objective study of higher nervous activity in 1913. Pavlov[16] began: "With full justice, Charles Darwin must be counted as the founder and instigator of the contemporary comparative study of the higher vital phenomena of animals; for, as is known to every educated person, through his highly original support of the idea of evolution, he fertilized the whole mentality of mankind, especially in the field of biology. The hypothesis of the origin of man from animals gave a great impetus to the study of the higher phenomena of animal life. The answer to the question as to

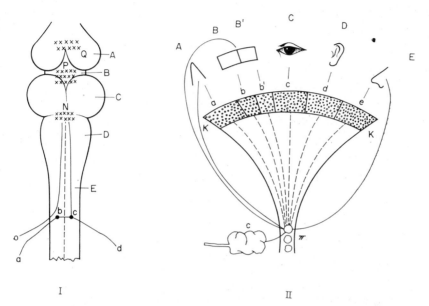

FIG. 3. Diagram of the central nervous system of the frog (*left*), from Sechenov[19]. Stimulation of the sites marked by crosses inhibited spinal reflexes, illustrating the hierarchy of neural levels and the domination of higher over lower.
In a diagram of the mechanism of the Pavlovian conditional reflex (right), the animal makes adaptive adjustments to its environment by means of new cortical links between the analyzers and connections from them to subcortical, unconditioned reflex arcs. From Brazier[2].

how this study should be carried out and the study itself have become the task of the period following Darwin."

Sigmund Freud

Passing now to Freud, his autobiography (reprinted in ref. 14) refers to the influences leading him to medicine: "At the time the theories of Darwin, which were then of topical interest, strongly attracted me, for they held out hopes of an extraordinary advance in our understanding of the world; and it was hearing Goethe's beautiful essay on *Nature* read aloud at a popular lecture, just before I left school, that decided me to become a medical student." Instances of a recurring effort to interpret neural organization and function in evolutionary terms can be noted in Freud's works.

In a letter written in 1896[12], Freud referred to his "latest bit of speculation, the assumption that our psychical mechanism has come about by a process of stratification." A quarter of a century later, he made two attempts to diagram these ideas, with interesting differences in the form of the figures. The first (Fig. 4, left), prepared in 1923, resembled an inverted brain, although reference was made to it as an ovum. The second (Fig. 4, right), prepared a decade later, was on the other hand really egg-shaped. In his lectures on the anatomy of the mental personality, Freud[19, 12] elaborated upon the contents of these figures: "Superego, ego and id are the three realms, regions or provinces into which we divide the mental apparatus of the individual, and it is their mutual relations with which we shall be concerned.

"The *id* is the obscure, inaccessible part of our personality. We can come nearer to the id with images, and call it a chaos, a cauldron of seething excitement. We suppose that it is somewhere in direct contact with somatic

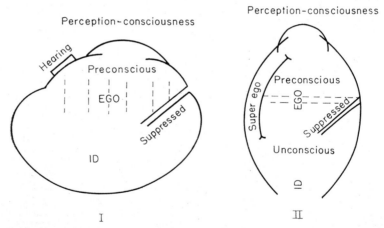

FIG. 4. Two diagrams by Freud[11, 12], presenting the mental apparatus as though spatially stratified.

processes and takes over from them instinctual needs. These instincts fill it with energy, but it has no organization and no unified will, only an impulsion to obtain satisfaction for the instinctual needs in accordance with the pleasure principle."

"The *ego* is directed onto the external world; it mediates perceptions of it and in it are generated, while it is functioning, the phenomena of consciousness. The ego also controls the path of access to motility, but it interpolates between desire and action the procrastinating factor of thought, during which it makes use of the residues of experience stored up in memory.

In this way, it dethrones the pleasure principle, which exerts undisputed sway over the processes in the id, and substitutes for it the reality principle, which promises greater security and success. What, however, especially marks the ego out in contradistinction to the id is a tendency to synthesize its contents, to bring together and unify its mental processes, which is absent entirely from the id. In popular language, we may say that the ego stands for reason and circumspection, while the id stands for the untamed passions."

"The role which the *superego* undertakes later in life is at first played by an external power, by parental authority. It can be traced back to the influence of parents, teachers and so on, and is based upon an overwhelmingly important biological fact, namely, the lengthy dependence of the human child on his parents. We have allocated to the superego the activities of self-observation, conscience and the holding up of ideals. It is the representative of all moral restrictions, the advocate of the impulse toward perfection. In short, it is as much as we have been able to apprehend psychologically of what people call the 'higher things in human life.' It becomes the vehicle of tradition and of all the age-long values which have been handed down from generation to generation. The ideologies of the superego perpetuate the past, the traditions of the race and the people, which yield but slowly to the influence of the present and to new developments."

Marx, Engels and Darwin

During their long residence in England, Marx and Engels were contemporaries of Darwin and took considerable interest in his work. It may be appropriate in conclusion to pass from a discussion of Darwin's influence upon concepts of brain function to a consideration of Marx and Engels' discussion of the relation of Darwin's views to their own ideology. It will be noted that in Engels' case this extended also to a deep interest in the evolution of the function of the brain.

In a period of great personal tribulation, from the illness of his wife, Karl Marx read Darwin's *Origin of Species* and, just a century ago, wrote to Engels[15]: "During my time of trial, these last four weeks, I have read all sorts of things. Among others Darwin's book on Natural Selection. Although it is developed in the crude English style, this is the book which contains the basis in natural history for our view."

It is clear that Engels too became familiar with the *Origin of Species*, for he presented an exposition of its central theme in his *Anti-Dühring* (1878), as follows[6]: "Darwin brought back from his scientific travels the view that plant and animal species are not constant but subject to variation. In order to follow up these ideas after his return home, there was no better field available than that of the breeding of animals and plants. Darwin found that this breeding has produced artificially, among animals and plants of the same species, differences greater than those found in what are generally recognized as different species. Thus was established, on the one hand, the variability of species and, on the other, the possibility of a common ancestry for organisms with different specific characteristics.

"Darwin then investigated whether there were not possibly causes to be found in nature which—without conscious purpose on the part of the breeder—would nevertheless in the long run produce in living organisms changes similar to those produced by artificial breeding. He discovered these causes in the disproportions between the immense number of germs created by nature and the insignificant number of organisms which actually attained maturity. But as each germ strives to develop, there necessarily arises a struggle for existence which manifests itself not merely as direct bodily combat or devouring, but also as a struggle for space and light, even in the case of plants. And it is evident that in this struggle those individual organisms which have some particular characteristic, however insignificant, which gives them an advantage in the struggle for existence will have the best prospect of reaching maturity and propagating themselves, while organisms which do not possess these characteristics succumb more easily in the struggle for existence and gradually disappear. In this way a species is altered through natural selection, through survival of the fittest."

Although recognizing the importance of Darwin's general conceptions, both Marx and Engels objected to emphasis upon the struggle for existence as the sole factor leading to natural selection. In particular, they opposed Darwin's proposal that this was simply "the doctrine of Malthus, applied to the whole animal and vegetable kingdom." Marx wrote Engels in 1862[15]: "As regards Darwin, whom, I have looked at again, it amuses me that he says he applies the 'Malthusian' theory also to plants and animals, as if Malthus' whole point did not consist in the fact that his theory is applied not to plants and animals but only to human beings. It is remarkable that Darwin recognizes among brutes and plants, his English society with its divisions of labor, competition, opening up of new markets, inventions, and Malthusian struggle for existence. It is Hobbe's *bellum omnium contra omnes* (the war of every man against every man)."

In his *Dialectics of Nature* (1872–78), Engels elaborated these objections and particularly condemned the application of Darwinism to the support of current *laissez-faire* economic policies[7]: "Darwin did not know what a bitter satire he wrote on mankind, and especially upon his countrymen, when he showed that free competition, the struggle for existence, which economists celebrate as the highest historical achievement, is the normal state of the *animal* kingdom . . ."

"Darwin's mistake lies precisely in lumping together, in 'natural selection' or 'the survival of the fittest,' two absolutely separate things:

(1) Selection by pressure of overpopulation, where perhaps the strongest survive (and)

(2) Selection by greater capacity of adaptation to altered circumstances, to which the survivors are better suited."

In a letter to Lazarow, in 1875, Engels added[15]: "I cannot agree that the war of every man against every man was the first phase of human development. In my opinion, the social instinct was one of the most essential levers in the development of man from the ape." Engels went on to elaborate this latter concept in an essay entitled "The Part Played by Labor in the Transition from Ape to Man," included in his *Dialectics of Nature* (7).

Anticipating many concepts of current anthropology, Engels proposed adaption of an erect posture as the decisive initial step in man's evolution. Freeing the hand from locomotory function, it enabled man to develop manipulative skill. Succeeding manual labor, undertaken gregariously, led man to communicate verbally with this fellows. This, in turn, was responsible for the development of speech and language.

Engels emphasized the correlations between "the adaptation of the feet for erect gait, the gradual perfecting of the human hand and the origin of language from and in the process of labor." The precise sequence of these serial events was not invariably made clear, however: "First comes labor," he wrote, "after it, and then side by side with it, articulate speech. These were the two most essential stimuli under the influence of which the brain of the ape gradually changed into that of man."

"The labor process," he continued, "begins with the making of tools, the most ancient of which were hunting and fishing implements, the former at the same time serving as weapons. These presuppose the transition from an exclusively vegetable diet to the concomitant use of meat. This, in turn, led to two new advances of decisive importance: to the mastery of fire and the training of animals. By the cooperation of hands, organs of speech, and brain, agriculture was added to hunting and cattle breeding, then spinning, weaving, metal working, pottery and navigation. Along with trade and industry, there appeared finally art and science."

"The animal merely *uses* external nature; man by his changes makes it serve his ends, *masters* it. This is the final, essential distinction between man and other animals, and once again it is labor that brings it about. Let us not, however, flatter ourselves overmuch on account of our human conquest over nature. All of our mastery of it consists in the fact that we have the advantage over all other beings of being able to know and correctly apply its laws. In particular, after the mighty advances of natural science in this century, we are more and more getting to know, and hence to control even the more remote natural consequences of our more ordinary productive activities."

With the passage of time, both Marx and Engels came to regard Darwin's contributions as outweighing their objections to special aspects of his views. In 1873, when a new edition of his *Capital* appeared Marx presented Darwin with a copy. Although the work apparently remained unread, the gift was politely acknowledged as follows (Aveling, 1897):

"Dear Sir,—I thank you for the honour which you have done me by sending me your great work on *Capital*; and I heartily wish that I were more worthy to receive it, by understanding more of the deep and important subject of political economy. Though our studies have been so different, I believe that we both earnestly desire the extension of knowledge; and this, in the long run, is sure to add to the happiness of mankind. I remain, dear sir, yours faithfully, Charles Darwin."

In his *Ludwig Feuerbach* (1886), Engels[8] rated as one of "the three great discoveries, by which the main processes of nature are explained and traced back to natural causes, the proof which Darwin just developed in connected form that the stock of organic products of nature surrounding us today, including mankind, is the result of a long process of evolution from a few unicellular germs; and that these have arisen from protoplasm or albumen which came into existence by chemical means."

"Thereby not only has an explanation been made possible for the existing stock of the organic products of nature, but the basis has been given for the pre-history of the human mind, for following all its various stages of evolution from the protoplasm, simple and structureless yet responsive to stimuli, of the lower organisms right up to the thinking human brain. Without this pre-history, the existence of the thinking human brain remains a miracle.

Finally and climactically, in the year following Darwin's death and burial in London, in 1882, Engels chose to select Darwin's discovery to compare with that of Marx himself. At Marx's funeral, also in London, but a year later, in 1883, Engels eulogized[9]: "Just as Darwin discovered the law of evolution in organic nature, so Marx discovered the law of evolution in human history."

REFERENCES

1. AVELING, E., Charles Darwin and Karl Marx: a comparison. *New Century Review* **1**, 232–243, 321–327 (1897).
2. BRAZIER, M. A. B. (Ed.), *CNS and Behavior*. Macy Foundation, New York 1958.
3. DARWIN, C., *On the Origin of Species by means of Natural Selection, or the Preservation of Favoured Races in the Struggle for Life*, London 1859.
4. DARWIN, C., *The Descent of Man, and Selection in Relation to Sex*, London 1871.
5. DARWIN, C., *The Expression of the Emotions in Man and Animals*, London 1872.
6. ENGELS, F., *Herr Eugen Dühring's Revolution in Science (Anti-Dühring)*. C. H. Kerr and Company, Chicago 1935.
7. ENGELS, F., *Dialectics of Nature*. C. Dutt (Trans. and ed.). Lawrence and Wishart, London 1940.
8. ENGELS, F., *Ludwig Feuerbach and the Outcome of Classical German Philosophy*. C. Dutt (ed.). International Publishers, New York 1941.
9. ENGELS, F., (In) *Reminiscences of Marx and Engels*. Foreign Language Publishing House, Moscow, no date.
10. FREUD, S., *New Introductory Lectures on Psycho-analysis*. Tr. W. J. H. Sprott. Norton, New York 1933.
11. FREUD, S., *The Ego and the Id*. Tr. J. Riviere. Hogarth Press, London 1950.

12. FREUD, S. *The Origins of Psycho-analysis*. Basic Books, New York 1954.
13. JACKSON, J. H., *Selected Writings of John Hughlings Jackson*. Two volumes. Basic Books, New York 1958.
14. JONES, E., *The Life and Work of Sigmund Freud*. Three volumes. Basic Books, New York 1953–1957.
15. MARX, K. and F. ENGELS, *Selected Correspondence*, 1845–1895. (with explanatory notes). D. Torr (Transl.). International Publishers, New York 1942.
16. PAVLOV, I. P., *Selected Works*. K. S. Koshtoyants (Ed.). Foreign Languages Publishing House, Moscow 1955.
17. PISAREV, D., *Selected Philosophical Social and Political Essays*. R. Dixen (Trans.). Foreign Languages Publishing House, Moscow 1958.
18. PLATONOV, G., *Kliment Arkadyevich Timiryazev*. Foreign Language Publishing House, Moscow 1955.
19. SECHENOV, I., *Selected Works*. Ed. A. A. Subkov, Moscow–Leningrad, 1935.
20. SPENCER, H., *The Principles of Psychology*. Two volumes. Fourth edition, London 1899.
21. SPENCER, H., *An Autobiography*. Two volumes. London 1904.

THE PHYSIOLOGICAL ROLE
OF CHEMICAL TRANSMITTERS
IN ONTOGENESIS

An Examination of the Enzymochemical Basis of Motor Activity
in Mollusc Embryos

B. N. MANUKHIN and G. A. BUZNIKOV

Laboratory of General and Comparative Physiology, Institute of Animal
Morphology, U.S.S.R. Academy of Sciences, Moscow

Translated by Dr. R. Crawford

A CONSIDERABLE number of papers in contemporary literature deal with chemical transmitters and the enzymes concerned in their synthesis and breakdown in the embryos of various animals. These substances were generally examined in relation to the establishment of various definitive mechanisms. For example, a close connexion has been established between development of the central nervous system in vertebrate embryos and cholinesterase activity in nerve tissue (Nachmansohn, 1938; Kakushkina and Arkhipova, 1941; Kakushkina, 1946; Boell and Shen, 1944, 1949, 1950; Boell *et al.*, 1955; Metzler and Humm, 1951; Elkes and Todrick, 1955; Bonichon, 1957; and others). The influence of transmitter substances (primarily acetylcholine and adrenaline) on the work of the heart in various stages of the development of extrinsic cardiac innervation has been investigated in considerable detail (Crozier, 1927; Armstrong, 1935; Cullis and Lucas, 1936; Shidlovskii, 1946; Koshtoyants, 1950; Barry, 1950; Hall, 1957; Jones, 1958; and others). Study of the direct participation of transmitter substances or their functional precursors in processes of morphogenesis is of special interest. Koshtoyants (1938) drew attention to this promising line of investigation, but as yet, there is still very little information on this subject. We know that acetylcholine esterase inhibitors in concentrations sufficient for complete suppression of embryo movement do not produce any appreciable disturbances of embryogenesis in ascidians or amphibians (Sawyer, 1943, 1955; Durante, 1958). On the other hand, anticholinesterases lead to characteristic disturbances of the development of chick embryos (Bucker and Platner, 1956).

According to Buller *et al.* (1959), the differentiation of mammalian muscles apparently proceeds under the control of substances secreted in the endings of motor nerves.

Investigations on echinoderms, testaceans, fishes and amphibians have established the physiological importance of the "acetylcholine–cholinesterase" system in the motor activity of embryos. The first appearance and development of motor activity in the embryo coincides with corresponding changes in the content of acetylcholine and in cholinesterase activity. Inactivation of cholinesterase or disturbance of its synthesis led to suppression of embryonic movements, and restoration of its activity was associated with restoration of motor activity (Youngstrom, 1938; Artemov, 1941; Sawyer, 1943, 1944, 1955; Augustinsson and Gustafson, 1949; Brinley, 1954; Durante, 1956, 1958, 1959; Koshtoyants, 1957a).

It may be assumed that the physiological roles of chemical transmitters in the reflex motor activity of the embryos of fishes and amphibians are similar to those in the fully grown animals. In other cases, such as molluscs, for example, the motor activity of the embryos remains "spontaneous" even after innervation by motor cells has been effected (Carter, 1926, 1928), whereas the definitive motor activity is reflex in nature (Koshtoyants, 1957a). The enzymochemical basis of embryonic movement may in these cases be different from that in the fully grown animals.

The purpose of our experiments was to examine the role of transmitter substances on the motor activity of the embryos of certain marine gastropod molluscs.

METHOD

The work was carried out at the White Sea Biological Station of Moscow State University in June–August 1959. Seven species of opisthobranchiate molluscs (Gastropoda, Nudibranchiata) were examined: *Dendronotus frondosus*, *Coryphella rufibranchialis*, *Aeolidia papillosa*, *Acanthodoris pilosa*, *Onchidoris muricata*, *Cadlina laevis*, *Cuthona* sp. (*concinna*?) and the prosobranchiate molluscs, *Lacuna divaricata* (Gastropoda, Prosobranchia). The development of all these molluscs, with the exception of *Cadlina laevis*, proceeds with the formation of a motile larva of veliger type. The embryonic organ of movement is the prototroch, which is later converted into the velum. The cilia of the prototroch and, later, of the velum begin to be active before the nerves have grown out to the motor cells and the activity takes the form of continuous rhythmic movement. In the later stages of development, soon after the development of innervation, pauses begin to be seen in the movements of the cilia. Isolation of the velum cells abolishes these pauses without disturbing the rhythmical activity of the cilia. Central influences on the motor activity of the cilia are thus inhibitory and not initiatory (Carter, 1926). Opisthobranch molluscs lose their velum during metamorphosis and their motor activity becomes definitive (Raven, 1958). The embryos

of *C. laevis* develop without metamorphosis and their organ of movement is not a velum but the foot which is covered with ciliated epithelium.

The spawn of opisthobranch molluscs is available for work throughout
the entire summer season. A large quantity of simultaneously developing
material can readily be obtained under aquarium conditions. Opisthobranch spawn was incubated in crystallizing dishes at temperatures not
exceeding 10–15°C.

The microtitrometric method was used for chemical estimation of cholinesterase activity. The experiments lasted 1·5–2·5 hr at temperatures of
12–15°C; the indicator used was cresol red. In the controls the specific
acetylcholine esterase inhibitor 62-C-47 (Bayliss and Todrick, 1956) was
added to the samples in concentration of 10^{-4} g/ml. The Kelly method
(Pierce, 1956) with a few changes was used for histochemical estimation
of cholinesterase. In the control experiments 62-C-47 (2×10^{-5} g/ml)
was added to the substrate, or the solution of the substrate was prepared
without acetylthiocholine. The embryos were enclosed in glycerol/gelatine
for histochemical treatment.

The effects of a number of transmitter substances on the motor activity
of the embryos or of isolated velum cells were also investigated. Velum
cells were isolated by homogenization of the embryos for 30–60 sec in the
cold. The effects of the substances examined were assessed visually. The observations were made with a low power of the microscope in diffuse light.
Photomicrographs of the embryos were made for purposes of morphological control.

RESULTS

(1) *Cholinesterase and Acetylcholine in the Motor Activity of the Embryos
of Opisthobranch Molluscs.*

In their morphology and the nature of the ciliary activity, the motor
cells of the prototroch and velum are very similar to the cells of ciliated
epithelium (Carter, 1926, 1928). In all cases examined, the spontaneous
motor activity of the cilia of ciliated epithelium has been connected with
the "choline acetylase–acetylcholine–cholinesterase" system. Acetylcholine
can be regarded as a movement-exciting local hormone for such varied
objects as the flagella of protozoons, the ciliary apparatus on the feelers of
Actinia, the ciliated epithelium on the gills of Medusa, the oesophagus
of the frog and the rabbit trachea, the flagella of sea-urchin embryos, etc.
(Burn, 1956; Koshtoyants, 1957a). We, therefore, first of all attempted to
verify whether acetylcholine and cholinesterase were concerned with the
motor activity of the embryo in opisthobranchiate molluscs.

The results of chemical analyses indicated that the trochophores and early
veligers of holobranchs did not contain cholinesterase in detectable quantities. This enzyme was first demonstrated in veligers with small shells, that
is almost at the same time as the development of the pause in the activity

of the velum cilia. Cholinesterase activity continued to increase thereafter; the increase was not associated with any appreciable changes in the character of the embryonic movements. The experiments with the preparation 62-C-47 indicated that the cholinesterase in the embryos of opisthobranches apparently belonged to the group of acetylcholine esterases.

In keeping with the results of chemical analysis, the trochophores and early veligers of all the opisthobranchs examined, with the exception of

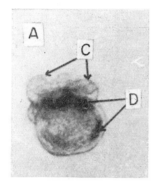 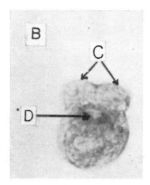

FIG. 1. Cholinesterase in embryos of *Acanthodoris pilosa*.

A—half-developed veliger. B—the same after inactivation of esterase with 62-C-47.
c—velum. d—ganglia.

A. papillosa, did not exhibit any positive histochemical reactions for cholinesterase. Two symmetrical brown spots, apparently identical with the cerebral ganglia, were noted at the base of the velum in slightly more advanced veligers of *D. frondosus*. Still later (veligers without shells but with a velum with well developed lamellae—Fig. 4, C) the cholinesterase content of the zone increased sharply; condensations corresponding to the cerebral, pedal and visceral ganglia were visible within this zone. Soon after hatching of the veligers (Fig. 4, E), the cholinesterase was located as before solely in nervous tissue (ganglia and commissures) and was absent in the motor cells of the velum and muscles. A similar histochemical picture was observed in the embryos of *C. rufibranchialis*, *A. pilosa* (Fig. 1, A), *O. muricata* and *Cuthona* sp. In all these species cholinesterase was present in nervous tissue only, appeared after the development of embryonic motor activity and, as was shown by the 62-C-47 experiments (Fig. 1, B), belonged to the group of acetylcholine esterases.

A different histochemical picture was seen in embryos of *A. papillosa*, in which cholinesterase synthesis began much earlier—simultaneously with the development of rhythmical activity of the prototroch cilia. At first cholinesterase was found only in the cells of the prototroch (Fig. 2, A). The cholinesterase content of the velum cells was increased in early veligers; at this time appreciable spots of staining, apparently identical with the cerebral ganglia (Fig. 2, B), became apparent. In moderately advanced veligers the cholinesterase was also located in the ciliated cells of the velum and in the ganglia (Fig. 2, C).

Another series of experiments showed that acetylcholine 10^{-4} g/ml or less had no effect on the rhythmic movement of the velum cilia in opisthobranchs.

(2) *Serotonin in the Embryonic Motor Activity of Opisthobranch Molluscs*

The results obtained indicated that in all the opisthobranchs examined, with the possible exception of *A. papillosa*, the embryonic motor activity was not directly connected with the "acetylcholine–cholinesterase" system. Another nervous system transmitter, serotonin, was, therefore, examined in the next series of experiments. The physiological role of serotonin has been studied in considerable detail in fully grown molluscs. Serotonin and related substances have been demonstrated in various molluscan tissues;

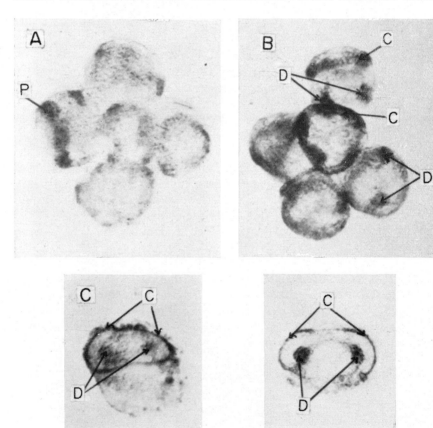

FIG. 2. Cholinesterase in embryos of *Aelidia papillosa*.

A—trochophores. B—early veligers. C—half-developed veligers. p—prototroch.
c—velum. d—ganglia.

there is much of it particularly in the central nervous system. Serotonin is probably the chemical transmitter for the extracardiac accelerator nerves; it has also been suggested that it is concerned in the activity of the central nervous system, in the control of muscular movements, the reactions of chromatophores, etc. (Koshtoyants, 1957a, 1957b; Erspamer, 1957; Welsh, 1957; Fange and Mattisson, 1958; Kahr, 1958; Meng, 1958; Page, 1958; Fan Tyan-Tsi, 1959; Kerkut and Laverack, 1960; and others).

Our experiments revealed that serotonin produced considerable acceleration and intensification of the beating of the cilia of prototroch and velum in all the opisthobranch species which have these embryonic organs of movement. The sensitivity of the embryo to serotonin changed with development (Fig. 3). The embryos first reacted to serotonin in the trochophore stage (Fig. 4, A). The motile activity of these embryos was in the nature of feeble jerks produced by the activity of the prototroch cilia. When serotonin was introduced (10^{-6} to 10^{-12} g/ml), the embryos began to turn round within the egg capsules. The subsequent development of the embryos to the stage of the early veliger (Fig. 4, B) was accompanied by increase of sensitivity to serotonin. It reached its maximum in veligers which were still without shells but had well developed velum lobes (Fig. 4, C). Having achieved this stage of development, the embryos rotated slowly as a result of continuous action of the velum cilia. Serotonin (10^{-5} to 10^{-16} g/ml) increased the rate of the embryo rotation considerably. Later, the sensitivity to serotonin began to decline (Fig. 3). This coincided with essential changes in the motor activity of the embryos and in their morphological state. The velum lobes were reduced in relative size and the shell appeared and increased steadily (Fig. 4, D, E). The beating of the cilia was interrupted by more or less prolonged

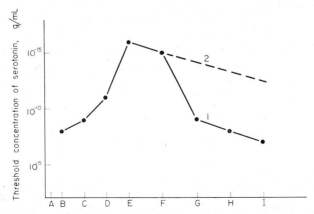

FIG. 3. Sensitivity to serotonin of embryos (1) and isolated velum cells (2) of *Dendronotus frondosus*.

A—trochophore. B—trochophore. C—commencement of the formation of velum. D—early veliger. E—veliger without shell. F—veliger with small shell. G—veliger with well developed shell. H—veliger before hatching, I—veliger after hatching.

pauses due, according to Carter (1926), to the development of central inhibitory influences. Soon after hatching the opisthobranch embryos shed their shell. Serotonin continued to influence their motor activity, probably right up to the time that the velum was lost. The serotonin effect on ciliary action was very persistent. When the embryos were kept for long periods in serotonin solutions, its effect persisted for not less than two or three days.

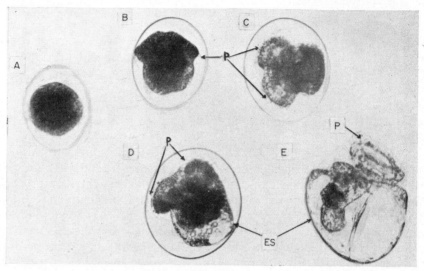

FIG. 4. Embryos of *Dendronotus frondosus*.

A—trochophore. B—early veliger. C—veliger without shell but with well developed velum lobes. D—veliger with a shell about half the maximum size. E—veliger seen after hatching. P—cilia of prototroch or velum. ES—embryo shell.

Serotonin stimulated the motor activity of both intact embryos and isolated velum cells. The beating of the cilia of these cells, when placed in sea water, continued for about 1–3 hours after isolation. Serotonin increased the background activity of the velum cells and also restored and intensified the activity of cilia which had stopped beating. The sensitivities of isolated velum cells and intact embryos to serotonin in the early stages of development were approximately the same. The sensitivity of intact embryos declined in later stages but that of isolated velum cells remained high (Fig. 3).

The anti-serotonin preparation LSD (the diethylamide of D-lysergic acid) in concentrations of 10^{-5} to 10^{-7} g/ml inhibited the spontaneous motor activity of intact embryos until there was complete arrest of ciliary movements and partial loss of the stimulating effect of serotonin. Serotonin restored the background activity of veligers when it was suppressed by LSD and had a protective effect when applied beforehand. Suppression of spontaneous motor activity was also observed when isolated velum cells were placed in

LSD solution. There was not, however, complete arrest of ciliary move-ment as in the intact embryos. In this case also serotonin abolished the in-hibition of motor activity produced by LSD and had a protective action. The effective concentrations of serotonin were much lower than for intact embryos (experiments on *Cuthona* sp.).

DISCUSSION

According to our findings, acetylcholine (also adrenaline and noradre-naline) has no effect on the beating movement of the cilia of the prototroch and velum in opisthobranch molluscs. Absence of cholinesterase from the motor cells of the velum was demonstrated histochemically in all the species examined with the exception of *A. papillosa*. On the other hand, serotonin in very low concentrations intensified the spontaneous motor activity of the velum cells and restored the activity of cilia which had stopped beating. The anti-serotonin preparation LSD abolished the serotonin effect and suppressed the spontaneous motor activity of intact embryos and of isolated velum cells. The motor cells of the prototroch and velum in *A. pa-pillosa* contain cholinesterase; but serotonin has the same effect on ciliary movement in *A. papillosa* as in the other opisthobranchs. These facts suggest that serotonin (or some closely related substance) has the function of a local hormone exciting movement of the cilia of the prototroch and velum in nudibranch embryos.

It may be that movement of the cilia in the veligers of other molluscs and the trochophores of Polychaeta are also connected with serotonin. It was, in fact, demonstrated that serotonin accelerated rhythmic movement of the cilia of the velum in the embryos of *Lacuna divaricata* (*Prosobranchia*). In certain opisthobranchs, as, for example, *Cuthona* sp., the foot, which is covered with ciliated epithelium, is also an organ of movement, along with the velum. Serotonin and LSD have no effect on the movement of the cilia on the foot. This points to different biochemical mechanisms for the motor activity of the ciliated epithelium and for that of the velum in opistho-branch embryos. In *C. laevis*, the development of which proceeds without the formation of a velum, the cilia on the foot give distinct reactions to serotonin and LSD.

The embryos begin to react to serotonin at the stage of the trochophore. The increase of sensitivity to serotonin seen during further development (Fig. 3) can be explained by the continuing formation of the corresponding receptors in the cells of the velum. Changes in receptor structures are also indicated by the fact that the antagonist of serotonin, LSD, which suppresses motor activity in the late veligers, excites ciliary movement in the early stages of development. The decline of sensitivity to serotonin in the second half of embryogenesis is not connected with any changes in the cells of the velum themselves. Isolated velum cells retain completely their ability to react to low concentrations of serotonin. This decline is probably determined by the establishment of central inhibitory influences over the activity of cilia. We know that innervation of the velum cells takes place just at the stages of development in which, according to our findings, the sensitivity of the embryos to serotonin begins to decline (Carter, 1926). The chemical factor responsible for the central inhibitory influences is not apparently identical with acetylcholine, as the latter has no influence on the motor activity of the embryos.

The importance of serotonin as a substance exciting motor activity disappears at the same time as the embryos lose the velum. In fully grown nudibranchs, as also in other *Gastropoda*, serotonin is probably one of the nervous system transmitters. There is thus considerable change in the physiological significance of serotonin in the course of ontogenetic development in opisthobranch molluscs.

CONCLUSIONS

(1) Acetylcholine esterase was present only in nerve tissue and not in the cells of the prototroch or velum in the embryos of all the opisthobranchs examined with the exception of *A. papillosa*.

(2) Acetylcholine, adrenaline and noradrenaline in concentrations of 10^{-4} g/ml or less, had no effect on movement of the cilia in the prototroch or velum.

(3) Serotonin (10^{-5} to 10^{-16} g/ml) stimulated the activity of the prototroch and velum cilia in all the molluscs examined. Ability to react to serotonin developed in the embryos at the stage of the trochophore and persisted up to the time of metamorphosis. The antagonist of serotonin, LSD, inhibited the spontaneous motor activity of cilia and abolished the stimulating effect of serotonin.

(4) The reduced sensitivity to serotonin developing in the later stages of embryogenesis was probably due to the development of inhibitory effects from nerve centres. Isolation of velum cells restored their high sensitivity to serotonin.

(5) Serotonin would appear to be the endogenous factor exciting the activity of the cilia of prototroch and velum in the embryos. The functional significance of this biologically active substance thus undergoes change in the course of molluscan ontogenesis.

REFERENCES

ARMSTRONG, P. B., *J. Physiol.* **84**, 20 (1935).
ARTEMOV, N. M., Bull. of the U.S.S.R. Academy of Sciences biol. series (*Izv. Akad. Nauk SSSR, seriya biol.*) **2**, 272 (1941).
AUGUSTINSSON, K. B. and T. GUSTAFSON, *J. Cell. Comp. Physiol.* **34**, 311 (1949).
BARRY, A., *Circulation* **1**, 1362 (1950).
BAYLISS, B. J. and A. TODRICK, *Biochem. J.* **62**, 62 (1956).

BOELL, E. J., P. GREENFIELD and S. C. SHEN, *J. Expl. Zool.* **129**, 415 (1955).

BOELL, E. J. and S. C. SHEN, *J. Expl. Zool.* **97**, 21 (1944).

BOELL, E. J. and S. C. SHEN, *Anat. Rec.* **105**, 490 (1949).

BOELL, E. J. and S. C. SHEN, *J. Expl. Zool.* **113**, 583 (1950).

BONICHON, A., *C. R. Acad. Sci.* **245**, 1345 (1957).

BRINLEY, F., *J. Pharmacol. Expl. Therap.* **112**, 257 (1954).

BUCKER, E. D. and W. S. PLATNER, *Proc. Soc. Expl. Biol. Med.* **91**, 539 (1956).

BULLER, A. J., R. M. ECCLES and J. C. ECCLES, XXI Int. Congress of Physiological Sciences. Abstracts of Communications. 45 (1959).

BURN, J. H., *Functions of Autonomic Transmitters*, Baltimore 1956.

CARTER, G. S., *J. Expl. Biol.* **4**, 1 (1926).

CARTER, G. S., *J. Expl. Biol.* **6** 97 (1928).

CROZIER, cited by KOSHTOYANTS, KH. S., *Principles of Comparative Physiology*, Moscow 1950.

CULLIS, W. C. and C. L. T. LUCAS, *J. Physiol.* **86**, 53 P (1936).

DURANTE, M., *Experientia* **12**, 307 (1956).

DURANTE, M., *Acta Embryol. Morphol. Exper.* **1**, 273 (1958).

DURANTE, M., *Acta Embryol. Morphol. Exper.* **2**, 234 (1959).

ELKES, J. and A. TODRICK, *Biochemical Development of the Nervous System* p. 309, New York 1955.

ERSPAMER, V., *Z. Vitamin, Hormon, Fermentforsch.* **9**, 74 (1957).

FANGE, R. and A. MATTISON, *Acta Zool.* **39**, 53 (1958).

FAN TYAN-TSI, *Comparative Analysis of the Physiological Role of Serotonin in Nervous System Activity* (Sravnitel'nyi analiz fiziologicheskoi roli serotonina v deyatel'nosti nervnoi sistemy), Moscow 1959.

GARREY, W. E., *Am. J. Physiol.* **119**, 314 (1937).

HALL, E. K., *J. Cell. Comp. Physiol.* **49**, 187 (1957).

JONES, D. S., *Anat. Rec.* **130**, 253 (1958).

KAHR, H., *Naturwissenschaften* **45**, 243 (1958).

KAKUSHKINA, YE. A., Bull. Experimental Biology and Medicine (*Byull. eksp. biol. i med.*) **22**, 21 (1946).

KAKUSHKINA, YE. A., and A. D. ARKHIPOVA, Bull. Experimental Biology and Medicine (*Byull. eksp. biol. i med.*) **11**, 533 (1941).

KERKUT, G. A. and M. S. LAVERACK, *Comp. Biochem. Physiol.* **1**, 62 (1960).

KOSHTOYANTS, KH. S., Physiol. J. U.S.S.R. (*Fiziol. zh. SSSR*) **24**, 221 (1938).

KOSHTOYANTS, KH. S., *Principles of Comparative Physiology* (*Osnovy sravnitel'noi fiziologii*), Vol. I, Moscow 1950.

KOSHTOYANTS, KH. S., *Principles of Comparative Physiology*, Vol. II, Moscow 1951a.

KOSHTOYANTS, KH. S., Bull. Armenian Academy of Sciences (*Izv. Akad. Nauk Arm. SSR*) **10**, 13 (1957b).

MENG, K., *Naturwissenschaften* **45**, 470 (1958).

METZLER, C. J. and D. G. HUMM, *Science* **113**, 382 (1951).

NACHMANSOHN, D., *C. R. Soc. Biol.* **127**, 630 (1938).

PAGE, J. H., *Physiol. Rev.* **38**, 277 (1958).

PIERCE, E., *Histochemistry*, Moscow 1956.

RAVEN, C. P., *Morphogenesis: Analysis of Muscular Development*, Pergamon Press, London 1958.

SAWYER, C. H., *J. Expl. Zool.* **92**, 1 (1943).

SAWYER, C. H., *J. Cell. Comp. Physiol.* **24**, 71 (1944).

SAWYER, C. H., *J. Expl. Zool.* **129**, 561 (1955).

SHIDLOVSKII, V. A., cited by KOSHTOYANTS, KH. S., *Principles of Comparative Physiology,* Moscow 1950.

WELSH, J. H., *Ann. N.Y. Acad. Sci.* **66**, 618 (1957).

YOUNGSTROM, K. A., *Anat. Rec.* **70**, 85 (1938).

THE ROLE OF TISSUE SULPHYDRYL GROUPS IN THE PRODUCTION OF AFFERENT IMPULSE DISCHARGE FROM INTEROCEPTORS

S. A. MIRZOYAN and S. V. DOVLATYAN

Erevan Medical Institute

Translated by Dr. R. Crawford

ACCORDING to Koshtoyants' enzymochemical theory of nerve excitation (1938), the influence of the nervous system is closely connected with the course of metabolic processes in the effector organ.

The investigations of Koshtoyants and his co-workers have shown that controlled change in the enzyme processes connected with carbohydrate metabolism leads to complete or partial loss of the effect of nerve stimulation (Koshtoyants, 1939, 1944, 1951; Ryabinovskaya, 1939).

It has been established that tissue sulphydryl groups play an important part in the actions of acetylcholine and of the vagus nerve on the cardiac muscle (Koshtoyants and Turpayev, 1946; Koshtoyants and Logunova, 1950), in the transmission of excitation from nerve to skeletal muscle (Koshtoyants, 1950), in interneural synapses in sympathetic ganglia (Smirnov et al., 1954) and in the effect of the sympatho-adrenal system (Manukhin, 1954). It has been shown that reversible changes can be produced in conditioned reflex activity in rats by blocking and restoration of sulphydryl groups (Galoyan, 1956).

Investigations on strychnine convulsions in frogs in relation to binding and restoration of sulphydryl groups demonstrated the importance of the integrity of protein structures in receptor elements (Putintseva, 1951).

An attempt was made in a further series of investigations (Turpayev, 1952, 1955, 1958; Turpayev and Nistratova, 1959; Nistratova, 1959) to discover the manner in which acetylcholine interacted with cholinoreceptors both in the intact frog heart and in tissue homogenate.

Koshtoyants' group have carried out investigations on the part played by the sulphydryl groups of the specific proteins of afferent systems in the production of reflex reactions, in addition to their work on the role of tissue sulphydryl groups in the production of the acetylcholine effect and the vagus inhibitory effect on cardiac muscle and on the interaction between acetylcholine and cholinoreactive structures in the effector organ.

Mirzoyan and Dovlatyan (1953) demonstrated, for example, that the sensitivity of receptor structures in the vessels of the rabbit ear depended on the state of the tissue sulphydryl groups.

Experiments in which gastric interoceptors were stimulated and cardiac activity was suppressed by the Goltz method revealed that the reflex depression of cardiac activity disappeared after binding of the sulphydryl groups in the proteins of the interoceptors and that sensitivity which had been lost was restored after the introduction of cysteine into the stomach (Putintseva, 1951). Binding of the sulphydryl groups in the protein molecules of sensory structures in the intestine likewise led to reduction in the quantity of pancreatic juice secreted in response to hydrochloric acid. Restoration of the integrity of the proteins led to restoration of secretion (Serbenyuk, 1952). The first investigations carried out by us on these lines revealed that the response of receptor mechanisms in the afferent nervous system to acetylcholine depended on the state of the tissue sulphydryl groups.

In the experimental part of this paper we describe the results of further investigations demonstrating the role of tissue sulphydryl groups in the production of afferent impulse discharge from interoceptors in several different kinds of material.

METHOD

The methods employed for investigation of the role of tissue sulphydryl groups in relation to change in reflex reactions to acetylcholine were Chernigovskii's (1943) perfusion of an intestinal loop in the cat and perfusion of the isolated rabbit ear with intact nerve supply, as developed by Mirzoyan and Dovlatyan (1955).

The results of our investigations indicated that the vessels in the rabbit ear constituted a reflexogenic, mainly depressor, zone, the action of various substances on which led to reflex changes in blood pressure and respiration.

Reflex reactions in the animals (cats and rabbits) in response to action of the several chemical stimuli were recorded by means of mercury or membrane manometers, with which were recorded arterial pressure, respiration and, in some experiments on cats, change in the volume of the spleen. The chemical stimuli were injected with a syringe into the blood vessels of the perfused intestinal loop in the cat or the ear of the rabbit.

RESULTS

Our investigation showed that acetylcholine, perfused through the vessels of the rabbit ear, had a considerable reflex influence on the cardiovascular system. When perfusion was effected with acetylcholine 10^{-5} g/ml there was a considerable fall of arterial pressure (50–60 mm) with a clearly evident prolonged after-effect, following a latent period of 8–10 sec. The depressor effect which developed was observed for 200–240 sec and was of protracted character. Only after the lapse of this period did the blood pressure return to somewhere near its original level. There were equally important reflex changes in the animal's respiratory function. Respiration began to be intensified and accelerated 10–12 sec after the commencement of acetylcholine injection, and this continued both during the period of perfusion and for 160–180 sec afterwards.

When the chemoreceptors in the vessels of the rabbit ear had first been treated with cadmium chloride, perfusion with acetylcholine of the same strength produced much reduced reflex effects on blood pressure and respiration. The injection of free cysteine into the stream of perfusion fluid led after 40–50 sec to restoration of the reflexes to acetylcholine stimulation of the chemoreceptors: acetylcholine perfusion again led to a considerable fall in blood pressure (50–60 mm) and noticeable intensification of respiration (Fig. 1).

These findings thus indicate that the specific structures in the tissue systems responsible for the production of reflex reactions to acetylcholine were blocked by cadmium chloride and reactivated by solutions of free cysteine; it follows, therefore, that tissue sulphydryl groups play an important part in the production of afferent impulse discharges from the receptors in the vessels of the rabbit ear.

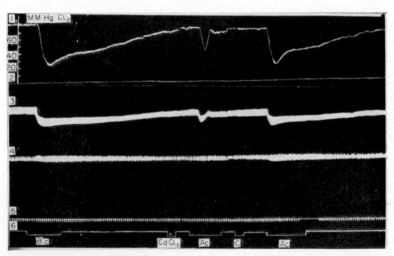

FIG. 1. Reflex changes in blood pressure and respiration produced by acetylcholine (Ac) in the normal state and after the injection of cadmium chloride 10^{-3} g/ml. Restoration of the normal response reaction to acetylcholine after treatment of the receptors in the vessels of the rabbit ear with cysteine (c).

1—blood pressure recorded with a mercury manometer. 2—zero line for the mercury manometer. 3—blood pressure recorded by a membrane manometer. 4—respiration. 5—time (3 sec). 6—interoceptive stimulation.

A series of experiments revealed that acetylcholine sensitivity in the receptor formations of the vessels in the rabbit ear, which had been lost as a result of binding of the tissue sulphydryl groups by cadmium chloride, was restored after injection of urea into the stream of perfusion fluid.

When the tissue sulphydryl groups were blocked and the reflex responses to acetylcholine were reduced, the injection of a solution of urea into the vascular stream restored the reflex reaction to acetylcholine completely.

The results of the experiments (Mirzoyan and Dovlatyan, 1957) in which we investigated the reflex responses to acetylcholine when the chemoreceptors in the intestinal loop were stimulated with Dzhermuk mineral water showed clearly that this substance had different effects in different concentrations. Weak solutions of the mineral water injected into the vessels of the perfused intestine intensified the reflexes to acetylcholine, whereas stronger solutions led to the opposite effect, namely weakening of the reflexes and the development of an inverted reaction: instead of rising, the blood pressure fell considerably.

An extremely important point was that this unusual type of reflex reaction in the blood pressure was reversible. Flushing with Tyrode solution could abolish the inverted reaction and lead to partial restoration of the pressor reflex, the amplitude of the respiratory movements and the characteristic curve for change in the volume of the spleen.

It should be emphasized that inversion of the blood pressure reaction developed gradually and that transitional stages, following one another in definite order, could be detected: reduction of the reflexes from the chemoreceptors in the intestine to acetylcholine was followed by a diphasic pressor–depressor reaction, the depressor phase being more pronounced in most cases, and, finally, there was a phase of complete disappearance of the pressor reaction, leaving only the depressor effect.

Consideration was given to factors connected with the possible disturbance of isotonicity in assessing the nature and strength of reflex responses to acetylcholine during prolonged perfusion with high concentrations of Dzhermuk mineral water in Tyrode solution. Inverted reactions to acetylcholine in response to stimulation of intestinal chemoreceptors by prolonged action of stronger solutions of the mineral water could likewise be produced in control experiments in which changes in the physiochemical property of the perfusion fluid were almost completely excluded. Tyrode solution prepared with Dzhermuk water, all the constituents of the latter being accounted in order to preserve isotonicity and constant ionic strength, likewise caused weakening of the reflexes at first, and later, complete inversion of the reflex reaction to acetylcholine (Fig. 2).

An interesting point was that weakening of the pressor reflex, reduction in the volume of the spleen and sometimes also inversion of the reflex responses from the intestinal chemoreceptors to acetylcholine could also

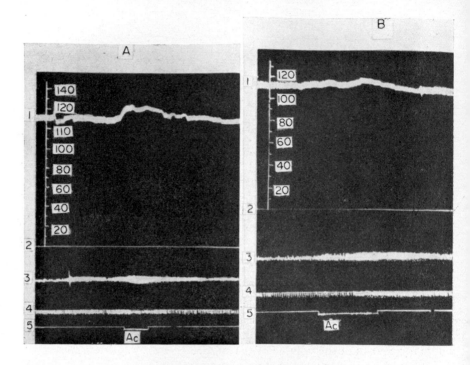

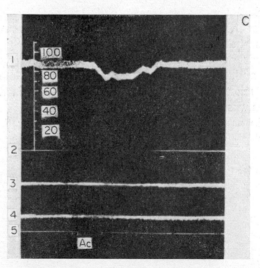

FIG. 2. Reflex changes in blood pressure and respiration on the injection of acetylcholine 10^{-5} g/ml before (A) and after (B, C) perfusion of Dzhermuk mineral water through the vessels of an isolated loop of small intestine.

1—blood pressure. 2—zero line for mercury manometer. 3—respiration. 4—time (3 sec). 5—interoceptive stimulation.

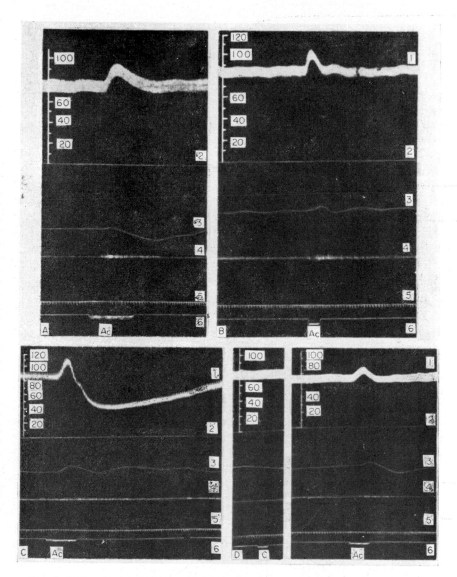

FIG. 3. Reflex changes in blood pressure, respiration and spleen volume in response to acetylcholine 10^{-5} g/ml.

A—before action of the trace elements. B, C—weakening and inversion of the reflex reactions to acetylcholine (Ac) produced from thermoreceptors in the intestine after action of the trace elements on the intestine. D—restoration of normal response reaction to acetylcholine on treatment of the intestine with cysteine (c).

1—blood pressure. 2—zero line for mercury manometer. 3—spleen volume. 4—respiration. 5—time (3 sec). 6—interoceptive stimulation.

be observed when the mucosa of the intestinal loop was irrigated with Dzhermuk mineral water.

We have put forward the hypothesis that the effect of this mineral water on the intestinal receptors depends on the presence of trace elements in the water. It is known that mineral waters, including also that of Dzhermuk, contain certain quantities of trace elements from the group of heavy metals, namely zinc, copper, iron, manganese, etc. The salts of certain heavy metals may influence the reactivity of sulphydryl groups. We regard this as the mechanism responsible for weakening and inversion of the reaction from intestinal chemoreceptors to acetylcholine produced by the action of the mineral water.

It is evident that tissue sulphydryl groups in the proteins of receptor structures both in the vascular bed and in the walls of the digestive tube are of material importance in the production of afferent impulse discharge from interoceptors in the intestine resulting from the action of the mineral water.

Experiments in which combinations of trace elements (copper, iron, manganese) prepared with Tyrode solution in concentrations corresponding to those in Dzhermuk mineral water were injected into the stream of fluid perfusing an intestinal loop were carried out in order to obtain direct proof of the importance of trace elements in the production of change in the course of reflex reactions to acetylcholine.

The results indicated that trace elements produced marked attenuation and inversion of the reflex responses from the intestinal chemoreceptors to acetylcholine. Only perfusion with free cysteine was capable of restoring normal intestinal reception (Fig. 3).

Assessing our findings, we can conclude that the quality of the reflexes produced from chemoreceptors in the vessels of the rabbit ear and in the intestine in response to acetylcholine after exposure to cadmium salts and to trace elements is determined by change in the chemodynamics of the receptor mechanisms.

Changes in the individual links of metabolic processes in the receptor structures of the vessels in the ear and intestine through interaction between cadmium chloride or trace elements and thiol groups in the specific proteins of the afferent systems lead to pronounced changes in the animal's reflex reactions to acetylcholine.

Tissue sulphydryl groups play an important part in the production of afferent impulse discharge from interoceptors.

REFERENCES

CHERNIGOVSKII, V. N., *Afferent Systems of the Viscera* (Afferentnyye sistemy vnutrennykh organov), Moscow 1943.

GALOYAN, SH. A., Reports of the Armenian SSR Academy of Sciences (*Dokl. Akad. Nauk Arm. SSSR*) **22**, 141 (1956).

Koshtoyants, Kh. S., Reports of the U.S.S.R. Academy of Sciences, new series (*Dokl. Akad. Nauk SSSR, novaya seriya*) **19**, 317, (1938).

Koshtoyants, Kh. S., Reports of the U.S.S.R. Academy of Sciences (*Dokl. Akad. Nauk SSSR*) **24**, 358 (1939).

Koshtoyants, Kh. S., Reports of the U.S.S.R. Academy of Sciences (*Dokl. Akad. Nauk SSSR*) **43**, 376 (1944).

Koshtoyants, Kh. S., Reports of the U.S.S.R. Academy of Sciences (*Dokl. Akad. Nauk SSR*) **52**, 981 (1950).

Koshtoyants, Kh. S., *Proteins Metabolism and Nerve Regulation* (Belkovyye tela, obmen veshchestv i nervnaya regulyatsiya) (1951).

Koshtoyants, Kh. S. and K. S. Logunova, Reports of the U.S.S.R. Academy of Sciences (*Dokl. Akad. Nauk SSSR*) **53**, 429 (1950).

Koshtoyants, Kh. S. and T. M. Turpayev, Reports of the U.S.S.R. Academy of Sciences (*Dokl. Akad. Nauk SSSR*) **54**, 181 (1946).

Manukhin, B. N., *Dependence of the Effect of the Sympathetic-adrenal System on Tissue Sulphydryl Groups* (Zavisimost' deistviya simpatiko-adrenalovoi sistemy ot tkanevykh sul'fgidril'nykh grupp), Moscow 1954.

Mirzoyan, S. A. and S. V. Dovlatyan, Pharmacology and toxicology (*Farmakol. i toksikol.*) **6**, 60 (1953).

Mirzoyan, S. A. and S. V. Dovlatyan, Pharmocology and Toxicology (*Farmakol. i toksikol.*) **18**, 11 (1955).

Mirzoyan, S. A. and S. V. Dovlatyan, Collection of papers of the Institute of Balneology and Physiotherapy (*Sbornik trudov In-ta kurortologii i fizicheskikh metodov lecheniya*) **3**, 71 (1957).

Nistratova, S. N., *Biochemical Nature of Cholinoreceptor in Connexion with the Mechanism of Acetylcholine Action* (O biokhimicheskoi prirode kholinoretseptora v svyazi s mekhanizmom deistviya atsetilkholina), Moscow 1959.

Putintseva, T. G., cited by Koshtoyants, Kh. S. in *Proteins, Metabolism and Nerve Regulation* (1951).

Ryabinovskaya, A. M., Reports of U.S.S.R. Academy of Sciences (*Dokl. Akad. Nauk SSSR*) **23**, 953 (1939).

Serbenyuk, Ts. V., *The Part of the Nervous System in the Production of the Effects of Chemical Factors Controlling Pancreatic Secretion* (Uchastiye nervnoi sistemy v osushchestvlenii vliyaniya khimicheskikh faktorov regulyatsii podzheludochnogo sokootdeleniya), Moscow 1952.

Smirnov, G. D., A. L. Byzov and Yu. I. Rampan, Physiol. J. U.S.S.R. (*Fiziol. zh. SSSR*) **40**, 424 (1054).

Turpayev, T. M., Reports of the I.M.Zh., U.S.S.R. Academy of Sciences (*Trudy IMZh Akad. Nauk SSSR*) **6**, 19 (1952).

Turpayev, T. M., Biochemistry (*Biokhimiya*) **20**, 456 (1955).

Turpayev, T. M., Biochemistry (*Biokhimiya*) **23**, 71 (1958).

Turpayev, T. M. and S. N. Nistratova, Biochemistry (*Biokhimiya*) **24**, 171 (1959).

CHEMICAL FACTORS CONTROLLING ION MOVEMENTS DURING NERVE ACTIVITY*

DAVID NACHMANSOHN

Departments of Neurology and Biochemistry,
College of Physicians and Surgeons, Columbia University,
New York, N.Y.

INTRODUCTION

One of the characteristic features of living cells is their high potassium ion (K^+) concentration compared to that of the surrounding fluid. In contrast, the sodium ion (Na^+) concentration is high in the outside fluid and low in the interior. However, only conducting tissues such as, for instance, nerve and muscle fibers are endowed with the special property to use these ionic concentration gradients for the generation and propagation of small electric currents along the fibers. The ionic concentration gradients between the inside and the outside of the cell are the source of electromotive force. The electric currents are carried by Na^+ and K^+. During activity Na^+ move to the inside, followed by an outflow of K^+ to the outside, as was first proposed by Overton[1], in 1902, and substantiated by measurements with radioactive ions after World War II[2]. The ion movements are made possible by a sudden transitory change in ionic conductance of the conducting membrane, the structural or functional barrier separating the cell interior from the outside fluid.

The fundamental question for the understanding of nerve activity is that of the mechanism by which the ionic conductance is so dramatically changed. The increase of conductance takes place within a fraction of a millisecond and the return to the resting condition is nearly as fast. What makes the potential source of energy, inactive at rest, suddenly effective? What are the forces controlling the ion movements with the extraordinarily high degree of precision and with the great speed indicated by the electrical recordings? It is difficult to conceive that electricity in a fluid system such as the living cell can be generated and regulated without chemical reactions. The membranes of conducting cells must be endowed with a special chemical system

* This work was supported in part by the National Science Foundation Grant No. G-12,901, and by the Division of Research Grants and Fellowships of the National Institutes of Health, Grant No. B-3304, U.S. Public Health Service.

208

capable of changing rapidly and reversibly the conductance and controlling the movements of ions in a specific way.

Any doubt as to the chemical nature of the process controlling the ion movements across the conducting membrane has been removed by the recent heat production measurements of A. V. Hill and his associates[3]. Their experiments, carried out on *Maja* nerve at 0°C with very fast recording equipment, have revealed that the previously recorded small initial heat consists of two distinct phases: a rather large positive heat, roughly coinciding with activity, followed by a negative heat taking place within 100–300 milliseconds. The positive heat, after appropriate corrections, is about 14×10^{-6} cal/g nerve/impulse. Actually, as pointed out by the authors, the heat produced should not be referred to g nerve but to g active material. The conducting membrane is about 50 Å thick. The surface area of 1 g *Maja* nerve is about 10^4 cm². Referred to g active material, the amount of heat produced is 2.0×10^{-3} cal/impulse. This is a remarkably high amount, similar to that produced per g muscle during a twitch. As stated by Hill, these results have made untenable the hypothesis that nerve impulse conduction is a purely physical process[4].

Additional support for the chemical nature of the conductance changes is their high temperature coefficient reported by several investigators. According to the studies of Schoffeniels on the isolated single electroplax, the Q_{10} of the action current is 3.6 and the activation energy is 20,000 cal/mole[5].

ROLE OF THE ACETYLCHOLINE SYSTEM
IN THE GENERATION OF BIOELECTRIC CURRENTS

About thirty years ago a chemical compound, acetylcholine (ACh) was linked to a special phase of nerve activity. The well known theory of neuro-humoral transmission assumed that ACh is secreted from nerve terminals and after crossing the intercellular space stimulates the second cell, nerve or muscle, thus acting as a mediator of nerve impulses. The idea of neuro-humoral transmission was based on observations in which classical methods of pharmacology were used. The theory was vigorously opposed by leading neurophysiologists, such as Erlanger, Gasser, Lorente de No, Fulton, and many others. The experimental observations were not questioned, but their interpretation was. In this impasse, a new approach appeared necessary.

The high speed of the events and the smallness of the energy transformations during electrical activity offers many difficulties for chemical analysis. But the rapid progress of physics and chemistry has provided powerful tools for the analysis of cellular function. The rise of biochemistry, the development of highly sensitive physicochemical methods, the spectacular advances in protein and enzyme chemistry, have profoundly changed the situation as to the understanding of the function of living cells in terms of physics and chemistry. In several fields the analysis of elementary processes has reached molecular levels. Investigations of the role of ACh based on biochemistry appeared to offer the best promise for finding a more satisfactory answer.

An approach with biochemical methods was initiated 25 years ago. The enzymes effecting the hydrolysis and the formation of ACh were analyzed, the sequence of energy transformations during electrical activity was established, and a number of chemical reactions, studied in the test tube, were correlated with electrical events recorded on intact cells. In the center of these studies have always been the proteins and enzymes, in particular those specifically linked to ACh. Two of these proteins have been isolated and purified from the electric organs of the electric fish. This material is particularly suitable. The organs are the most powerful bioelectric generators created by nature and they are, moreover, highly specialized in their function. The electricity, as was well recognized in the 19th century, is basically similar to that of nerve and muscle fibers. The organs contain only 3 per cent protein and 93 per cent water. Nevertheless, the concentration of the proteins and enzymes of the ACh system is extraordinarily high compared with other conducting tissues, thereby greatly facilitating their isolation. These organs have been used systematically, since 1937, for the analysis of the chemical basis of bioelectricity. The knowledge obtained from the studies of the protein *in vitro* has been applied wherever possible to the analysis of their role in cellular function.

It soon became apparent that the hypothesis of neurohumoral transmission must be abandoned. A new concept was proposed which explains the original observations and reconciles the facts with the view of many electrophysiologists[6]. ACh is not, as was originally proposed, secreted from the nerve endings, and acts as a mediator between two cells; its action is an *intracellular* or rather an *intramembranous* process, taking place within the membranes of conducting cells. The action of the ester is responsible for the rapid and reversible changes of ionic conductance, the elementary process by which bioelectric currents are generated and propagated. ACh is the "specific operative substance" in conduction in the sense applied by Otto Meyerhof to the role of ATP in muscular contraction. The ACh system is the special chemical system with which all conducting cells of the animal kingdom are endowed and which enables them to control the ion movements in the rapid and precise way required for their function.

The picture of the role of ACh in the elementary process which has emerged from these studies may be described as follows (Fig. 1): ACh is in resting condition bound to a protein (or conjugated protein) (S for storage form). During activity the ester is released and reacts with a receptor protein (R). It is this reaction with the receptor protein, leading apparently to a local change in the configuration of the protein, which is responsible for the increase in ionic conductance, probably by the removal of charge located at strategic points. It is the trigger which controls the ion movements and makes the potential sources of energy, the ionic concentration gradients, effective. The ACh-receptor complex is in dynamic equilibrium with the free ester and the protein. The free ester is attacked by ACh-esterase (E) and rapidly inactivated by hydrolysis. Thereby, the receptor and the membrane conductance are able to return to the resting condition. The barrier for ion movements is re-established. The rapidity of the chemical reactions, taking

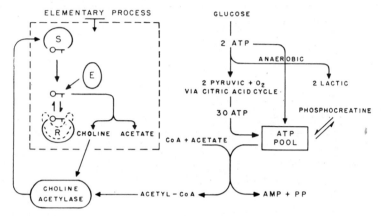

FIG. 1. Sequence of energy transformations associated with conduction, and integration of the acetylcholine system into the metabolic pathways of the nerve cell.

The tentative picture of the elementary process is described in the text.

place within a fraction of a millisecond, accounts for the speed of the electrical events and for the ability of nerve fibers to conduct a thousand or more impulses per second. In the recovery period ACh is restored by choline acetylase and the other constituents of the acetylating system.

The developments have been reviewed in a monograph[7]. In the present article recent evidence in favor of the concept proposed is discussed.

INSEPARABLE ASSOCIATION OF ELECTRICAL AND ACh-ESTERASE ACTIVITY

Studies on ACh-esterase have revealed that the enzyme satisfies many prerequisites for the assumption of the primary role of ACh proposed. But the crucial evidence for its essential role in conduction is based on the interdependence of electrical and enzyme activity. If the proposed picture is correct, a block of ACh-esterase activity should stop electrica lactivity. It has been demonstrated with a great variety of extremely potent and specific enzyme inhibitors, that it is impossible to separate electrical from ACh-esterase activity. In all types of conducting fibers of the animal kingdom tested, central and peripheral, motor and sensory, cholinergic and adrenergic, vertebrate and invertebrate fibers, electrical activity invariably fails when enzyme activity is blocked. The process is reversible with reversible inhibitors, irreversible with irreversible ones.

Some investigators objected to this evidence because of the high concentration of inhibitor used, which is much higher than that required to inhibit the enzyme in solution. It is not difficult to explain this apparent discrepancy. Inhibition of an enzyme in an intact cell requires always higher concentrations than in solution. Many compounds do not readily enter the cell interior, since cells are protected by structural barriers. The outside concentration of an inhibitor is irrelevant, only that at the site of action is pertinent. When squid giant axons are exposed to 1 mg of DFP/ml, less than 1 μg/g is found inside the axon at the time when conduction fails. The functional interdependence of enzyme and electrical activity has been demonstrated on intact fibers by using a substrate which penetrates into the interior. The interdependence of electrical and chemical activity was shown with a multifiber preparation of crab axons[8], and, quite recently, with the squid giant axon[9]. When the enzyme activity falls below a certain level of the initial value, electrical activity is blocked.

A refined preparation was used by Dettbarn[10]. At the Ranvier node of myelinated frog nerve fibers the conducting membrane is covered by a thin and porous structure only[11]. Applying Staempfli's technique[12] for recording electrical activity of a single Ranvier node of a single frog sciatic fiber, Dettbarn obtained with 300 μg of eserine per ml reversible block of activity in 30 seconds, with 30 μg/ml in a few minutes, a thousandfold increase in the potency compared to that on intact frog sciatic nerve.

PROTEINS OF THE ACh SYSTEM AND THEIR RELATION TO FUNCTION

When the essential role of ACh in the elementary process was ascertained, about 15 years ago, the situation was analogous to that reached in the investigations of muscular contraction in 1939, when by the startling discoveries of Engelhardt and Ljubimova the interaction between ATP and myosin moved into the center of interest of the analysis of the primary events in muscular contraction[13]. It became apparent that a better understanding of the processes underlying the generation of bioelectric currents required the knowledge of the proteins tied to the function of ACh. The forces must be similar in all four proteins, since a molecule such as ACh has only a limited number of features permitting the interaction with a macromolecule. However, for many reasons the enzyme ACh-esterase appeared to be the most favorable for an analysis of the molecular forces acting between proteins and small molecules.

The enzyme process is usually formulated as follows: $E + S \rightleftharpoons ES \rightarrow E +$ products, where E is the enzyme, S the substrate, ES the enzyme-substrate

(Michaelis–Menten) complex. Analysis of the molecular forces acting in the active surface of the enzyme, carried out with appropriate substrates and inhibitors, has revealed that the surface has two functionally and spatially separated sub-sites: an anionic site and an esteratic site. The former attracts the cationic group by Coulombic and van der Waals' forces. The esteratic site has an acidic and a basic, or nucleophilic, group symbolized by H and G. The nucleophilic group forms a covalent bond with the electrophilic carbon of the carbonyl group. Fig. 2 is a schematic presentation of

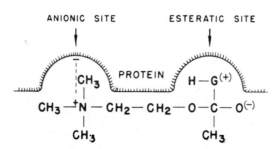

FIG. 2. Schematic presentation of interaction between the active groups of acetylcholinesterase and its substrate (the Michaelis–Menten complex).

the Michaelis–Menten complex. The hydrolytic process takes place in two phases: in the first step the alcohol (choline) is eliminated from the enzyme substrate complex by an electronic shift. As a result an acetylated enzyme is formed. This acetylated enzyme reacts rapidly, in microseconds, with water to form acetate and restored enzyme[14, 15].

Knowledge of the molecular forces acting in the proteins of the ACh system has greatly helped the understanding of various aspects of nerve function. One illustration is the story of the nerve gas poisoning and the development of an extremely potent and efficient antidote. Certain organophosphorus compounds are widely used as insecticides. Some of them are volatile and extremely toxic. To this group belong the famous nerve gases, the most powerful potential chemical warfare agents ever developed. The compounds have the general formula: $(RO)_2(X)P = O$, where X is an electronegative group. $P-X$ can be readily hydrolyzed by esterases. All esterases are irreversibly inhibited by the action of these compounds, but the lethal action is due to the inhibition of ACh-esterase[16].

The understanding of the hydrolytic process by ACh-esterase led to the explanation of the mechanism of alkylphosphate action: it is a nucleophilic attack of the enzyme on the P atom in an S_N2 reaction[17]. Instead of an acylated enzyme, the physiological intermediary, a phosphorylated enzyme is formed. But whereas the acylated form reacts extremely fast with water to form acetate and restored enzyme, the phosphorylated enzyme does not react with water at all or extremely slowly, in days or weeks.

8 a*

Once the mechanism of alkylphosphate poisoning was recognized, it appeared possible to reverse the inhibition of the enzyme by a nucleophilic group which would restore the enzyme activity in a displacement reaction removing the phosphoryl group from the enzyme. Hydroxylamine was known from Hestrin's experiments[18] to form hydroxamic acid from acetate, a reaction catalyzed by ACh-esterase. The effect is produced by an attack of hydroxylamine on the carbon of the carbonyl group of the acetylated enzyme. With hydroxylamine it is possible to restore the enzyme activity of the phosphorylated enzyme, but this reaction is slow and requires extremely high concentrations[19].

The question naturally arose whether it was possible to increase the reactivating power of the nucleophilic group attacking the P atom of the phosphorylated enzyme and to obtain eventually an efficient antidote. Wilson proposed to attach a quaternary nitrogen group to the active nucleophilic group in a proper atomic distance. The reactivating power should thereby be greatly promoted since the cationic group of the molecule would be attracted to the anionic site and the nucleophilic atom would be thereby directed towards the P atom. This would be analogous to the great superiority of ACh as a substrate when compared to ethyl acetate, because the presence of the cationic group increases the forces of binding by a factor of more than 1000 and helps the structure to be attracted and oriented in the protein surface. Among a series of compounds proposed by Wilson and synthesized by Ginsburg, the most powerful reactivator turned out to be 2-pyridine aldoxime methiodide (PAM)[20]. Its power to reactivate alkylphosphate inhibited ACh-esterase *in vitro* is about one million as high as that of hydroxylamine.

When Kewitz, in 1955, applied PAM to animals the compound turned out to be the first really efficient antidote against organophosphorus poisoning. The first experiment was striking. Twenty mice were exposed to a 100 per cent sure lethal dose of alkylphosphate. Ten were treated with PAM. These ten survived, the other ten were dead within half an hour[21]. No statistics were required. In combination with atropine, which protects the receptor protein, animals survived 10 to 20 fold lethal doses of nerve gas[22]. Later, modifications of PAM were developed, such as a bisquaternary PAM, which seem to be still more potent than PAM itself[23]. These developments have provided an extremely efficient and potent treatment of nerve gas poisoning. Animals may be protected against 100 fold lethal doses of sarin. PAM has been successfully applied in severe insecticide poisoning of men, particularly in Japan, where it has been used on a large scale[24].

The extraordinary reactivating power of PAM is quite striking. In order to explain this potency, Wilson and his associates studies in the following years the inhibition of ACh-esterase by a number of phenyl trimethyl ammonium derivatives as to the degree of binding in terms of the respective position of various atoms of the inhibitor and of the enzyme. The results seemed to suggest a high degree of molecular complementarity between PAM and phosphorylated enzyme [25]. However, subsequent observations have cast considerable doubt as to the validity of this explanation (see e.g. Hobbiger [25a]).

The development of the antidote supports the view of the author proposed fifteen years ago and vigorously opposed at that time, that the effects of organophosphorus compounds must be attributed to a specific biochemical lesion and not to a general toxic effect. It has been experimentally ascertained that PAM actually repairs the biochemical lesion, i.e. restores the activity of ACh-esterase as postulated by theory. This mode of action was demonstrated by Kewitz[26] in the periphery and by Rosenberg in the brain[27].

THE ACh RECEPTOR

Another example of how the study of the proteins has provided valuable insight into the forces underlying nerve activity is the information obtained about the ACh receptor. The quaternary nitrogen group is a tetrahedral structure, i.e. it has a more or less spherical shape. Investigations with the enzymes ACh-esterase and choline acetylase in solution suggest that the extra methyl group on the nitrogen induces a conformational change of the protein in the active state. A change of configuration of a protein might be a possible basis of the change of permeability to ions during conduction by the removal of a charge located in the pathways of Na in the membrane and slowing down its flow from the outside to the inside. Does acetylcholine produce such an effect when reacting with the receptor? A receptor was postulated fifty years ago by Langley. Its existence as a cell constituent different from ACh-esterase has been experimentally demonstrated about 10 years ago by a combination of two methods which permitted a distinction to be made between compounds acting predominantly on the receptor and those acting on the enzyme or on both[28]. Segments of electric tissue containing 1–3 rows of electroplax were isolated. The effects upon the electrical activity of compounds acting on the ACh system were measured with microelectrodes inserted into the interior of a cell. At the same time the ACh-esterase activity was determined on the row of intact cells. In this way it has been demonstrated that some compounds, such as for instance ACh, carbamylcholine, procaine and D-tubocurarine block conduction without affecting the esterase. In the presence of these compounds the enzyme activity remains at a high level even at a much higher concentration than that producing block. Consequently, the blocking action observed cannot be attributed to the effect on the esterase but to that of a similar cell constituent, the long postulated receptor. There are, of course, other compounds which decrease enzyme activity to a low level at the time when electrical activity stops.

In these cases the blocking action on conduction may be attributed, either partly or entirely, to the decrease of enzyme activity to a level incompatible with electrical activity.

The compounds acting on the receptor may be divided into two distinctly different types according to the way in which they affect electrical activity. One type blocks conduction without depolarization, the other blocks and simultaneously depolarizes the membrane. In one case the barrier to ion movements evidently remains unchanged when activity stops, in the other case it is reduced. Quaternary compounds, such as ACh, carbamylcholine, decamethonium and others, usually belong to the latter category. Most tertiary analogues, as for example procaine and related local anesthetics, block but do not depolarize.

If one associates the transient change of permeability in conducting tissues with the reaction between ACh and the receptor, one must assume that ACh not only combines with the receptor but that during the formation of the complex a change of the proteins takes place. We have, therefore, introduced the distinction between receptor activators which effect this change, and receptor inhibitors which combine with the receptor but do not produce a change. The latter apparently block the access of ACh to the active site. These two different types of interaction are analogous to those in enzyme chemistry where we distinguish between enzyme substrates and inhibitors.

If one accepts the idea that the molecular forces acting between ACh and the proteins associated with its function are more or less similar, one may visualize that the receptor in the active state undergoes a change in configuration comparable to that suggested to occur in the enzyme during activity. Such an action may well be associated with the change of permeability taking place in the active membrane. One possible picture would be that positively charged amino groups may form an obstacle for the rapid passage of Na^+. A small, even very limited change in a long protein chain may remove a strategically located positive charge by a few A, thereby greatly increasing the rate of flow. Folding or unfolding of a small section of a helical or nonhelical portion of a protein may be enough for such a process and thus act as a trigger. The data available indicate that the action of one ACh molecule may permit the passage of about 1000–2000 Na ions. This is a relationship of an order of magnitude consistent with that which is expected for a trigger process in which the controlling energy required must be small.

MONOCELLULAR ELECTROPLAX PREPARATION

Of great value for the studies on the receptor has been the monocellular electroplax preparation developed by Schoffeniels[29]. In this preparation one single electroplax, dissected from the bundle of Sachs of *Electrophorus* is kept between two nylon sheets, one with a window adjusted to the dimensions of the cell, the other with a grid consisting of nylon threads by which the cell is pressed against the window. The two sheets are mounted between two blocks of lucite, each containing a pool of fluid. When the two blocks are fixed, the two pools of fluid are completely separated by the cell, so that ions or other chemicals dissolved in the solution cannot pass from one pool to the other except through the cell. The solution of one pool bathes the conducting, that of the other pool that of the nonconducting membrane. The preparation has been greatly improved during the last few years, especially by the introduction of a switching device for the recording of potentials with intracellular electrodes across the conducting and nonconducting membranes and across the whole cell (Higman and Bartels[30]). It offers a sensitive method for testing the potency of compounds acting on the receptor and for recording the resulting changes of electrical characteristics. As an illustration an experiment with ACh is shown in Fig. 3. It demonstrates that ACh in low concentrations rapidly and reversibly blocks electrical activity and simultaneously depolarizes the cell, as postulated for a receptor activator (Bartels[31]). A receptor inhibitor such as tetracaine, shown in Fig. 4, blocks but does not depolarize.

In view of its great sensitivity to small modifications of structure of compounds reacting with the receptor, the preparation is most suitable for studying structure–activity relationships. It offered the possibility to test whether in the reaction of ACh with the receptor the presence of an extra methyl group has such a potent effect as was observed in the reactions with ACh-esterase and choline acetylase. When the potency of mono-, di-, and

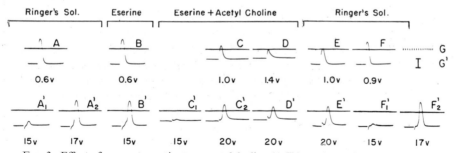

FIG. 3. Effect of a receptor activator: acetylcholine (ACh) on the resting and action potentials of a single isolated electroplax.

The figure shows the inseparable association of the blocking and the depolarizing action. The recordings were made with the cathode ray oscilloscope by means of microelectrodes, one of them intracellular. The value for the resting potential, measured by the distance between the two base lines is usually about 85 mV. A–F direct, A'_1–F'_2 indirect stimulation. The voltages refer to stimulus strength. A–A'_2 control in Ringer's solution; after A–A'_2 physostigmine 5×10^{-5} M added at 0 time; B, B' 5 min later. ACh 5×10^6 M + physostigmine 5×10^{-5} M added at $5\frac{1}{2}$ min; C–C'_2 30 sec, D, D $3\frac{1}{2}$ min later. Returned to Ringer's solution at $9\frac{1}{2}$ min after 0 time. E, E'. 1 min, F–F'_2 15 min recovery. Calibration in this and the following Fig.: 1000 c/s and 50 mV (Bartels[33]).

trimethylaminoethyl acetate on electrical activity was determined, the dimethyl compound was found to be about 20–25 times more potent than the monoester. This increase in potency may be attributed, at least to a considerable extent, to a stronger binding by van der Waals' forces due to the presence of an extra methyl group. But the trimethylated compound (ACh) is 200 times more potent than the dimethylated one and 5000 times as potent

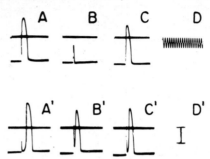

FIG. 4. Effect of a receptor inhibitor: tetracaine on the resting and action potentials of a single isolated electroplax.

The compound blocks electrical activity but without depolarization. Recordings as in the preceding Figure. A–C direct stimulation; A′–C′ indirect stimulation; A, A′ control in Ringer's solution; B′ B′ 5½ min after the addition of tetracaine 5 × 10⁻⁵ M. Returned to Ringer's solution at 6 min.; C, C′ 11 min recovery (stimulus strength: A′ 30 V, B′ 100 V, C′ 60 V (Highman and Bartels[35]).

as the monomethylated. A 200-fold increase in potency by the extra methyl group in the quaternary ion can hardly be explained on the basis of increased binding. The results parallel the findings of a marked increase of enzyme activity when ACh-esterase and choline acetylase activity are tested with substrates in presence of the extra methyl group, where the increase cannot be attributed to increased binding[32, 33]. The binding forms only part of the biological activity. It is a prerequisite for some additional changes. Since the quaternary group is a tetrahedral structure and has a more or less spherical shape, folding of a few amino acids of the protein around the extra methyl group may be an explanation for the effect on the protein activity. The assumption of conformational changes in all three proteins in their active state is further supported by the differences of the entropy of activation of ACh-esterase during the hydrolysis of tertiary and quaternary esters: the entropy of activation is much more favorable, by about 30–40 entropy units, in the presence of the extra methyl group[34].

Curare (D-tubocurarine) is formed by 6 rings; 2 of them are heterocyclic and contain quaternary nitrogens. The compound is a relatively potent inhibitor of ACh-esterase[35]. However, it has a markedly higher affinity to the receptor. The "apparent" dissociation constant of the D-tubocurarine –receptor complex was tested on the monocellular electroplax preparation and found to be 2.4 × 10⁻⁷[36].

The high affinity of curare suggests its usefulness for attempts to isolate the receptor protein. Curare like compounds have been first used by Chagas and his assoiates for studying curare "receptors" in general[37]. Subsequetly, attempts were initiated for isolating the ACh receptor protein by precipitation with curare. A compound such as curare will react by Coulombic and van der Waals' forces with a variety of macromolecules, proteins, nucleic acids, acidic polysaccharides, etc. But there is a protein fraction which precipitates with curare. One of the proteins precipitated seemed to have a high affinity to curare and to other compounds related in structure to ACh and appeared to consist of a single component according to electrophoretic analysis and sedimentation velocity[38]. However, purification of this protein on columns revealed that it could still be resolved into several fractions; one of the protein precipitable by curare seems to have a rather high affinity to curare and is at present under investigation (S. Beychok, unpublished observations).

INSEPARABLE ASSOCIATION OF ELECTRICAL ACTIVITY WITH THE ACh RECEPTOR PROTEIN

Of particular interest is the reaction of the receptor protein with local anesthetics, related in structure to ACh such as procaine:

$$\overset{\oplus}{R}\!\!-\!\!R\ N CH_2CH_2O\overset{(+)}{C}\!\!-\!\!O^{(-)} \qquad \overset{\oplus}{R}\!\!-\!\!R\ N CH_2CH_2O\overset{(+)}{C}\!\!-\!\!O^{(-)}$$

Acetylcholine	Procaine

In tetracaine one proton on the N of the aniline group is replaced by a butyryl group. In contrast to ACh these tertiary structures are lipid soluble and therefore able to penetrate the structural barriers surrounding the conducting membrane. The author has maintained for many years that this type of local anesthetics act by competition with ACh for the active site of the receptor protein. These local anesthetics are receptor inhibitors; they act as antimetabolites by preventing ACh from reacting with the active site. Evidence for this mode of action has been obtained in experiments with procaine and tetracaine on the monocellular electroplax[29, 39, 40]. The data show conclusively that the local anesthetics compete with ACh for the receptor: a cell depolarized by receptor activators, ACh or carbamylcholine, is completely repolarized by tetracaine, even in the presence of the activator. The effects are in contrast to those with compounds which block electrical activity but have no affinity to the ACh system, such as for instance the potent marine toxin obtained from puffer fish. No competition is observed in this case.

The results provide a chemical explanation of the mode of action of certain local anesthetics. Moreover, since it is known that these local anesthetics block conduction in all conducting fibers, the observations provide evidence that the ACh receptor protein is essential for the generation of bioelectric currents in axons; they thus supplement the evidence previously obtained for the inseparable association of electrical and ACh-esterase activity.

THE BASIS OF THE NEUROHUMORAL TRANSMITTER THEORY VIEWED IN THE LIGHT OF BIOCHEMICAL ANALYSIS

When a new approach leads to new knowledge, a more satisfactory interpretation of previous observations frequently becomes possible. The two main facts on which the hypothesis of neurohumoral transmission was based was (I) the appearance of ACh in the fluid perfusing junctions or synapses, following stimulation, and (II) the powerful action of ACh on junctions in contrast to the absence of any effect on axonal conduction. However, as was repeatedly and emphatically stressed by Dale, one of the leading pioneers of the theory, and his associates, ACh appears only in the presence of physostigmine in the perfusion fluid; not a trace appears in its absence. Physostigmine is a powerful inhibitor of ACh-esterase and inactivates the ester released in microseconds. If this physiological mechanism of removal is blocked, ACh of necessity must leak out. The appearance of ACh outside the cell clearly is an artifact. Moreover, contrary to previous assumption, ACh is released from both sides of the junction[41]. According to recent data of Hayes and Riker[42], just as much ACh is released per impulse at the neuromusculatur junction on direct stimulation of the denervated muscle as is in the innervated control. By combining staining techniques with electron microscopy Barrnett[43] has shown that ACh-esterase is located in the pre- and postsynaptic membranes of the neuromuscular junction. The ACh system is not only present in the two membranes, but is is functional there since ACh, curare and prostigmine act on both sides of the junction[44].

Since the famous observations of Claude Bernard—that the action of curare is limited to the neuromuscular junction and does not affect conduction in nerve and muscle fibers—this demonstration was used as evidence for a special mechanism at junctions different from that in axons. However, curare, ACh, and similar mono- and diquaternary nitrogen derivatives are lipid-insoluble. The explanation was offered that the conducting membrane of axons is protected by structural barriers impervious for lipid-insoluble compounds except at junctions. Experimental evidence for the existence of these barriers was offered in a great variety of ways. Lipid-soluble analogues, such as local anesthetics, are able to penetrate, and therefore, to compete with ACh released intracellularly. Moreover, if ACh cannot penetrate, it cannot, when released internally, leak to the outside except at junctions.

However, in the last three years, actions of curare and ACh on axonal electrical activity have been obtained in various ways. Preparations were tested in which the protecting barriers are so weak as to be unable to prevent this type of compounds from reaching the membrane. In other cases, the structural barriers were reduced by chemical treatment.

Applying curare to a Ranvier node of a single fiber of a frog's sciatic nerve (which contains several thousand fibers) Dettbarn obtained reversible block of axonal electrical activity within 30 seconds[45]. An effect of ACh was obtained by Armett and Ritchie[46] in fibers of the desheathed vagus of rabbit. Dettbarn and Davis[47] recently obtained a depolarizing action of ACh on axonal electrical activity of sheathed somatic fibers of crustaceans. After treatment of frog sciatic nerves with a detergent, Walsh and Deal[48] obtained reversible block of axonal conduction with curare, ACh, and other quaternary nitrogen derivatives. After exposure of the giant axon of squid to cottonmouth moccasin venom in a concentration which by itself had no effect, Rosenberg and Podleski obtained rapid and reversible block of electrical activity with curare and with ACh[49]. The effects have been demonstrated to be due to increased permeability after venom treatment (Rosenberg and Hoskin[50]). Thus, what is considered as a direct evidence for the role of ACh in the thinking of some investigators, has now been provided with a variety of preparations and procedures.

However, the effects of ACh and curare now obtained on axonal conduction would by themselves not be significant without the large amount of biochemical data in favor of the essential role of ACh in this process. The fact that the ACh system is present in all conducting fibers, the various unusual properties of the system satisfying the prerequisite for being in control of the ion movements during activity, the evidence that specific and competitive inhibitors of either ACh-esterase or receptor protein block electrical activity, in the light of all these facts the depolarizing action of ACh and the blocking effect of curare become significant.

There are many observations which indicate that the ACh system is present, complete and functional in the axonal, the pre- and the post-synaptic membranes[7, 51]. There is no justification for assuming a role of the system at the junction fundamentally different from that in the axon. However, the complex structural organization of the junction differs greatly from the simple form of the axon. Even if the ACh system has the same function on both sides of the gap, i.e. that of changing ionic conductance of the membranes, physical events must be greatly influenced and almost certainly be modified by the difference in structure. Our techniques, in spite of all refinements, are not adequate as yet for direct recordings of the physical events taking place between two cellular units in a space which is only a few hundred Å wide and sometimes even less. Whether additional chemical factors are present at the junction, but not in the axon, is not known. A more complete understanding thus remains a problem for further investigations.

REFERENCES

1. E. OVERTON, *Pflueg. Arch. ges. Physiol.* **92**, 346 (1902).
2. M. A. ROTHENBERG, *Biochim. Biophys. Acta*, **4**, 96 (1950); R. D. KEYNES, *J. Physiol.* **113**, 99 (1951); A. L. HODGKIN, *Biol. Rev.* **26**, 338 (1951).
3. B. C. ABBOTT, A. V. HILL and J. V. HOWARTH, *Proc. Roy. Soc. B.* **148**, 149 (1958).
4. A. V. HILL, in: *Molecular Biology*, D. Nachmansohn, Ed., Academic Press, New York, p. 17 (1960).
5. E. SCHOFFENIELS, *Science* **127**, 1117 (1958).
6. D. NACHMANSOHN, *Harvey Lectures 1953/54*, Academic Press, New York, p. 57 (1955).
7. D. NACHMANSOHN, *Chemical and Molecular Basis of Nerve Activity*, Academic Press, New York 1959.
8. I. B. WILSON and M. COHEN, *Biochim. Biophys. Acta* **11**, 147 (1953).
9. W. D. DETTBARN and F. C. G. HOSKIN, *Biochim. Biophys. Acta*, **62**, 566 (1962).
10. W. D. DETTBARN, *Biochim. Biophys. Acta* **41**, 377 (1960).
11. J. D. ROBERTSON, in: *Molecular Biology*, D. Nachmansohn, Ed., Academic Press, New York, p. 87, 1960.
12. R. STAEMPFLI, *J. Physiol.* (Paris) **48**, 710 (1956).
13. W. A. ENGELHARDT and M. N. LJUBIMOVA, *Nature* **144**, 668 (1939).
14. I. B. WILSON, F. BERGMANN and D. NACHMANSOHN, *J. Biol. Chem.* **186**, 781 (1950).
15. D. NACHMANSOHN and I. B. WILSON, *Advanc. Enzymol.* **12**, 259 (1951).
16. D. NACHMANSOHN and E. A. FELD, *J. Biol. Chem.* **171**, 715 (1947).
17. I. B. WILSON and F. BERGMANN, *J. Biol. Chem.* **185**, 479 (1950).
18. S. HESTRIN, *Biochim. Biophys. Acta* **4**, 310 (1950).
19. I. B. WILSON, *J. Biol. Chem.* **199**, 113 (1952).
20. I. B. WILSON and S. GINSBURG, *Biochim. Biophys. Acta* **18**, 168 (1955).
21. H. KEWITZ and I. B. WILSON, *Arch Biochem. Biophys.* **60**, 261 (1956).
22. H. KEWITZ, I. B. WILSON and D. NACHMANSOHN, *Arch. Biochem. Biophys.* **64**, 456 (1956).
23. E. J. POZIOMEK, B. E. HACKLEY and G. M. STEINBERG, *J. Org. Chem.* **23**, 714 (1958).
24. T. NAMBA and K. HIRAKI, *J. Am. Med. Assoc.* **166**, 1834 (1958).
25. I. B. WILSON, S. GINSBURG and C. QUAN, *Arch. Biochem. Biophys.* **77**, 286 (1958).
25a. F. HOBBIGER, in: *Handbuch der experimentellen Pharmakologie*, Erg. Band 15, G. Koelle, Ed., p. 921, Springer Verlag, Heidelberg (1963).
26. H. KEWITZ, *Arch. Biochem. Biophys.* **66**, 263 (1957).
27. P. ROSENBERG, *Biochem. Pharmacol.* **3**, 212 (1960).
28. M. ALTAMIRANO, W. L. SCHLEYER, C. W. COATES and D. NACHMANSOHN, *Biochim. Biophys. Acta* **16**, 268 (1955).
29. E. SCHOFFENIELS and D. NACHMANSOHN, *Biochim. Biophys. Acta* **26**, 1 (1957); E. SCHOFFENIELS, *Biochim. Biophys. Acta* **26**, 585 (1957).
30. H. B. HIGMAN and E. BARTELS, *Biochim. Biophys. Acta* **57**, 77 (1962).
31. E. BARTELS, *Biochim. Biophys. Acta* **63**, 365 (1962).
32. I. B. WILSON, *J. Biol. Chem.* **197**, 215 (1952).
33. R. BERMAN, I. B. WILSON, and D. NACHMANSOHN, *Biochim, Biophys. Acta* **12**, 315 (1953).
34. I. B. WILSON and E. CABIB, *J. Am. Chem. Soc.* **78**, 202 (1956).
35. F. BERGMANN, I. B. WILSON and D. NACHMANSOHN, *Biochim. Biophys. Acta* **6**, 217 (1950).
36. H. B. HIGMAN, T. R. PODLESKI, and E. BARTELS, *Biochim. Biophys. Acta* **75**, 187 (1963).

37. C. CHAGAS, *Ann. N.Y. Acad. Sci.* **81**, 345 (1959); A. HASSON and C. CHAGAS, in: *Bioelectrogenesis*, C. Chagas and A. Paes de Carvalho, Eds., Elsevier, Amsterdam, p. 362 (1961).
38. S. EHRENPREIS, *Biochim. Biophys. Acta* **44**, 561 (1960).
39. H. B. HIGMAN and E. BARTELS, *Biochim. Biophys. Acta* **54**, 543 (1961).
40. T. R. PODLESKI and E. BARTELS, *Biochim. Biophys. Acta*, in press.
41. A. R. McINTYRE, in: *Curare and Curare-like Agents*, D. Bovet, F. Bovet-Nitti and G. B. Marini-Bettolo, Eds., Elsevier, Amsterdam, p. 211 (1959).
42. A. H. HAYES and W. F. RIKER, *Fed. Proc.* **215** (1963).
43. R. J. BARRNETT, *J. Cell. Biol.* **12**, 247 (1962).
44. R. L. MASLAND and R. S. WIGTON, *J. Neurophysiol.* **3**, 269 (1940); W. F. RIKER, G. WERNER, J. ROBERTS and A. KUPERMAN, *J. Pharmacol. Exptl. Therap.* **125**, 150 (1959); G. WERNER and A. S. KUPERMAN, in: *Handbuch der experimentellen Pharmakologie*, Erg. Band 15, G. Koelle, Ed., p. 570, Springer Verlag, Heidelberg (1963).
45. W. D. DETTBARN, *Nature* **186**, 891 (1960).
46. C. J. ARMETT and J. M. RITCHIE, *J. Physiol.* **152**, 141 (1960).
47. W. D. DETTBARN and F. A. DAVIS, *Biochim. Biophys. Acta* **66**, 397 (1963).
48. R. R. WALSH and S. E. DEAL, *Am. J. Physiol.* **197**, 547 (1959).
49. P. ROSENBERG and T. R. PODLESKI, *J. Pharmacol. Exptl. Therap.* **137**, 249 (1962).
50. P. ROSENBERG and F. C. G. HOSKIN, *J. Gen. Physiol.* **46**, 1065 (1963).
51. D. NACHMANSOHN, in: *Actualités Neurophysiologiques* (Vol. III), A. M. Monnier, Ed., Masson, Paris, p. 299 (1961); D. NACHMANSOHN, in: *Handbuch der experimentellen Pharmakologie*, Erg. Band 15, G. Koelle, Ed., Springer Verlag, Heidelberg (1963).

A PROBLEM IN MUSCULAR EXCITATION
IN THE ANTHOZOA

C. F. A. PANTIN

Professor of Zoology in the University of Cambridge

THE use of simple models to elucidate complex mechanical principles is well known to the engineer. Similarly, the analysis of living machinery by study of its principles in the simplest organisms is one of the most powerful weapons in the hands of the physiologist. A vivid illustration of this was the discovery by Metchnikoff (1892) of phagocytosis as a major defence mechanism against infection. He studied the phenomenon in every grade of organism, and one of his many demonstrations of it was to show the manner in which amoebocytes migrate to the site of an injury by a foreign body in the Medusae *Rhizostomum* and *Aurelia*. The work of Professor Koshtoyants has been in this same tradition, and it is a pleasure to offer a small contribution from one who has worked in fields allied to his own.

The problem I wish to consider in this essay is how far our existing knowledge of the nervous and muscular organization in the simplest cellular animals, particularly the Anthozoa, suffices to account for the different kinds of contraction which the muscles can undergo.

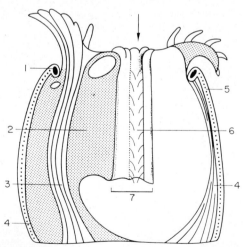

FIG. 1. Chief musculature of *Metridium*. (From: Batham and Pantin, 1950. *J. exp. Biol.* **27**, 264, Fig. 1.)

224

Investigation by lapse-rate cinematography and other means (Batham and Pantin, 1950; Pantin, 1952) shows that Actinians, or sea-anemones, can execute a remarkable variety of behaviour patterns despite the simplicity of their organization. We will not now discuss the local responses of the disk and tentacles of the complex activities associated with feeding and locomotion. Let us confine our attention to the simple reflex closure resulting from strong stimulation of the column. Figure 1 shows the muscles involved; the retractors of the mesenteries which pull down the disk, the marginal sphincter which closes it, and the parietal and circular muscle systems of the body wall.

Following the work of Parker (1919), Pantin (1935a–d) and Hall and Pantin (1937) on *Metridium* and *Calliactis*, it seems clear that excitation of the column initiates nervous impulses which can be conveyed in any direction without hindrance over a through-conduction system leading to the responding muscles. There is evidence that this system is particularly well developed in tracts running up the mesenteries and connected round the column, particularly at the level of the marginal sphincter (Pantin, 1935b).

A succession of impulses causes a contraction of the retractors or the sphincter, the extent of these contractions being governed by facilitation between the excitable system and the contractile system of the muscle (Pantin, 1935d). A single impulse is without mechanical effect, but it so influences the contractile system that a subsequent impulse may cause a very rapid contraction of the muscle. The extent of this contraction decreases as the interval between stimuli is lengthened. Consequently a succession of shocks causes a steplike succession of rapid contractions; as in Fig. 2 which records the response of the retractors of *Metridium*.

The histological evidence agrees well with the requirements of this system. Running up the retractor face of the mesenteries is a well developed nerve-net of bipolar cells (Pantin, 1952; Batham, Pantin and Robson, 1960). These make simple non-syncytial synaptic contacts with each other. The structure of the net indicates no preference for conduction in one direction rather than another. The net extends over the retractor and other muscles.

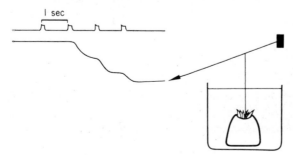

FIG. 2. *Metridium* retractor response to four condenser shocks. (From: Batham and Pantin, 1954. *J. exp. Biol.* **31**, 86, Fig. 1a.)

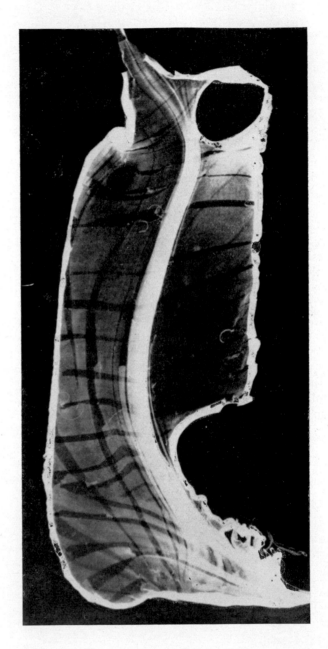

FIG. 3. (a) Whole perfect mesentery of *Metridium* showing retractor and muscle fields. (From: Batham and Pantin, 1951. *Quart. J. micr. Sci.* **92**, 27, Fig. 3.)

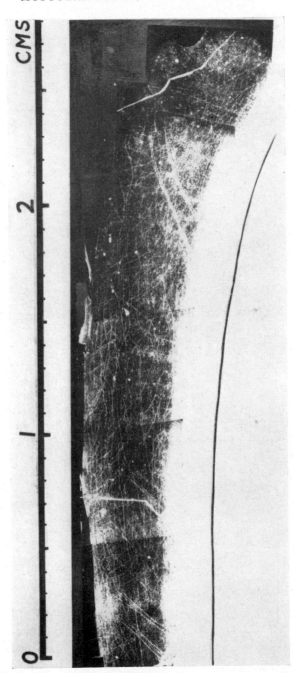

FIG. 3 (b) *Metridium* upper two thirds of "perfect" mesentery as in Fig. 3 a. Stained with Holmes' silver method. Under darkground illumination. Showing network of nerve fibres running alongside, and into, the retractor (white, on right).

Figure 3 shows (a) an isolated mesentery to show the retractor muscle and its neighbouring muscle field, (b) a mesentery stained with silver after Holmes' method (cf. Pantin, 1952) examined under low magnification with darkground illumination. The net is clearly shown running by, and into the retractor. Figure 4 shows under direct illumination an enlargement of

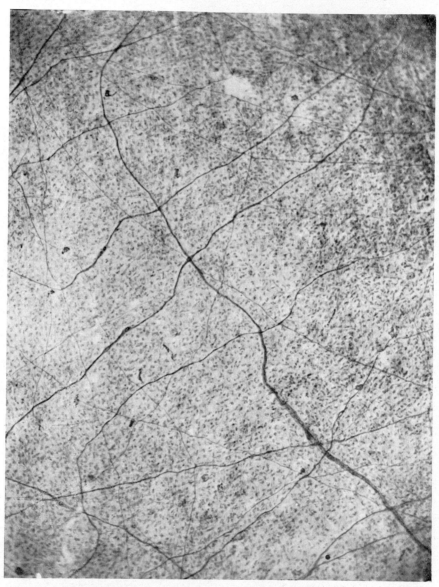

FIG. 4. Nerve-net of bipolar nerve cells on retractor surface of perfect mesentery of *Metridium*. Preparation by E. J. Batham.

the nerve-net, stained with silver, from the region between the retractor and the body wall. The net continues over the retractor and the processes of the bipolar nerve cells mostly appear to end in expansions on the muscle fibres. In addition, it is possible to show that an abundance of simple sense-cells connect with this nerve-net (Pantin, 1952). The sensory stimulation of the system has been analysed by Passano and Pantin (1955), for mechanical stimuli.

So far, the physiological requirements of sensory system, through-conduction system, and access from this to the retractor muscle all have histological structures in the right position to correspond to them; sense cells, nerve network and the contacts between this and the muscle. If the system gave only facilitated contractions such as those recorded in Fig. 2 the accordance between the physiological and histological pictures would be complete. In fact there are additional physiological features which complicate the matter: there is evidence in certain muscles of reciprocal inhibition, notably between the circular muscles and the parietals (Batham and Pantin, 1954): there is also evidence that muscles like the retractor and the marginal sphincter can give more than one kind of contraction, a quick and a slow.

Elsewhere in the animal kingdom as in the Crustacea and the Mollusca, inhibition and ability of a muscle to give more than one sort of contraction are commonly associated with multiple innervation of the muscle by different sets of nerve fibres. In the varied histological methods my colleagues and I have used, we have found no evidence for this in the actinian nerve-net, and this conclusion does not run counter to the fine classical description of the nervous system of these animals given by the Hertwigs (1879). We have not yet attacked the question of the histological basis of inhibition. But we have begun an analysis of the two distinct kinds of contraction which can be given by the same muscle.

The facts are as follows. Some muscles like the retractor can give quick facilitated responses. These take place to stimuli at frequencies about 1 per sec. All muscles, including those like the retractor, can however give a very slow contraction often taking a minute or more to reach its maximum and even longer to decay. This slow contraction can usually be initiated by stimuli at frequencies of the order of 1 per 5 sec; that is below the frequency required for facilitated responses. These slow contractions may vary considerably in extent and in the latent period following stimulation. The parietals and the circular muscle sheet of the column (apart from the marginal sphincter) only give such slow contractions. On the other hand, the retractor and the marginal sphincter can give these slow contractions as well as the quick facilitated ones (Fig. 5). The quick and the slow contractions are excited by stimuli at exactly the same threshold intensity—that of the through-conduction system. There is no evidence of their being called into action by independent excitatory systems. Their appearance or nonappearance depends solely upon the frequency of stimulation. Low frequencies, one every 3 to 5 seconds, call forth slow contractions in all muscles. High frequencies, one per second, may also call forth quick facilitated responses in some muscles, like the retractor.

Even at the electron microscope level of magnification there is no histological difference except size between the muscle fibres which give quick contractions and those which only give slow. The "quick" muscle fibres,

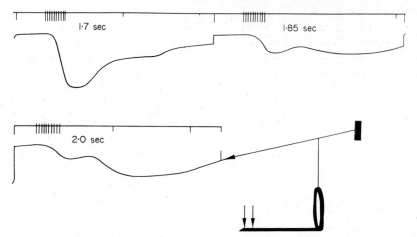

FIG. 5. *Metridium:* responses of muscle ring including sphincter to series of shocks at different intervals. (From: Batham and Pantin, 1954. *J. exp. Biol.* **31**, 84, Fig. 6.)

however, are longer and thicker (Grimstone and others, 1958). There is no evidence of any differentiation of the nerve-net except that those muscles so far investigated which have a facilitated response have a much richer nerve-net over them.

To prove the negative, that there are not two independently excitable systems serving the quick and the slow contractions, is difficult. But the fact that the threshold for both is always the same—that of the through-conduction system—suggests that there is only one system; and the fact that the two contractions are called up over different ranges of frequency suggests that the method by which they are brought about must be different.

Another striking difference between the quick and the slow contractions rests in this. In the quick contraction the muscle develops tension at once after a latent period of a few msec, due to conduction time. In contrast, the slow contraction develops in a sigmoid manner with no sharp onset. This suggests that this is a recruitment phenomenon in which more and more of the contractile system becomes involved as the contraction proceeds. This does seem to be the case.

Figure 6(a) shows a slow isometric contraction developed in a ring, 4 cm across, of the circular muscle sheet from the middle of the column or

Metridium. A series of 5 shocks at 1 per sec interval is followed by a long latent period and a slow sigmoid rise in tension over a period of minutes. Figure 6(b) shows a similar contraction in which the isometric tension is suddenly released by allowing 2·1 mm of shortening, during the development of the contraction, after the manner of the classical experiments of A. V. Hill (1926). It will be seen that the re-development of tension is far more rapid than during its slow sigmoid onset. Initially, therefore, the full tensile state has not been developed but is very gradually recruited.

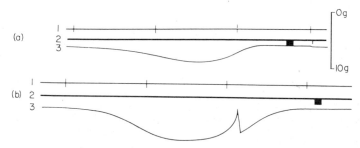

FIG. 6. Isometric responses of ring tissue from middle of column of *Metridium* to 5 condenser shocks at intervals of 1 sec (middle signal). Width of ring 40 mm. Time marker in minutes.

(a) Simple contraction, note very long latent period followed by slow sigmoid rise of tension.
(b) The same, with a quick release of 2·15 mm during the rising phase of tension. Note the very rapid re-development of tension.

This gradual recruitment of the contraction in the circular muscle takes place very long after the stimulus which initiated the contraction. We do not yet know how it is produced. But there is evidence which suggests that it may involve spread of contraction by muscular conduction rather than nervous. These slow contractions can occur at a stage during magnesium anaesthetization long after indirect excitation of the muscle has failed. Moreover peristalsis of the circular muscle is conducted down the column far more slowly than the rate of conduction over the column by the nervenet.

Histological studies of the nerve-net by intra-vital staining with methylene blue (Batham, Pantin and Robson, 1960) show a very sparse nerve-net over the circular muscle sheet in which it seems impossible that more than a few of the individual muscle fibres are in contact with nerve fibres.

If this hypothesis is correct we must suppose that the slow recruitment of the slow Actinian muscles is due to gradual spread of the contractile state through the muscle sheet. In contrast the richly innervated muscles could, under appropriate conditions, be activated almost simultaneously over the whole sheet. Low frequency stimulation of such muscles might involve muscular conduction as in the weakly innervated slow circular muscle sheet of the body wall. Two kinds of contraction would then be possible in the one muscle.

Such an hypothesis must of course be tested. It is elaborated here, simply to remind us that even the fact that two kinds of contraction can be elicited from the same muscles does not necessitate the assumption of multiple innervation of the muscle. The physiological potentialities of even simple neuromuscular systems are greater than is commonly assumed (Pantin, 1956).

REFERENCES

BATHAM, E. J. and C. F. A. PANTIN, Phases of activity in the sea-anemone *Metridium senile* (L.), and their relation to external stimuli. *J. exp. Biol.* **27**, 377 (1950).

BATHAM, E. J. and C. F. A. PANTIN, Slow contraction and its relation to spontaneous activity in the sea-anemone *Metridium senile* (L.) *J. exp. Biol.* **31**, 84 (1954).

BATHAM, E. J., C. F. A. PANTIN and E. A. ROBSON, The nerve-net of the sea-anemone *Metridium senile:* the mesenteries and the column. *Quart. J. micr. Sci.* **101**, 487 (1960).

GRIMSTONE, A. V., R. W. HORNE, C. F. A. PANTIN and E. A. ROBSON, The fine structure of the mesenteries of the sea-anemone *Metridium senile*. *Quart. J. micr. Sci.* **99**, 523 (1958).

HALL, D. M. and C. F. A. PANTIN, The nerve-net of the Actinozoa. V. Temperature and facilitation in *Metridium senile*. *J. exp. Biol.* **14**, 71 (1937).

HERTWIG, O. and R. HERTWIG, *Studien zur Blättertheorie*. Heft 1. Die Actinien. Jena, Gustav Fischer 1879.

HILL, A. V., The laws of muscular motion. *Proc. Roy. Soc. B.* **100**, 87 (1926).

METCHNIKOFF, E., *Leçons sur la Pathologie Comparée de l'Inflammation*. Paris, Masson 1892.

PANTIN, C. F. A., The nerve-net of the Actinozoa. I. Facilitation. *J. exp. Biol.* **12**, 119 (1935a).

PANTIN, C. F. A., The nerve-net of the Actinozoa. II. Plan of the nerve-net. *J. exp. Biol.* **12**, 139 (1935b).

PANTIN, C. F. A., The nerve-net of the Actinozoa. III. Polarity and after-discharge. *J. exp.. Biol.* **12**, 156 (1935c).

PANTIN, C. F. A., The nerve-net of the Actinozoa. IV. Facilitation and the "staircase". *J. exp. Biol.* **12**, 389 (1935d).

PANTIN, C. F. A., The elementary nervous system. *Proc. Roy. Soc. B.* **140**, 147 (1952).

PANTIN, C. F. A., The origin of the nervous system. *Publ. Staz. Zool. Napoli* **28**, 171 (1956).

PARKER, G. H., *The Elementary Nervous System*. Philadelphia and London, Lippincott 1919.

PASSANO, L. M. and C. F. A. PANTIN, Mechanical stimulation in the sea-anemone *Calliactis parasitica*. *Proc. Roy. Soc. B.* **143**, 226 (1955).

THE HEAT-REGULATING MECHANISM
AND ITS DEVELOPMENT
IN POIKILOTHERMIC ANIMALS

V. A. Pegel' and V. A. Remorov

State University, Tomsk

Translated by Dr. R. Crawford

Metabolic processes in cold-blooded animals are known to depend on the temperature of the environment. Study of the quantitative aspect of this relationship has shown that it takes the form of an exponential curve (Krogh, referred to by Vinberg, 1956). Subsequently, the "Krogh curve" obtained wide recognition and received repeated confirmation by many authors working with a great variety of materials (Vinberg, 1956).

Under these circumstances the normal vital activity of poikilothermic animals is secured by a mechanism of co-ordination which maintains constancy of function within wide temperature limits (Pegel', 1949).

The publication of Krogh's investigations was followed by a number of papers in which doubt was thrown on the universality of the van't Hoff rule and the applicability of physico-chemical rules to biological material (Yel'tsina, 1940). In the opinion of Slonim (1937), deviations from the exponential curve observed in metabolism are possibly indicative of vestiges of active chemical thermoregulation in allotherms. This conclusion is not, however, accepted by all. Vinberg (1956, 1957) for example, regards it as unproven and he tends to regard the facts published merely as manifestations of individual variations.

It must therefore be recognized that there is still no unanimity of opinion on this "central" problem of biology (Precht, 1949). What then are the actual facts which have been omitted from Krogh's schema?

Stroganov (1939a, 1939b, 1940, 1956) has shown that if, prior to experiment, a fish is kept within a certain temperature range for a considerable time, then within this temperature range, metabolism will no longer exhibit an exponential dependence on temperature and there will be development of the so-called flattened segment, within the limits of which there is establishment of a definite level of physiological processes. Deviation of the temperature from the zone of adaptation produces qualitative changes in metabolism as shown by increase in the value of the respiratory quotient and

233

decline in the oxygen consumption per respiratory movement. Stroganov detects here a certain similarity between fishes and homoiotherms. He is of the opinion that we still know little of the mechanism responsible in poikilotherms for the constancy of physiological processes within the zone of temperature adaptation.

Similar results have been obtained by other authors. Schmeing-Engberding (1953) failed to observe any relationship between oxygen consumption and change of temperature within the "zone of preferred temperatures" in fishes. This was also established by Nikiforov (1958) in experiments with adapted salmon.

Similar disturbances of respiratory exchange have been found in insects (Kozhanchikov, 1936a, 1936b, 1941; Zenyakin, 1937; Lozina-Lozinskii, 1943), in molluscs (Grayevskii, 1946) and other animals in addition to fishes. These authors found that the flattened segment of the Krogh curve was formed by virtue of the fact that the rate of oxygen consumption fell as the temperature rose beyond the zone of adaptation. According to Kozhanchikov, this disturbance of the form of the curve reflects a thermoregulatory reaction and is characteristic only of eurythermic insects exposed to new conditions for a short period. There is no such reaction in stenothermic species.

Schlieper (1950, 1952) has also demonstrated differences in the reactions of stenothermic and eurythermic fishes and of crustaceans to temperature changes. Raising or lowering of the temperature readily leads to metabolic disequilibrium in stenothermic species (trout) but metabolism rapidly becomes stabilized under the new conditions (after 40–50 hours). In contrast, metabolism in eurythermic animals such as the river crab (*Astacus fluviatilis*) or the swordfish (*Xiphophorus helleri*) is resistant to falling or rising temperatures for a certain length of time and then gradually reaches its new level (on the 5th or 6th day). Schlieper's conclusion was that although basal metabolism in eurythermic animals also exhibited a certain degree of stability, it was insufficient to protect the fish against fluctuations in metabolism on prolonged temperature change.

Of still greater interest are his experiments on basal metabolism in relation to the adaptation of animals to daily fluctuations in temperature of up to 10°C. When the temperature was changed from 15° to 25° or from 25° to 15°, the change in basal metabolism was never greater than 25 per cent whereas, according to van't Hoff's rule, it should have been 200–300 per cent.

Disturbance of the exponential curve within the limits of the temperatures in which the animals had been kept before an experiment was also observed by Rao and Bullock (1954). Concerning the reasons for the fall of Q_{10} to 1 observed under these conditions, Bullock (1955) draws attention to the absence of experimental evidence on mechanisms for the regulation of metabolism, independent of temperature, and suggests that these cannot be regarded as simple chemical processes.

An important investigation was carried out by Precht *et al.* (1955) on temperature adaptation as revealed by metabolic adjustment in relation to slow changes in environmental temperature. Precht distinguishes five types of temperature adaptation. In animals classed as showing the first three types of temperature adaptation the intensity of functional activities changed with change of temperature but later there was return to the original levels. The basal metabolism of these animals thus remained independent of temperature to a greater or lesser extent. Precht points out that the reactions to temperature changes of the animals regarded as having the third type of adaptation are similar to those of terrestrial animals with primitive forms of heat-regulation.

Precht's fourth type consisted of animals with no power to regulate metabolism and in which the latter always followed the "Krogh curve." This was the particular type of temperature adaptation seen when the normal environmental temperature was unusually stable.

Precht's opinion is that temperature adaptation of cell enzymes constitutes the basis of metabolic regulation in animals. Change in the activity of cell enzymes as a means for the regulation of functions was known previously (Kreps, 1945). Precht's merit lies in the fact that he attempted to prove that functions were regulated by temperature through changes in the properties of the respiratory enzymes and their adaptation to actual environmental conditions.

Precht's conclusions receive some support from other investigations (Kozhanchikov, 1936a; Grayevskii, 1946; Privol'nev, 1947, 1952; Verzhbinskaya, 1957; Stroganov, 1939a, 1939b, 1940, 1956; and others). According to this view, reduction of temperature should lead to intensification and increase of temperature to reduction of oxidative processes in the body. This of course is not a complete statement of the mechanism for the influence of temperature in poikilothermic animals. Precht himself recognizes that it is much more complex and involves participation of the nervous system.

Other investigations (Wells, 1935a, 1935b; Samokhvalova, 1938; Shkorbatov, 1958) are also of considerable importance for an understanding of temperature adaptation. These papers have shown that adaptation to the actual environmental conditions is associated with certain changes in the physiological state of the animal. These differences may reveal themselves in dissimilar gaseous exchange values, dissimilar respiration rates and increased or reduced resistance of cells to temperature.

It has, however, also been found that animals exposed for long periods to environmental factors adapt themselves to the latter and that the indices for a number of functions then become identical (Selye, referred to by Mantel'man, 1958; Precht *et al.*, 1955).

Some authors distinguish several stages in the general adaptation reaction of the animal to changing temperature (Selye, referred to by Mantel'man,

1958; Stroganov, 1939a, 1939b, 1940, 1956; Serbenyuk and Manteifel', 1958; and others). In the first stage the organism tries to counteract the temperature effect and in subsequent stages slow changes occur in the organism for the purpose of adapting it to the new conditions.

Freeman (1950) and, more particularly, Serbenyuk and Manteifel' (1958) have demonstrated the important part played by the nervous system in the reactions of fishes to change of temperature. They established that fluctuation of the environmental temperature was followed by change in the respiratory exchange of the brain, as a result of which the organism's metabolism became adjusted to the new temperature.

In summing up these findings on the effect of temperature on vital activity one must emphasize the complexity of the problem and the absence of complete unanimity of view.

While existing views hold that poikilothermic aquatic animals are unable to regulate body temperature (Genn, 1944) or metabolism (Vinberg, 1956, 1957; Ivlev, 1958), evidence is accumulating that fishes and other cold-blooded animals do have mechanisms for such regulation.

At the same time Vinberg and Ivlev rightly state that many investigators who have expressed the view that fishes do have powers to regulate metabolism do not adduce any serious proofs. This reproach refers mainly to the lack of a physiological basis for such regulation.

For example, papers which describe experimental results supporting regulation of metabolism in fishes make no reference to heat-regulation, the assumption being that the body temperature of these animals follows the temperature of their environment accurately (Stroganov, 1956). Such a separation of metabolism and body temperature is unnatural. If the elements in the regulation of metabolism in the course of temperature adaptation in fishes find expression in flattening of the exponential curve, then it must be assumed that the same must also occur in connexion with the animal's body temperature.

Direct measurements of the body temperatures of fishes have shown that it is usually 0·002–0·7°C higher than that of the surrounding water (Genn, 1944). Even greater differences, reaching 4–10°C in the tunny (*Tunnus alalonga*) for example, are known (Kanitts, referred to by Ryumin, 1939).

So far, however, there have been no direct investigations on the subject of change in the body temperature of fishes within the zone of adaptation.

Our experiments (Pegel' and Remorov, 1957, 1959c) on three species of fish adapted to various temperature zones between 4° and 24° degrees revealed that the relationship between body temperature and environmental temperature was much more complex than is generally thought. We measured body temperature with a thermocouple inserted to a depth of 8–10 mm into the dorsal muscles of the fish.

It was found that, when the water temperature was raised or lowered slowly beyond the fish's adaptation zone, the fish's temperature began to lag behind the temperature of the surrounding water. When the water was heated the animal's temperature was found to be 0·1–0·2° below the water temperature and when the water was cooled, it was 1·5–2·0° higher. The curves for the relationships of the respiratory and cardiac rates to temperature were at the same time flattened.

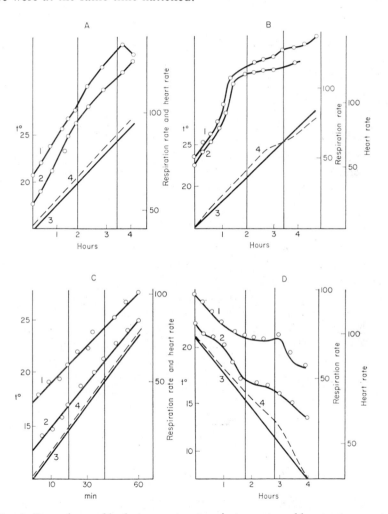

FIG. 1. Dependence of body temperature, respiratory rate and heart rate on water temperature in non-adapted fishes (A), adapted fishes (B and D) and adapted fishes in a state of general narcosis (C).

A and B—gourami (*Esphromenius olfax*), C and D—dace (*Leuciscus leuciscus*). 1— respiratory rate. 2—heart rate. 3—water temperature. 4—fish's temperature. Between vertical lines—zone of temperature adaption.

Control experiments on fishes not subjected to adaptation showed that their functions maintained direct relationships with the water temperature.

This was also typical of adapted fishes when in a state of general narcosis (Fig. 1). Our observations led us to the conclusion that elements of a heat-regulating mechanism, the purpose of which was probably to mitigate the effects of fluctuation of environmental temperature on the organism's metabolism, took shape in the course of the adaptation of the fishes to different temperatures. The mechanism apparently increased metabolism and heat production in response to cooling and reduced these on heating.

This view received a certain amount of support from our latest investigations (Pegel' and Remorov, 1959c) which demonstrated that respiratory exchange was increased in adapted fishes when the temperature was reduced by 2°C. There was simultaneous increase of lactic acid and reduction of sugar (Hagedorn–Jensen) in the blood. Heating of the water by 2°C led to reduction of oxygen consumption and raising of the RQ to 1·4–1·6. Blood lactic acid and sugar were also increased.

The content of residual nitrogen in the blood was practically unchanged by temperature fluctuations. The slight reduction that occurred on cooling after several hours was restored completely (Figs. 2 and 3).

In control experiments with non-adapted dace the respiratory exchange retained its direct relationship to temperature.

The metabolic changes described in fishes might be accompanied by vascular reactions.

We have only indirect evidence of the occurrence of vascular reactions in fish. Such evidence is derived from comparison of body temperatures in live and dead fish. In the latter it lags 0·3° behind the water temperature, whereas in living adapted fishes the lag is only 0·1–0·2° and in non-adapted fishes the temperature is always higher. These facts can apparently be explained if account is taken of the fact that the rate at which heat pene-

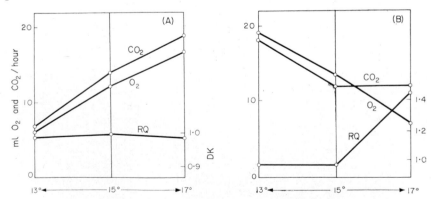

FIG. 2. Dependence of respiratory exchange on surrounding temperature in non-adapted (A) and adapted (to 15°C) dace (B) on increase of temperature above and decrease below the zone of adaptation.

trates the body from the surrounding water depends on the rate of blood-flow (Stacey *et al.*, 1959).

Another factor which may actively influence the course of the curve for the relationship between metabolic processes and temperature is the muscular activity or movement of the fish, which, according to Vinberg (1956) and Ivlev (1958) is increased when the animal is cooled and reduced when it is heated. This may be regarded as a manifestation of chemical thermoregulation in fishes.

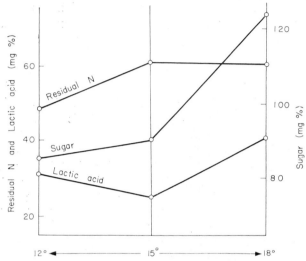

FIG. 3. Changes in the lactic acid, sugar and residual nitrogen contents of the blood in adapted dace on increase or decrease of the water temperature beyond the zone of adaptation (15°C).

In our investigations on temperature adaptation and also oxygen adaptation we gave particular attention to the signs of gradual stabilization of metabolic processes in fish within fairly wide temperature limits.

Amplifying the facts already known (Wells, 1935; Stroganov, 1956; Vinberg, 1956; Privol'nev, 1947; Mints, 1952; Precht, 1949, 1955; Lozinov, 1952, 1956; Nikiforov, 1952, 1953, 1958), our special experiments revealed that the physiological functions of fishes tended to fluctuate less as adaptation to temperature and oxygen conditions proceed (Pegel' and Remorov, 1959a, 1959b, 1959c). These findings serve to explain both the considerable individual fluctuations in various physiological indices described in the literature (Adrianov, 1937; Pavlov, 1936, 1939; Kalashnikov, 1933; Puchkov, 1954; and others) and for which there has hitherto been no satisfactory explanation (Vinberg, 1956), and also the possibility of their elimination. It follows from our experiments that this may be achieved if, before physiological investigations, poikilothermic animals are kept for a certain period under constant conditions leading to adaptation to these conditions.

This statement does not, of course, exhaust all the forms of adaptation to temperature in fish.

The fact is that, while a "normal Krogh curve" is the general form of the relationship between physiological processes and temperature in cold-blooded animals, these animals are capable of elaborating various adaptations to the actual conditions of existence in the course of their individual lives.

Although inhabiting areas with wide temperature limits, poikilothermic animals generally strive to live in more restricted zones of "preferred temperatures" (Ivlev, 1958; Strel'nikov, 1959). The result is that, as Beklemishev (referred to by Grayevskii, 1946) pointed out, the animal lives under much more constant temperature and humidity conditions than would appear to be the case at first sight.

The statement by Kalabukhov (1956) that the adaptational importance of many features is evidenced by the maintenance of the body's energy balance, also has a bearing on this question. This balance can, in the opinion of Aleksandrov (1952) and Ushakov (1955), be achieved in many ways, including system adaptation.

The active maintenance of constant conditions in this way favours the development of regulating mechanisms mitigating the effects of transient, slight temperature changes on the organism. This is the most probable way in which the elementary regulation of body temperature develops in poikilothermic animals. As in homiotherms, its purpose is to maintain the constancy of the organism's "internal medium."

The feature of heat regulation in poikilothermic animals, as compared with homoiothermic, is its impermanence. It develops on each occasion in the course of adaptation to an actual temperature and disappears when the latter changes, to reappear when fresh temperature conditions persist for a certain period of time.

It is probable that these forms of adaptation to environmental temperature in poikilothermic animals also represent an initial stage in the evolution of the heat-regulating mechanism generally, the theoretical aspects of which have been discussed in the works of Korzhuyev (1940, 1949) and Koshtoyants.

REFERENCES

ADRIANOV, V. B., Scientific Papers of Moscow University 9, *Biology* **5** (1937).
ALEKSANDROV, V. YA., Reports of the U.S.S.R. Academy of Sciences (*Dokl. Akad. Nauk SSSR*) **83** (1), 149 (1952).
BARCROFT, D., *Advances in Experimental Biology VIII* (2) (1929).
BULLOCK, T. H., *Biol. Rev.* **30** (3), 311 (1955).
FREEMAN, J. A., *Biol. Bull.* **99**, 416 (1950).
GRAYEVSKII, E. YA., J. of Gen. Biol. (*Zh. obshch. biol.*) **7**, 6, 475 (1946).
GENN, D. L., Recent advances in biology (*Usp. sovr. biol.*) **17**, 1, 87 (1944).
IVLEV, V. S., *Papers at a Congress on the physiology of fishes*, 288, Leningrad 1958.

IVLEV, V. S., Papers at a Congress on the physiology of fishes 288, Leningrad 1958.
KALABUKHOV, N. I., J. Gen. Biol. (*Zh. obshch. biol.*) **17**, 7, 417 (1946).
KALASHNIKOV, G. N., Composition of the blood of fishes. Scientific papers of Moscow University 33. *Hydrobiology*, 65.
KOZHANCHIKOV, I. V., *Papers of Z.I.N.* **4**, 2, 313 (1936a).
KOZHANCHIKOV, I. V., Zool. J. (*Zool. zh.*) **15**, 2, 217 (1936b).
KOZHANCHIKOV, I. V., Reports of the U.S.S.R. Academy of Sciences (*Dokl. Akad. Nauk SSSR*) **32**, 7, 515 (1941).
KORZHUYEV, P. A., Recent advances in biology (*Usp. sovr. biol.*) **12**, 3, 488 (1940).
KORZHUYEV, P. A., *Evolution of the Respiratory Function of the Blood*, Moscow 1949.
KREPS, YE. M., Bull. of the U.S.S.R. Academy of Sciences, division of biological sciences (*Izv. Akad. Nauk SSSR otd. biol. nauk*) **3**, 197 (1945).
KREPS, YE. M. and N. A. VERZHBINSKAYA, Bull. of the U.S.S.R. Academy of Sciences. Biological series. (*Izv. Akad. Nauk SSSR seriya biol.*) **6**, 855 (1959).
LOZINA-LOZINSKII, L. K., *Izv. Akad. Nauk SSSR* **3**, 125 (1943).
LOZINOV, A. B., Zool. J. (*Zool. zh.*) **31**, 5, 686 (1952).
LOZINOV, A. B., *Dokl. Akad. Nauk SSSR* **107**, 2, 337 (1956).
MANTEL'MAN, I. I., *Izv. V.N.I.O.R.Kh.* **47**, 1 (1958).
MINTS, A. G., *Adaptability of Young Fishes to Oxygen Changes*, Leningrad 1952.
NIKIFOROV, N. D., *Dokl. Akad. Nauk SSSR* **86**, 6, 1231 (1952).
NIKIFOROV, N. D., *Izv. V.N.I.O.R.Kh.* **33**, 36 (1953).
NIKIFOROV, N. D., *Papers at a Congress on the physiology of fishes*, Leningrad 1958.
PAVLOV, V. A., *Papers of the Vorodinsk Biological Station* **9**: **1**, 29 (1936).
PAVLOV, V. A., *Izv. V.N.I.O.R.Kh.* **21**, 127 (1939).
PEGEL', V. A., *Scientific Papers of Tomsk University* **12**, 117 (1949).
PEGEL', V. A., *Papers of the All-Union Congress on the biological basis of pisciculture, Tomsk 1959.*
PEGEL', V. A. and V. A. REMOROV, *Proceedings of Congress on Oedological Physiology* **1**, 44 (1959a).
PEGEL', V. A. and V. A. REMOROV, Papers of Congress on General Biology, commemorating the centenary of Darwinism. *Papers of Tomsk University* **237** (1959b).
PEGEL', V. A. and V. A. REMOROV, *Scientific addresses for institutes of Higher Education, biol. series* **3**, 86 (1959c).
PEGEL', V. A. and V. A. REMOROV, *Papers of Tomsk University* **151**, 29 (1960).
PRECHT, H., Zeitschr. f. Naturforsch. **4b**, 1, 25 (1949).
PRECHT, H., J. CHRISTOPHERSEN and H. HENSEL, *Temperatur und Leben*, Berlin 1955.
PRIVOL'NEV, T. I., *Izv. V.N.I.O.R.Kh.* **25**, 2, 125 (1947).
PRIVOL'NEV, T. I., *Papers of Congress on acclimatization of fishes and edible invertebrates* **40** (1952).
PUCHKOV, I. V., *Physiology of Fishes*, Moscow 1954.
RAO, K. P. and T. H. BULLOCK, Amer. Nat. **88**, 1, 33 (1954).
RYUMIN, A. V., Scientific papers by students of Moscow University. Biology **6** (1939).
SAMOKHVALOVA, G. V., *Dokl. Akad. Nauk SSSR* **20**, 6, 475 (1938).
SCHLIEPER, C., Biol. Zbl. **69**, 5/6, 216 (1950).
SCHLIEPER, C., Verh. dtsch. zool. Ges. **2**, 267 (1952).
SCHMEING-ENGBERDING, F., Zeitschr. f. Fisch **2**, 1/2, 125 (1953).
SERBENYUK, TS. V. and YU. B. MANTEIFEL', *Papers of Congress on the Physiology of Fishes* 278. Leningrad 1958.
SHKORBATOV, L. G., Papers of Congress on the Physiology of fishes. Moscow 1958.
SLONIM, A. D., Recent advances in biology (*Usp. sovr. biol.*) **6**, 1, 52 (1937).
STACEY, R., D. WILLIAMS, R. JORDEN and R. MACMORRIS, *Principles of Biological and Medical Physics* (1959).
STREL'NIKOV, I. D., *Proceedings of Congress on Oecological Physiology* **61**, Leningrad 1959.
STROGANOV, N. S., Physiol. J. U.S.S.R. (*Fiziol. zh. SSSR*) **26**, 1, 68 (1939a).

STROGANOV, N. S., Scientific Papers of Moscow University 33. *Hydrobiology* **30** (1939b).
STROGANOV, N. S., *Dokl. Akad. Nauk SSSR* **28**, 8, 744 (1940).
STROGANOV, N. S., *Physiological Adaptability of Fishes to Water Temperature.* Moscow 1956.
USHAKOV, B. P., *Investigations on Heat-stability in the Muscles of Poikilotherms in Relation to the Conditions of Species Existence.* Leningrad 1955.
VERZHBINSKAYA, N. A., *Evolution of Energy Metabolism in the Vertebrate Brain.* Leningrad 1957.
VINBERG, G. G., Papers of Belorussian University, Minsk 1956.
VINBERG, G. G., *Bulletin of the Moscow Society of Naturalists. Biological Division* **12**, 3, 91 (1957).
WELLS, N. A., *Physiol. Zool.* **8**, 2, 196 (1935a).
WELLS, N. A., *Physiol. Zool.* **8**, 2, 318 (1935b).
YEL'TSINA, N. V., Recent advances in Biology (*Usp. sovr. biol.*) **12**, 1, 52 (1940).
ZENYAKIN, L. A., Entomological Review (*Entomologicheskoye obozreniye*) **28**, 32, 174 (1937).

THE EVOLUTION OF MUSCLE

J. W. S. PRINGLE

Department of Zoology, Oxford University

IN THE latter half of the nineteenth century Darwinian ideas about evolution stimulated a great outburst of interest in the comparative anatomy of animals. The first half of the twentieth century has seen a smaller but no less vital growth of the subject of comparative physiology, the study of the different ways in which animals perform their bodily functions. Already some progress has been made in the search for principles which have governed the evolution of these physiological systems.

There is one great difference between the two subjects. Whereas descriptive anatomy has now almost ceased to be studied in its own right, physiology progresses from strength to strength and seeks its explanations ever deeper in the laws of physics and chemistry. The purely analytical approach is extremely fruitful, and intensive studies of this sort make up most of the physiological literature. But to the zoologist or the comparative physiologist no account of the physiology of an organ of the body is complete unless it embraces the organ's evolutionary history; the zoologist is bound to take into account the fact that the mechanisms available for study today have become what they are through a process of evolution. He feels the need for extensive work on a wide range of vertebrate and invertebrate types in order to comprehend the varieties of mechanism which exists in the animal kingdom.

Because of the focal interest in the physiology of man, this extension of the subject to the lower animals makes slow progress, but particularly in that branch of physiology concerned with the working of nerves and muscles there is now a considerable body of established facts about invertebrate animals. In this field the science of comparative physiology can begin to advance beyond mere description to the formulation of laws and general hypotheses. By their very nature, generalizations about the course of evolutionary progress can never command certainty, and they may, for that reason, always remain suspect for the biophysicist and biochemist whose processes of analysis are not subject to the same limitation. Such generalizations should, however, be able to help the pure physiologist, for the course of evolutionary change is not random and the laws, once established, should enable him to narrow down the search for biophysical and biochemical explanations. The object of this essay is to suggest one way in which the synthetic approach of comparative physiology can help analytical biophysics; I want to try to show that muscle physiologists, by a neglect of the fact of evolution, have been misled in their search for an understanding of the mechanism of muscular contraction.

THE ORIGIN OF CONTRACTILE TISSUES

It was G. H. Parker (1919) who first gave clear formulation to the idea that the functioning of the nervous and muscular systems of the lower invertebrate Phyla might reproduce much that must have been characteristic of these systems in their earliest stages of evolution. This is an example of the applications to comparative physiology of a principle so successful in the science of comparative anatomy, and it led Parker to a study of the Porifera as the lowest form of metazoan organization.

In a sponge like *Stylotella*, he found contractility without coordination, the ability to respond by local contraction to a variety of forms of stimulation. The concept of the "independent effector" arose from this work: this is a cell or a tissue with the property not only of contractility as found in the effectors of higher animals but also of that sensitivity to stimuli which in higher animals is restricted to separate, specialized receptor cells. Sponges, says Parker (1919), represent that stage of evolution in which a primitive type of muscle tissue has made its appearance unaccompanied by nervous elements. They mark the beginnings of the neuromuscular mechanism in that they possess the original and most ancient of its constituents, muscle, around which the remainder of the system (nerves and sense organs) is supposed subsequently to have evolved.

Parker continued to build up his picture of the evolution of the differentiated neuromuscular system by consideration of the Coelenterata. The quickened rate of response to stimuli, which distinguishes the coelenterates from the sponges, is associated with the fact that the coelenterates possess not only muscles but also nervous organs in the form of simple sensory surfaces. In that their behaviour is still dominated by local responses, the coelenterates might be thought not yet to possess the elements of a complete neuromuscular system comparable to that of higher animals. But in fact there is already in these animals a large measure of overall coordination of movement (Pantin, 1956); it was recognized long ago in the swimming of medusae and in feeding responses throughout the phylum, and it has more recently been studied by Batham and Pantin (1954). It is now recognized that in their nerve nets the Coelenterata have a true counterpart of the central nervous systems of higher animals: a diffuse coordinating mechanism which completes, with the receptors and effectors, the three elements into which the behavioural machinery of higher animals is commonly analysed.

It can perhaps be argued, against Parker's ideas, that both the sponges and coelenterates are mainly sessile animals and that the types of neuro-muscular system found in them may not be typical of the primitive organization of a more active animal. One can reason then in a different way, and consider from a theoretical standpoint the factors which must have governed the earliest stages in the evolution of animal movement. If we accept the views of Lwoff (1944), the holozoic habit typical of animals evolved from a holophytic condition by a process of loss of synthetic capabilities. The organism was at first saprophytic, feeding by diffusion into itself of organic material in solution. Later, with the development of digestive enzymes, came the ability to utilize solid particles. At the saprophytic stage, movement is advantageous because it creates turbulence and so renews the layer of water immediately in contact with the absorbing surface; when solid particles form the bulk of the food, movement is necessary to bring them into contact with the surface. Two general requirements can be stated for any mechanism of animal movement evolved in this way; (1) the mechanism must be energetically efficient, so that the diversion of energy from growth processes is as small as possible and is outweighed by the gain in energy resulting from increased food supplied, and (2) the movement must be regulated to the optimum for the conditions of the moment, so that it is neither too slow to achieve the gain in food supplies nor so fast that energy is dissipated wastefully. If the mechanism of animal movement did not from the first satisfy these two conditions, it is unlikely that it would have persisted and developed as part of the organization of the animal body.

These two requirements set limits to the possible design of the mechanical effectors. If they are to be mechanically efficient, thermodynamic considerations demand that they comprise a mechanism working cyclically. It is now probable that a muscle is such an engine for the conversion of chemical energy into mechanical work, operating by means of reversible (cyclical) strains in the working substance, the muscle proteins (Pryor, 1950). It seems highly unlikely that animals with a mechanism of movement involving the continuous dissipation of fuel substance (as, for example, in a rocket) would ever have competed successfully with those possessing a cyclical mechanism. But the operation of a cyclical machine involves the discontinuous performance of mechanical work and this at once introduces further design limitations. General synchronization of effectors would lead to fluctuations in the velocity of movement which is inefficient in a medium where drag is proportional to the square of the velocity.

In order to produce the required continuous locomotion, the animal must from the first have possessed a large number of effectors whose cycles of activity were either randomly timed or else suitably phased in a meta-chronal rhythm. Considerations of this sort determine the nature of the coordinating mechanisms, which are, however, outside the scope of this essay.

9 a*

The second requirement, that the velocity of movement must be regulated to the optimum, has more direct implications on the design of the effector mechanism. In higher animals, whose physiology is more familiar, this regulation of the force and speed of muscular action is done through the nerves by means of proprioceptive and other reflexes. But it cannot be supposed that such a differentiated reflex system was present .in the early stages of the evolution of a muscular contractile mechanism. The effectors, because their evolution was from the start determined by their value to the animal, must nevertheless have possessed a mechanism of regulation; this means that, primitively, they must have contained within themselves the necessary means of adjustment to the mechanical conditions in which they were called upon to work. The initial adjustment will have occurred through natural selection in the design of the locomotor organ; thus, before the appearance of skeletal levers, muscles required to move large loads slowly will have had more contractile elements in parallel and those required to move light loads through a large distance will have had more elements in series. But over and above this, except in very special circumstances where the load against which the muscle operates is always the same, a means is still required of adjusting its activity to the mechanical conditions under which it is working at the moment. It is this self-regulating aspect of the primitive mechanism of movement which has not been taken into account in theories of muscular contraction. Physiologists who have paid more attention to the highly differentiated muscles of vertebrates and crustacea have tended to think of these as containing the elementary type of con-tractile mechanism; rather than trying, as they do, to explain the neuro-muscular physiology of the lower invertebrata in terms of the physiology of higher animals, the clue to an understanding of the higher animals should be sought in the physiology of the lower. It should be recognized that the absence of a self-regulating property in vertebrate or crustacean muscle is due to the secondary loss of a physiological character and is only made possible by the evolution of proprioceptive reflexes; the primitive contractile tissue must have had the properties of an independent effector in that its output of mechanical energy was directly related to the environ-mental conditions.

An example of the type of regulation required in a locomotor mechanism may help to explain this argument. Undulatory propulsion through the water is a form of locomotion found very widely in living organisms. In bacterial, protozoan and spermatozoan flagella, in invertebrates such as the Polychaeta Errantia and the Hirudinea, and in fish and snakes the same type of mechanical principle is invoked to achieve movement through the medium. The dynamics of the motion have been studied especially by Gray (1953, 1955), and it is clear that the similarities found in such widely dif-ferent organisms are an example of evolutionary convergence (the adoption of a common mechanical principle) and are not always produced by similar neuromuscular mechanisms. The snake and probably the fish have elaborate proprioceptive reflexes, the invertebrates have at least differentiated nerves and muscles, but the flagella of unicellular organisms have nothing, so far as we know, beyond the elementary fibrils of the contractile apparatus. Yet in all these cases, there is the same rhythmic activity (Pringle, 1957a) and the same self-adjustment of the frequency of the wave motion when mechanical conditions are changed (Sleigh, 1956). The isolated muscles of a snake or a fish do not show a rhythm of activity or an adjustment of the output of mechanical work to the optimum for the given external conditions; clearly the possession of muscles by themselves does not confer any advantage on the animal, and it is only the entirety of the nervous and muscular apparatus that has functional significance. But at some early stage in the evolution of animal movement the effectors alone must have been complete organs of locomotion; from this undifferentiated condition has come the variety of component parts of the neuromuscular system found now in the higher animals.

We see thus that whether the argument is based on a study of lower animals like sponges and coelenterates, or on theoretical considerations, the same conclusion is reached that the mechanical effector, muscle, is the most primitive component in the neuromuscular system, and that in its first form it must have contained within itself the necessary organization to make it effective in the production of animal locomotion. Faced with a conclusion like this, the comparative physiologist looks round the animal kingdom to see if there is anywhere an organism or a system which has preserved any features of the primitive organization. Is there a *Balanoglossus* of muscle physiology? Fortunately it seems that the search is not altogether hopeless, and that certain invertebrate muscles may give the clue which has so far been lacking in the understanding of the mechanism of contraction.

THE COMPARATIVE STUDY OF MUSCLE STRUCTURE

Various attempts have been made to classify the types of muscle tissue found in animals. The earliest division, still found in textbooks with a medical bias, was into three categories, skeletal (striated), smooth and cardiac muscles. This is adequate only for man and the higher vertebrates, and is of merely historical interest to the comparative physiologist; when a survey is made of the invertebrate phyla as well as the vertebrates, it is clear that there is a great variety of smooth and striated muscles, and also that the distinction between them is not absolute.

The limitations of the light microscope create serious difficulties in the formulation of a classification of muscles based in cellular structure, since even with the newer forms of optical microscopy it is impossible to resolve the cytoplasmic filaments which seem to be the basis of the property of contractility. A great deal of additional information about muscle structure is given by electronmicrographs of well-fixed material and it is already clear that any future classification must be based on the ultrastructure which can only be observed with this instrument.

A provisional scheme of this sort has been proposed by Hanson and Lowy (1960). These authors suggest that it is now possible to recognize four classes of muscles.

1. *Striated muscles*. In this type, which occurs sporadically in nearly all the invertebrate phyla as well as typically in the Arthropoda and Vertebrata, the contractile elements are axially differentiated into an alternating sequence of optically dense, birefringent A bands and less dense, less birefringent I bands. The electronmicrographs show that the banding is caused by the regular arrangement of two kinds of protein filaments (Hanson and Huxley, 1955). No essential differences in ultrastructure have yet been found between striated muscles from the different phyla; minor differences in the relative arrangements of the filaments have yet to be correlated with function or distribution. Mammalian cardiac muscle comes in this structural category.

2. *Helical smooth muscles*. These are muscles with myofibrils (i.e. bundles of filaments) which follow a helical course in the fibre. They are typical of the locomotor muscles of annelids and cephalopods and may be of much wider distribution than is known at present. This type of muscle must not be confused with other striated or smooth muscle types in which an appearance of helical structure is given by the helical arrangement of bands in longitudinally arranged filaments (Tiegs, 1955; Hanson and Lowy, 1957).

3. *Paramyosin smooth muscles*. In this type of non-striated muscle the fibres contain two sorts of filament, one thin (50 Å) corresponding to the thin filaments of striated muscle and one very thick (up to 1000 Å) and ribbon-like with the typical "paramyosin" X-ray diffraction diagram (Bear and Selby, 1956). The best-known of these muscles are the adductors and retractors of lamellibranch Mollusca, but the characteristic protein (tropomyosin B) is also found in the muscles from other invertebrate phyla and the type may be of more widespread occurrence.

4. *Classical smooth muscles*. The fibres of these muscles contain longitudinally oriented filaments but no signs of the paramyosin structure. Muscles of this type occur in all the animal phyla, and the category includes vertebrate smooth muscle. In an increasing number of cases, filaments of two different diameters have been found in these muscles, as in striated muscle, and their chief characteristic is a negative one, the absence of traverse alignment of the filaments.

From an evolutionary standpoint two points emerge from this latest study of comparative muscle structure. It is now clear that at this resolution there is a common structural basis for all muscles, smooth and striated, and that the presence of striation does not imply any essentially new feature in the contractile machinery. Striated muscle, because of the more orderly arrangement of the filaments, is an easier tissue to study with the electron-microscope, but in all the types of muscle, evidence, mainly from the X-ray diffraction studies, is growing for the fact that the process of contraction involves little or no change in length of the filaments, but rather a sliding of one past another (Huxley, H. E. and Hanson, 1954; Huxley, A. F. and Niedergerke, 1954). It will probably be some time, however, before the correlation between peculiarities of fine structure and peculiarities of physiology becomes sufficiently close for the structural evidence to be helpful in the problem of the origin of muscular tissues and their evolution in the animal kingdom.

THE COMPARATIVE PHYSIOLOGY OF MUSCULAR CONTRACTION

This is too large a subject to discuss in its entirety in an essay of this sort. It divides logically into two parts, the study of the nervous control of muscular contraction, the comparative physiology of which has been reviewed by Hoyle (1957), and the study of the mechanism of mechanical changes. It is this latter aspect which will be briefly discussed here, since few attempts have been made to present the subject from a comparative standpoint. Hanson and Lowy (1960) have surveyed what is known of mechanical phenomena in invertebrate muscles, but they have not tried to discuss the evolutionary problems.

As was mentioned earlier, the greatest attention has been paid by physiologists to those more specialized muscles from vertebrates, arthropods and molluscs in which it is to be expected that there would be a simplification of the relationships between the performance of the muscle and the mechanical features of the environment. Spontaneous rhythmic activity such as is required for locomotion does not lend itself to analysis so readily as the single twitch or tetanus which can be produced in one of these muscles by electrical stimulation of its motor nerve.

Although what is here left of the interaction with the environment is no longer of sufficient value to the animal to enable muscles to continue to function usefully when their nerves are cut, there does remain some direct action in the so-called Fenn effect. The total work done by a muscle undergoing one half-cycle of shortening depends on the distance through which it shortens (Hill, 1938), and in this way more chemical energy is converted into mechanical work when it is required than when tension is merely being maintained. It has long been recognized that this aspect of the mechanical performance of striated muscle has to be taken into account in any hypothesis about the mechanism of contraction (Huxley, A. F., 1957). It is suggested here that this particular feature is merely one of the ways in which the original primitive contractile machinery adjusted itself to the mechanical conditions under which it was working; the other aspects have been lost with the development of proprioceptive reflex mechanisms of control, but the explanation of what is left should be sought through a consideration of the whole. The present position is like trying to understand the construction of the mammalian ear without taking into account the stages through which it has passed in vertebrate evolution.

It follows logically from what has been said above that a study of the physiology of flagella and of the muscles of the lower invertebrates is required for an understanding of the physiology of the muscles of man. Unfortunately this is also technically difficult, since in many of these organisms differentiation has not even proceeded far enough to separate the locomotor apparatus from the parts of the body serving other functions. It may therefore be of particular importance that there are now two types of muscle known from higher phyla in which the properties of self-regulation to the mechanical features of the environment are present to a greater extent than in "normal" muscles. These are the paramyosin smooth muscles of lamellibranch Mollusca and the fibrillar flight muscles of the higher insects. These two unusual types may contain clues which are important for an understanding of what is generally regarded as "normal" muscular behaviour.

The paramyosin smooth muscle is characterized by the ability to maintain tension for long periods with small expenditure of energy, and also under certain circumstances to relax more rapidly. Two hypotheses have been put forward to explain this behaviour. According to one view, upheld by Abbott and Lowy (1958), tension is assumed to be maintained by spontaneous random re-excitation of a mechanism similarly to but much slower than the type of twitch found in "normal" muscles; the other view supposes that there is a special "catch" mechanism present in these muscles and that when this is brought into operation forced extension leads to a much greater rise of tension than it would otherwise do. Recent evidence for this view is given by Jewell (1959); it may be regarded functionally as a special case where mechanical changes in the environment have a direct effect on the performance of the muscle, making it useful to the animal even in the absence of proprioceptive reflexes. Insect fibrillar muscle is at the other extreme of the range of speeds at which muscles can work, since muscles of this type are known that will contract more than 1000 times per second (see Pringle, 1957b). The rhythmic activity of these muscles is originated in the muscle itself by a direct action of mechanical changes in the environment on the contractile mechanism (Machin and Pringle, 1960). As a result this system shows the primitive feature that it can operate even when all reflex action has been abolished by anaesthetics (the condition of "anaesthetic flight" or "Rauschflug", Pringle, 1949; Schneider, 1953); the muscle automatically adjusts the timing of its contractions so as to give a useful output of energy even if the frequency of beat is altered by accidental damage to the wings.

Figure 1 attempts to summarize in diagrammatic form the relationships between the muscle and its mechanical environment as illustrated by these examples. The essential difference between the classical view of muscle and that put forward here is that in the former the effect of excitation is thought to be to activate a contractile mechanism by an open loop of control, whereas in the latter excitation is thought to modify the operation of a

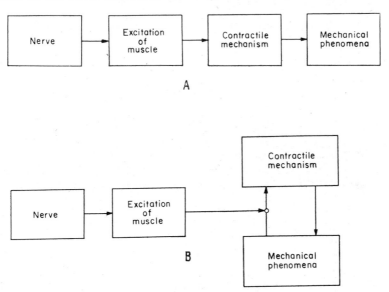

FIG. 1. Diagrammatic representations of the control sequence in muscle. A, the classical view with open loop control. B, closed loop control of mechanical phenomena.

closed loop between the contractile mechanism and its mechanical environment. If the "normal" type of muscle is considered alone, the former view may be adequate (see, however, Pringle, 1960); when paramyosin smooth muscle and insect fibrillar muscle are also taken into account, and when the origin of contractile systems is considered in the way that has been attempted here, it is clear that something on the lines of Fig. 1 B is a preferable analytical scheme.

REFERENCES

ABBOTT, B. C. and J. LOWY, Contraction in molluscan smooth muscle. *J. Physiol.* **141**, 385 (1958).

BATHAM, E. J. and C. F. A. PANTIN, Slow contraction and its relation to spontaneous activity in the sea-anemone *Metridium senile* (L.). *J. exp. Biol.* **31**, 84 (1954).

BEAR, R. S. and C. C. SELBY, The structure of paramyosin fibrils according to X-ray diffraction. *J. biophys. biochem. Cytol.* **2**, 55 (1956).

GRAY, J., Undulatory propulsion. *Quart. J. micr. Sci.* **94**, 551 (1953).

GRAY, J., The movement of sea-urchin spermatozoa. *J. exp. Biol.* **32**, 775 (1955).

HANSON, J. and H. E. HUXLEY, The structural basis of contraction in striated muscle. *Symp. Soc. exp. Biol.* **9**, 228 (1955).

HANSON, J. and J. LOWY, Structure of smooth muscles. *Nature, Lond.* **180**, 906 (1957).

HANSON, J. and J. LOWY, Structure and function of the contractile apparatus in the muscles of invertebrate animals. In *Structure and Function of Muscle* (Ed., Bourne, G. H.). Academic Press (1960).

HILL, A. V., The heat of shortening and the dynamic constants of muscle. *Proc. roy. Soc. Lond. B.* **126**, 136 (1938).

HOYLE, G., *The Comparative Physiology of the Nervous Control of Muscular Contraction.* Cambridge 1957.

HUXLEY, A. F., Muscle structure and theories of contraction. *Progress in Biophysics* **7**, 255 (1957).

HUXLEY, A. F. and R. NIEDERGERKE. Interference microscopy of living muscle fibres. *Nature, Lond.* **173**, 971 (1954).

HUXLEY, H. E. and J. HANSON, Changes in the cross-striations of muscles during contraction and stretch and their structural interpretation. *Nature, Lond.* **173**, 978 (1954).

JEWELL, B. R., The nature of the phasic and the tonic responses of the anterior byssus retractor muscle of *Mytilus*. *J. Physiol.* **149**, 154 (1959).

LWOFF, A., *L'Evolution Physiologique*, Paris 1944.

MACHIN, K. E. and J. W. S. PRINGLE, The physiology of insect fibrillar muscle. III. The effect of sinusoidal changes of length on a beetle flight muscle. *Proc. roy. Soc. Lond. B.* **152**, 311 (1960).

PANTIN, C. F. A., The origin of the nervous system. *Publ. Staz. Zool. Napoli*, **38**, 171 (1956).

PARKER, G. H., *The Elementary Nervous System.* Philadelphia 1919.

PRINGLE, J. W. S., The excitation and contraction of the flight muscles of insects. *J. Physiol.* **108**, 226 (1949).

PRINGLE, J. W. S., Myogenic rhythms. In *Recent Advances in Invertebrate Physiology* (Ed. Scheer, B. T.). University of Oregon Publications (1957a).

PRINGLE, J. W. S., *Insect Flight.* Cambridge (1957b).

PRINGLE, J. W. S., Models of muscle. *Symp. Soc. exp. Biol.* **14** (1960).

PRYOR, M. G. M., Mechanical properties of fibres and muscles. *Progress in Biophysics* **1**, 216 (1950).

SCHNEIDER, G., Die Halteren der Schmeißfliege (*Calliphora*) als Sinnesorgane und als mechanische Flugstabilisatoren. *Z. vergl. Physiol.* **35**, 416 (1953).

SLEIGH, M. A., Metachronism and frequency of beat in the peristomial cilia of Stentor. *J. exp. Biol.* **33**, 15 (1956).

TIEGS, O. W., The flight muscles of insects—their anatomy and histology; with some observations on the structure of striated muscle in general. *Phil. Trans. roy. Soc. Lond. B.* **238**, 221 (1955).

SOME PROBLEMS OF NEUROMUSCULAR ACTIVITY AND BEHAVIOUR IN THE "ELEMENTARY NERVOUS SYSTEM"

D. M. Ross

Department of Zoology,
University of Alberta, Edmonton, Alberta, Canada

COELENTERATE animals have long attracted the attention of comparative physiologists as animals possessing a primitive neuromuscular system. Consisting of co-ordinated systems of tissues, rather than co-ordinated organ systems, they are unique morphologically and physiologically. Focal points of interest in these animals are indicated by two works separated by 33 years, a monograph by G. H. Parker (1919) and a Croonian Lecture to the Royal Society by C. F. A. Pantin (1952), both bearing the title *The Elementary Nervous System*. It is natural that Kh. S. Koshtoyants should also have been led, by his broadly-based approach to the physiology of the nervous system, to include coelenterates amongst the many animals he has investigated. Together with his co-worker, N. A. Smirnova, he made important observations on one of the fundamental features seen in the sea anemone *Actinia equina*, the phenomenon of slow periodic activity (1955).

Physiological studies on coelenterates have centred on the ever remarkable *Hydra*, on the larger jellyfishes, and on the sea anemones. Any general views about the properties of nerve and muscle in coelenterates should be based on these three types of creatures, since they represent applications of the nerve net arrangement to three different modes of life. This article will be confined, however, to the sea anemones, which employ their nerves and muscles to carry out the activities associated with a sessile mode of life.

It is illusory to imagine that because the nervous system of sea anemones is primitive or "elementary," it is therefore easy to study. Some features, for instance, the quick closing response of certain anemones, are indeed based apparently on some simple quantitative principle. Other features, such as the slow long-delayed responses and the slow semi-rhythmical activity, have many properties that are difficult to interpret in terms of established hypotheses of nervous activity.

To the experimenter, these animals present many difficulties. The nervous system is not organized in recognizable tracts with clear-cut sensory and

motor components, and there is no definite concentration of nervous
tissue which functions as a co-ordinating centre. Muscles are arranged in
sheets surrounded by a relatively massive connective tissue, the mesogloea;
except for the sphincters and retractors involved in quick closing responses,
they are not firm masses of contractile tissue which can be studied in relative

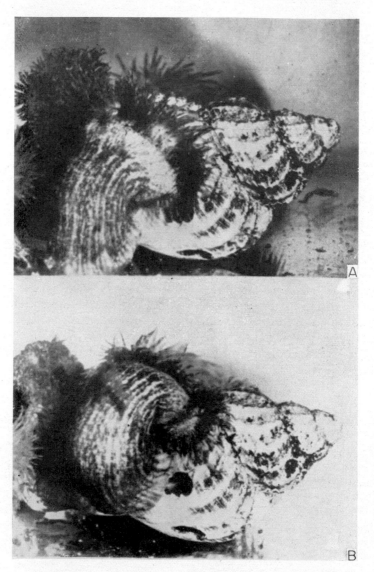

FIG. 1. *Calliactis parasitica* attaching itself to empty whelk shell.

A. Tentacles and oral disk adhering to shell, foot detaching itself from floor of vessel.
B. Foot lifted on to shell and beginning to re-attach. (7 min after A.)

isolation. Thus the usual methods of isolating and recording the activities of their muscles and nerves, are difficult to apply here. Yet to some extent, the whole animal can be regarded as a nerve-muscle preparation. Pantin's (1935) studies on *Calliactis parasitica*, which first revealed the beautiful relationships between stimuli and responses in this animal, were based on this approach. In spite of the difficulties mentioned above, isolated preparations of parts of the body have also been used very effectively. By their use it has been possible to see many of the neuromuscular phenomena which make up the movements and responses of the sea anemones, *Metridium senile* (Batham and Pantin, 1950 and 1954), and *Calliactis parasitica* (Ross, 1957; Needler and Ross, 1958; Ewer, 1960).

From these works the temporal and mechanical properties of these movements are now well known. Slow kymograph records and time-lapse cinematography show also that much of this activity is cyclical or phasic. This slow semi-rhythmical activity appears in isolated preparations of the column so that it is an inherent feature of the musculature, or of the associated nervous tissue (Batham and Pantin, 1950 and 1954; Needler and Ross, 1958).

There are other activities of particular sea anemones which are directly linked with some fairly obvious goal and which show certain analogies with behaviour patterns found in animals with central nervous systems. Batham and Pantin (1950) cite the slow locomotory movements of *Metridium* as an example of a complex behaviour pattern. Another complex activity is the swimming movement of the Pacific anemone, *Stomphia coccinea*, elicited by contact with two particular species of starfish, *Hippasteria spinosa* and *Dermasteria imbricata* (Yentsch and Pierce, 1955; Sund, 1958). Most remarkable of all, in my opinion, is the slow orderly series of movements by which *Calliactis parasitica* transfers itself to shells inhabited by the hermit crab, *Pagurus bernhardus* (Ross, 1960a). This is not a simple response but a programme of about six component movements in a definite sequence, each one involving a remarkable degree of adaptation to the shape and position of the shell in relation to the anemone (Fig. 1), and carried out over a period of about 10 to 30 min.

These examples show that the "elementary nervous system" provides for a considerable range of activities. Some of these are simple and almost automatic. Others are extremely complex and particularly difficult to interpret in conventional neuromuscular terms, considering the diffuse nature of the nervous system and the absence of any recognizable central elements.

NEUROMUSCULAR TRANSMISSION

Studies on sea anemones have provided some information bearing on the comparative physiology and evolution of processes of neuromuscular transmission. Like most animals, sea anemones exhibit two distinct types of movement, quick and slow, corresponding roughly with the movements found in skeletal and smooth muscles in the vertebrates.

The neuromuscular elements used in the quick closing responses of *C. parasitica* and *M. senile* are inactive unless stimulated, like skeletal muscle. When they respond, they do so with movements of short latency (*ca.* 0·1 sec) which travel quickly through the muscle. Unlike skeletal muscle, these movements cannot be produced by single stimuli, but they occur to all stimuli after the first stimulus within a narrow range of frequencies, and the closer the stimuli, the bigger the contraction (Pantin, 1935). Pantin (1937) suggested, and subsequent work has supported (Ross, 1945, 1952 and 1957) the hypothesis that neuromuscular transmission in this quick movement takes place not in a single step, as in vertebrate skeletal muscle but in two steps: (1) a preliminary sensitizing or facilitating step, which lasts about 3 sec and (2) an exciting or triggering step, which causes a contraction, the size of which depends on the amount of facilitation remaining from the preceding stimulus. This arrangement bears some likeness to facilitated transmission in Crustacea but there is an element of simplicity and regularity in these anemones that is almost unparallelled in a whole animal.

The neuromuscular elements involved in the slow movements are continuously active but they also respond to stimuli with movements of long latency (*ca.* 30–60 sec) and several minutes' duration. A few or many stimuli may be required to start a slow response, but in this case, transmission would appear to be a process occurring in a single step, involving only the release and accumulation of some slowly spreading excitatory condition through the musculature. However, recent work by Ewer (1960) shows that it may be more complicated in some circumstances. He suggests that a slow alternation of excitation and inhibition is the governing factor in the activity and responses of the slow musculature.

Ever since Dale, Loewi and their colleagues established that neuromuscular transmission in vertebrates is a chemical process and that acetylcholine is the transmitter at parasympathetic nerve-endings and at nerve-endings in skeletal muscle, comparative physiologists have attempted to establish the existence of similar chemical transmitters in invertebrates. In the main, the results have been disappointing. They have been reviewed by Bacq (1947) and Fredericq (1947). Only in annelid worms, in holothurians and in a single mollusc (*Venus mercenaria*) is there a satisfactory proof of the existence of a cholinergic mechanism. Many other animals in these phyla are sensitive to acetylcholine, and/or contain acetylcholine or choline esterase, without apparently using acetylcholine as a transmitter. In coelenterates and most arthropods, however, acetylcholine is neither present (some arthropod nervous tissues excepted) nor active (some crustacean hearts excepted).

Information is more scanty about the occurrence in the invertebrates of adrenergic mechanisms, which in the vertebrates function at postganglionic endings of the sympathetic system by the release of a transmitter now known to be noradrenaline (von Euler, 1959). There is a widespread sensitivity to adrenaline and other sympathomimetic amines in annelids, holothurians, molluscs and a few arthropods, but only in the leech, in *Aplysia*, and in cephalopods is there strong evidence for the existence of an adrenergic mechanism of transmission. Although there is still much work to be done in this field it is clear that there are big groups of animals whose musculature is insensitive to both classes of substance associated with chemical transmission in the vertebrates, and where no solid evidence for chemical transmission at nerve endings can be adduced. Even so, most authorities continue to believe that chemical transmitters must exist in these animals (e.g. Furshpan (1959) on Crustacea). One can conclude, therefore, that there is no clear evolutionary or systematic pattern in the distribution of chemical transmitters in the animal kingdom. One can state only that beginning with the annelids, a cholinergic mechanism is widely distributed.

The evolutionary position of the Coelenterata, and the remarkable relationships between stimuli and responses discovered in sea anemones by Pantin (1935), has justified a continuing search for chemical transmitters in these animals. Earlier studies on whole anemones (Ross, 1945) have now been extended by comprehensive tests on isolated preparations (Ross, 1960b, c). The results confirmed that acetylcholine and substances which affect cholinergic mechanisms in the vertebrates are totally without effect on these animals. In fact, effects of any kind were limited to very few substances and these showed no obvious links with other systems. For instance, adrenaline proved to be the most active substance of the group, causing direct slow contractions and raising the tone of the slow musculature (Fig. 2). Yet noradrenaline, the post-ganglionic transmitter in

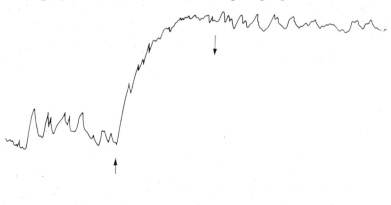

Fig. 2. *Calliactis* column preparation (slow) treated with adrenaline chloride (1×10^{-5}) for 30 min. Preparation fully contracted on upper level of trace.

Time trace: 15 min.

vertebrates, differing from adrenaline by the absence of a single methyl group, had no action of any kind on anemones. Moreover, drugs acting as inhibitors or potentiators of adrenergic effects had no effects of their own and did not affect the response to adrenaline.

Similarly, tryptamine caused direct contractions of both the slow and the quick musculature, and under its influence, quick responses frequently occurred to single stimuli (Fig. 3). Yet 5-hydroxytryptamine, which is much more active than tryptamine on most preparations, had only slight effects on anemone preparations. Tyramine was the only other substance having a marked effect on whole animals or on the preparations. In vertebrates it is classed as a sympathomimetic drug, as a less active but more stable substitute for adrenaline; it is believed by some workers to act as a releaser of noradrenaline. In anemones, tyramine enhanced the quick response, without causing any direct contractions and permitting only very tiny responses to single stimuli.

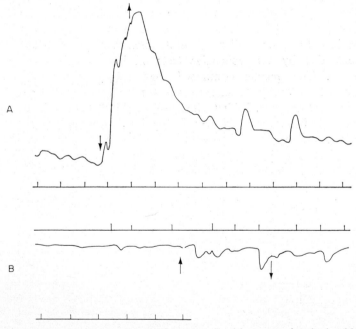

Fig. 3 A. *Calliactis* column preparation treated with tryptamine hydrochloride (1 × 10⁻⁴) for 4 min.

Time trace: 3 min.

B. *Calliactis* sphincter preparation (quick) treated with tryptamine hydrochloride (1 × 10⁻⁴) for 20 min. Upper signals indicate the application of single stimuli before, during and after treatment. Note responses to stimuli during treatment and also some direct responses to the treatment alone.

Time trace: 6 min.

Until now no pharmacological treatment has been found which depresses the whole animal and the isolated preparation. Ergotoxine, which had some effects on whole animals (Ross, 1945), had only slight effects on the quick responses of preparations, and no effect at all on the slow musculature. Clear-cut depressant effects were found only with certain inorganic treatments. The most effective of these was the heavy metal, cadmium. This has been used by Koshtoyants on isolated prepartions of a number of animals, including the sea anemone *A. equina* (Koshtoyants and Smirnova, 1955), on all of which it has powerful depressant effects. These are attributed by Koshtoyants to the specific depression of the metabolism of SH groups (Koshtoyants, 1951). Contrary to an earlier published statement (Needler and Ross, 1958), cadmium stops all activity and responses of preparations of *Calliactis* quickly and completely (Ewer, Pople and Ross, 1961). This effect can be removed by return to sea water and also, as Koshtoyants discovered, by the action of cysteine and other substances containing free SH groups. Further work suggests, however, that restoration after depression with cadmium can also be achieved by applying some other substances that have no specific connexion with SH metabolism.

The effects of adrenaline, tryptamine and tyramine on preparations of *Calliactis* and *Metridium* are important in two respects. (1) It is shown that these substances have different effects on the quick and slow contractions of the muscles. This is especially clear when the effects are obtained from the sphincter muscles of these anemones, which can contract quickly or slowly, according to the frequency of stimulation applied (Batham and Pantin, 1954; Ross, 1957). (2) Although the drug effects do not necessarily have any bearing on the nature of neuromuscular transmission in these animals, it is interesting that the preparations should be sensitive only to the substances mentioned. The effects of adrenaline and tyramine in particular give some indication of the possible importance of adrenergic mechanisms,

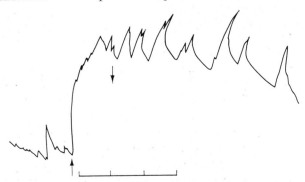

FIG. 4. *Calliactis* column preparation (slow) treated with extract of *Calliactis* column for 12 min. Sample given consisted of material extracted from 0·05 mg dry tissue per ml.

Time trace: 10 min.

a point of considerable interest in these lower invertebrates where any suggestion of a link with cholinergic mechanisms is totally lacking.

Pursuing this line of investigation, recent work (unpublished) has shown that extracts of sea anemones contain a substance which causes direct contractions and heightens the tonus of the slow musculature rather like the adrenaline effect (Fig. 4). From the activity of whole extracts and fractions separated by chromatography, this substance would seem to be more active than adrenaline. If it can be classified and identified, it should be possible to attack the problem of neuromuscular transmission in these animals in a more concrete way.

CO-ORDINATION AND BEHAVIOUR

In conclusion it is instructive to dwell briefly on the neuromuscular system of sea anemones as a co-ordinating system responsible for patterns of behaviour in the whole animal. The effectors consist basically of a general slow musculature some of whose components, e.g. the sphincter of *Calliactis*, are also able to contract quickly to the appropriate stimuli. The conducting system consists of a general nerve network, probably serving the entire musculature, with some specialized through-conduction tracts, reminiscent of giant fibres, which apparently innervate muscles involved in quick contractions.

This equipment permits a considerable variety of movements, local and general, characterized by differences in duration. If these activities are under nervous control, they imply an elaborate neural differentiation, with definite pathways in the network and sequences in its functioning. The programme of movements carried out by *Calliactis* in climbing on a shell, already mentioned and shown in Fig. 1 (Ross, 1960), can serve as an example of a complex motor reaction of this animal. There are usually six stages: (1) an active adhesive response of tentacles, margin and oral disk, triggered off by contact of the actinian with the shell; (2) oral–aboral peristalsis and constriction of the column; (3) lifting and detachment of the pedal disk; (4) bending of the column towards the shell; (5) swelling of the pedal margin and attachment of pedal disk to the shell; (6) release of tentacles and straightening of the column. This pattern can only be explained by postulating a series of nervous connexions providing specific pathways for sensory information, extero- and proprioceptive impulses travelling to centres which transmit the appropriate motor excitation to specific effectors in their turn. The centres involved in this process remain to be discovered, but in my opinion, they must exist. If this be true, even the so-called "elementary nervous system" must possess sensory, central and motor components performing functions similar to those of the higher animals. From the standpoint of the comparative physiology of the nervous system, to which

Professor Koshtoyants gave so much attention, the important point is that nerve and muscle of relatively simply organized animals possess components which make possible behaviour patterns of considerable complexity.

REFERENCES

BACQ, Z. M., *Biol. Rev.* **22**, 73 (1947).

BATHAM, E. J. and C. F. A. PANTIN, *J. Exp. Biol.* **27**, 377 (1950).

BATHAM, E. J. and C. F. A. PANTIN, *J. Exp. Biol.* **31**, 84 (1954).

EULER, U. S. VON, Autonomic neuro-effector transmission. In *Handbook of Physiology*, *pt. I. Neurophysiology*, 215. Am. Physiol. Soc. Washington 1959.

EWER, D. W., *J. Exp. Biol.* **37**, 812 (1960).

EWER, D. W., W. POPLE and D. M. ROSS, *Dokl. Akad. Nauk SSSR* **137**, 240 (1961) (in Russian).

FREDERICQ, H., *Biol. Rev.* **22**, 297 (1947).

FURSHPAN, D., Neuromuscular transmission in invertebrates. In *Handbook of Physiology*, *pt. I. Neurophysiology*, 239. Am. Physiol. Soc. Washington 1959.

KOSHTOYANTS, KH. S., *Protein Bodies, Metabolism and Nervous Regulation.* (Belkovyye tela, obmen veshchestri i nervnaya regulyatsiya) Moscow 1951.

KOSHTOYANTS, KH. S. and N. A. SMIRNOVA, *Dokl. Akad. Nauk SSSR* **104**, 662 (1955).

NEEDLER, M. and D. M. ROSS, *J. Mar. Biol. Ass. U. K.* **37**, 789 (1958).

PANTIN, C. F. A., *J. Exp. Biol.* **12**, 119 (1935).

PANTIN, C. F. A., *Proc. Roy. Soc., B* **123**, 397 (1937).

PANTIN, C. F. A., *Proc. Roy. Soc., B* **140**, 147 (1952).

PARKER, G. H., *The Elementary Nervous System.* Philadelphia–London, Lippincott 1919.

ROSS, D. M., *J. Exp. Biol.* **22**, 21 (1945).

ROSS, D. M., *J. Exp. Biol.* **29**, 235 (1952).

ROSS, D. M., *J. Exp. Biol.* **34**, 11 (1957).

ROSS, D. M., *Proc. Zool. Soc. London* **134**, 43 (1960a).

ROSS, D. M., *J. Exp. Biol.* **37**, 732 (1960b).

ROSS, D. M., *J. Exp. Biol.* **37**, 753 (1960c).

SUND, P. N., *Q. J. Micros. Sci.* **99**, 401 (1958).

YENTSCH, C. S. and D. C. PIERCE, *Science* **122**, 1231 (1955).

THE IMPORTANCE OF AFFERENTATION IN THE DEVELOPMENT OF RHYTHMIC ACTIVITY OF THE RESPIRATORY CENTRE IN FISH

Ts. V. Serbenyuk

Department of Animal Physiology, Faculty of Soil Biology,
State University, Moscow

Translated by Dr. R. Crawford

Our investigations of the nature of the rhythmic activity of the respiratory centre in fish established that the change in the activity of the centre that followed de-afferentation took place in two phases. During the first phase, which lasted 7–10 min, the periodic activity of the centre, as determined from its electrogram, persisted in the rhythm of the respiration of the intact animal. In the second phase this activity was replaced by a different, but still periodic activity of the centre, with a new rate (Serbenyuk *et al.*, 1959). The view was expressed that the rate of the periodic activity of the centre in the second phase was determined by automatic processes in the nerve structures of the respiratory centre in fish, whereas the rate of activity in the intact centre was determined by afferent reflex influences.

An attempt was made to obtain experimental confirmation of these views in experiments to demonstrate the importance of afferent influences from different reflexogenic zones in fish in determining the rate of rhythmical activity in the respiratory centre.

The work now discussed constitutes part of the research carried out under the direction of Koshtoyants on the nature of the rhythmical activity of nerve structures.

METHOD

The experiments were carried out on carp weighing 250–300 g. The potentials of the respiratory centre were recorded by means of constantan electrodes 156–160 μ in diameter. After suitable amplification the potentials were recorded by a loop oscillograph. Gill movements were recorded simultaneously, the mechanical energy of the movements being transformed

262

into electrical. During the experiment the fish was fixed in a special stand and placed in a crystallizer containing water. The cranium was opened and the electrodes were inserted into the region of the respiratory centre by means of a micromanipulator.*

CHANGES IN THE RHYTHMICAL ACTIVITY OF THE RESPIRATORY CENTRE IN FISH ON EXCLUSION OF INDIVIDUAL REFLEXOGENIC ZONES

(1) *Exclusion of afferent influences from the vessels of the gills and from the swim-bladder.* A number of authors have drawn attention to the great importance of afferent influences from the vessels of the gills in the activity of the respiratory centre (Lutz and Brenton, 1929; Powers, 1942; Kravchinskii, 1945; Puchkov, 1954). There is also oscillographic evidence that

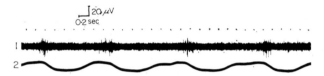

FIG. 1. Electrogram of the respiratory centre (1) and record of gill movements (2) after exclusion of reception in the vessels of the branchial region.

bursts of impulses at the rhythm of cardiac activity pass along the branchial nerves to the respiratory centre (Irving *et al.*, 1935). Afferent influences from the vessels of the branchial region were excluded in our experiments by ligature close to the heart and subsequent division of the large branchial vessels, so that the vessels were emptied.

The electrogram from the respiratory centre and the gill movements were recorded in the experimental fish before and after the operation.

There were considerable changes in the rate, depth and force of gill movements after the operation and there were also certain changes in the character of the electrogram of the respiratory centre but (1) respiration was maintained and (2) the bursts of impulses recorded from the respiratory centre did not differ essentially from the normal bursts and occurred in the rate of the respiratory movements in all experiments without exception (Fig. 1).

Exclusion of afferent influences from the zone of the swim-bladder was effected by puncture of the bladder or division of the corresponding branch of the vagus nerve. The changes then seen in respiration and in the character

* The method employed for collection and recording of the potentials of the centre was described in detail in an earlier paper (Serbenyuk *et al.*, 1959).

of the electrical activity of the centre were similar to those observed when vascular reception was excluded, but were more pronounced.

(2) *Exclusion of afferent influences reaching the respiratory centre from the spinal cord.* Transection of the spinal cord immediately behind the medulla led to considerable changes in respiration. As a rule, the transection was followed at once by respiratory arrest, but respiration was restored after 2–3 min and it was either rapid and superficial or slow and deep. The electrogram of the respiratory centre might exhibit certain changes in the

Fig. 2. Electrogram of the respiratory centre (1) and record of gill movements (2) after spinal transection.

nature of the bursts of impulses but the essential nature of the rhythmical activity of the respiratory centre remained unchanged even in this case (Fig. 2).

(3) *Changes in the rhythmical activity of the respiratory centre in fish on exclusion of gill movements.* The experiments in which de-afferentation of the respiratory centre was achieved by arrest of gill movements yielded different results. There were marked changes in the electrogram of the respiratory centre which, in our opinion, reflected the development of a new type of activity in the nerve cells of the centre (Serbenyuk *et al.*, 1959).

(4) *Exclusion of gill movements by curarization.* In our preceding investigation (Serbenyuk *et al.*, 1959) the gill movements were arrested by division of the motor (facial) nerve or by exclusion of the vagus nerves which would appear to be the main conductors for afferent influences from the branchial region. In this investigation similar changes developed in the activity of the respiratory centre in experiments in which the gill movements was arrested by curarization (curare, tubocurarine or novocain). Like the preceding series, these experiments were carried out on carp weighing 250–300 g. An electrogram of the respiratory centre and gill movements was recorded from the immobilized fish. Thereafter, the electrodes being left in position, the fish was given an intramuscular injection of 0·2–0·25 mg curare or tubocurarine, after which the electrical activity of the centre and gill movements were again recorded.

The injection of curare was followed by considerable changes in the nature of the gill movements and in the electrogram of the respiratory centre: after 1–3 min the bursts of impulses in the respiratory centre still had the rate of respiration in the intact fish but the gill movements were slower, apparently as a result of action of the poison on neuromuscular transmission. Gill movements ceased 3–4 min after the injection of curare but bursts of impulses continued to develop in the respiratory centre in the former rhythm. The rate and character of the bursts changed 7–10 min after the commencement of the experiment and very soon disappeared completely; there was then development of a new form of activity in the centre, reflected in the electrogram in the form of prolonged bursts of impulses with a rate of 5–7 per min.

The changes in the electrogram of the respiratory centre seen to result from the action of curare were similar in every way to those demonstrated by us in experiments in which gill movements were arrested by division of the motor nerves (Serbenyuk *et al.*, 1959).

(5) *Novocain exclusion of reception in the branchial region.* A 0·5 per cent novocain solution was passed for 3–5 min through the gill region. As was expected, the changes then seen in the electrogram of the respiratory centre and the nature of the gill movements were similar to those observed in experiments with bilateral vagotomy (Serbenyuk *et al.*, 1959): the electrogram of the respiratory centre retained its normal character and the gill movements were normal during the first 5–7 min. After 7–10 min the centre developed fresh activity—extended bursts of impulses with a rate of 5–7 per min.

Just as in the vagotomy experiments, gill movements ceased during the period in which the new electrical activity was developing.

The similarity of the results obtained with bilateral vagotomy and novocain respectively indicates that the influences from the receptors in the gill region were excluded in both cases. As we had suggested, the main afferent paths from receptors in the branchial region apparently run in the vagus nerves.

The separate exclusion of different reflexogenic zones (vascular region of the gills, swim-bladder) thus led to considerable changes in the nature of the gill movements without producing any essential changes in the rhythmical activity of the respiratory centre. Arrest of the gill movements, which obviously led to simultaneous loss of several reflexogenic zones (proprioceptors in muscles, mechanoreceptors and chemoreceptors excited by the passage of a stream of water through the gill region, etc.), resulted in arrest of the normal rhythmical activity of the centre and development of its automatic activity. It is natural to ask whether the different effects on respiration seen in these cases are due solely to difference in the number of afferent impulses reaching the centre or whether afferentation from the branchial region has a specific effect on the respiratory centre.

Special experiments were carried out in an attempt to determine this. It was first of all important to establish what effect simultaneous exclusion of the reflexogenic zones which, when excluded separately, merely produced changes in the regulation of respiration, would have on the activity of the respiratory centre.

CHANGES IN THE RHYTHMICAL ACTIVITY OF THE RESPIRATORY CENTRE IN FISHES ON SIMULTANEOUS EXCLUSION OF A NUMBER OF REFLEXOGENIC ZONES

The experiments in this series were carried out in the following manner. Afferent influences from the region of the branchial vessels and the region of the swim-bladder were excluded simultaneously. Sharp changes in respiration were then observed: it became slow and feeble and pauses in respiration were frequent but respiration generally persisted for a considerable length of time (an hour or more). There were also changes in the nature of the bursts of impulses recorded from the respiratory centre: the bursts were somewhat increased in length but the rate and amplitude of the impulses in a burst were reduced. The development of an automatic rate of activity in the respiratory centre, seen typically in the case of more profound de-afferentation, was not, however, observed. When spinal cord transection was added to the exclusion of these zones, gill movements died out gradually. The electrogram of the respiratory centre then exhibited the changes typical of bilateral vagotomy or novocainization: the bursts retained their normal character for 7–10 min, after which there was development of fresh periodic activity in the centre and gill movements ceased during this period.

The changes in the electrogram of the respiratory centre were thus similar when gill movements were arrested and when a number of reflexogenic zones were excluded simultaneously. The impression was created that the first essential for normal rhythmical activity in the respiratory centre was a certain total of afferent influences, and that the rhythmical influences from the branchial region associated with the respiratory act constituted one of the elements in this total. Another component consists of afferent influences reaching the respiratory centre with rates differing from that of respiration, namely afferent influences from vessels at the rhythm of cardiac activity, influences from the swim-bladder dependent on its degree of stretching, etc.

These facts are consistent with Koshtoyants' hypothesis on the dual nature of the afferent influences reaching the central nervous system. The essential feature of this hypothesis is that the nervous system receives constant afferentation which ensures an active state of the nerve cells and also periodic afferentation producing response activity of nerve structures with reflexion of this activity at the periphery (Koshtoyants, 1957).

We attempted to analyse the interrelationships between the various afferent effects determining the rhythmical activity of the respiratory centre.

THE ABILITY OF THE RESPIRATORY CENTRE IN FISH TO BECOME ADJUSTED TO THE RATE OF PRECEDING AFFERENT INFLUENCES

Experiments with artificial respiration were set up for detailed examination of the role of the afferent influences reaching the centre during periods of gill movements.

The experiments were carried out in the following manner. The normal background electrical activity of the centre was established and gill movements were then arrested either by division of the motor nerves or by the injection of curare. When the characteristic changes had developed in the electrogram of the respiratory centre, artificial respiration—opening and closing of the gills—was carried out.

These experiments showed that bursts of impulses at the rhythm of the artificial respiration developed in the electrogram of the respiratory centre after 10–15 artificial gill movements. These bursts became very distinct after 30–40 respiratory movements and persisted as long as artificial respiration was maintained.

After artificial respiration ceased, bursts of impulses of the same rate were recorded for 5–10 min and then their character began to change just as in any other case of arrest of gill movements. An interesting point was that bursts of impulses at the original rate of the intact fish's respiration were never observed after the cessation of artificial respiration. The bursts of impulses were always recorded at the new artificial rate but these were later replaced by long infrequent bursts similar to those seen in the first part of the experiment, after the arrest of natural respiration (Fig. 3).

When, therefore, with the respiratory centre in a state of automatic activity, the afferentation developing during artificial respiration reached the centre, there was subsequent development of periodic activity at the rate of the incoming afferent influences. There was a corresponding change in the character of the electrogram recorded. It was thus possible to "impose"

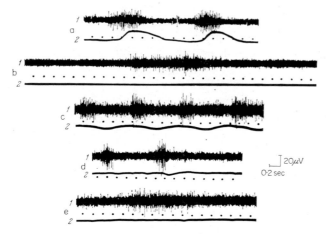

FIG. 3. Changes in the electrical activity of the respiratory centre in artificial respiration.

1—electrogram. 2—gill movements: a—normal; b—15 min after bilateral division of the facial (motor) nerves; c—development of bursts of impulses during artificial respiration; d—5 min after the cessation of artificial respiration; e—15 min after the cessation of artificial respiration.

a new rate of electrical activity on the respiratory centre in fish, a new rate entirely determined by the rate of preceding afferent effects.

It was also found that this imposed rate persisted for some time after the arrival of the artificial afferent influences had ceased. This affords quite convincing support, in our opinion, for the view expressed in our previous paper (Serbenyuk *et al.*, 1959) that the respiratory centre in fish is capable of adjusting itself to the rate of preceding afferent effects and maintaining this rate for a certain time even after de-afferentation.

It was also found that it was only possible to "impose" a new rate on the respiratory centre within certain frequency limits—in our experiments from 20 to 100 per min. With artificial respiration rates below 20 per min no synchronous bursts of impulses in the respiratory centre could be demonstrated. With rates higher than 100 per min the bursts of spike potentials fused and the electrical activity of the centre became indefinite.

It must be remembered in assessing these experiments that none of the reflexogenic zones studied—vascular region, swim-bladder, etc. — was interfered with in the production of artificial respiration.

In the next experiments we attempted to demonstrate the role of these reflexogenic zones in the production of the rhythmic activity of the respiratory centre in fish during artificial respiration.

RELATIONSHIP BETWEEN THE VARIOUS REFLEXOGENIC ZONES CONCERNED IN PRODUCTION OF THE RHYTHMICAL ACTIVITY OF THE RESPIRATORY CENTRE

The experiments were carried out in the following manner. The motor nerves were divided in the experimental fish and then either the region of the swim-bladder was excluded or the spinal cord was transected.

After 5–10 min the electrical activity became that typical of automatic activity of the centre—long protracted bursts of impulses with a rate of 5–7/min. On this background, artificial opening and closing of the gills led after 15–25 movements to the development of bursts of impulses corresponding to the rate of the artificial respiration. When, however, artificial respiration was performed after exclusion of both the zones referred to, the development of rhythmic bursts of impulses in the centre could not be demonstrated.

Nor were rhythmical bursts observed when artificial respiration was carried out after exclusion of the vascular region and the region of the swim-bladder, or after exclusion of the vascular region and transection of the spinal cord.

The results of these experiments thus led to the conclusion that one of the conditions essential for the development of rhythmic respiration is that a certain total of afferent effects should reach the centre.

The next point to be elucidated was the specificity of the afferent effects we were examining. For this purpose we carried out experiments in which we attempted to make compensation for the exclusion of one reflexogenic zone by additional afferentation from another zone. The experiments were carried out in the following way. The motor nerves were divided in fish with the vascular region excluded and the spinal cord transected. After 10–15 min, when the characteristic background of respiratory centre activity had been established, artificial respiration was started and at the same time, the swim-bladder was inflated.* Increase of pressure in the swim-bladder is known to increase the stream of afferent impulses travelling along the vagus nerve (Koshtoyants, 1957).

Artificial respiration under these conditions led to the development of bursts of impulses at the rate of the "imposed" respiration in the respiratory centre.

The flow of afferent impulses arriving rhythmically from the gill region when the respiratory act was effected could thus elicit a response reaction in the centre in the form of bursts of impulses synchronous with respiration only when the centre was receiving in addition to these impulses a certain total of afferent effects, the region of origin of which was not strictly specific.

In all our experiments hitherto the creation of a different flow of afferent influences has been effected by means of gill movements. It was of interest, therefore, to determine the specificity of these effects and the possibility of replacing them by rhythmic effects from another region. We therefore carried out the following experiments. Two per cent novocain solution was passed through the gill region for 5–7 min. When gill movements ceased and the changes characteristic of such experiments developed in the re-spiratory centre, the swim-bladder was distended rhythmically. After the bladder had been distended 10–20 times, definite, although not regular,

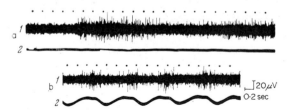

FIG. 4. Changes in the electrical activity of the respiratory centre on rhythmic distension of the swim-bladder.

a—after novocain. b—during rhythmic inflation of the swim-bladder. 1—electrogram. 2—gill movements.

* In our experiments pressure change was produced in the swim-bladder by inflation through a small fistula tube inserted into the bladder and connected with a rubber bulb and manometer.

10*

bursts of impulses, similar in character to those recorded normally, began to develop in the respiratory centre. After 30–40 distensions the bursts became more sharply defined and distinct gill movements developed in time with the bursts (Fig. 4).

It was thus found possible (by creating a rhythmic flow of afferent impulses from the swim-bladder) both to reproduce the effects of artificial respiration on the nature of the electrical activity of the centre, and to induce respiratory movements.

DISCUSSION

We believe that these experimental results afford a partial explanation of the complex process leading to rhythmic activity of the respiratory centre in fish. Schematically, the process appears to us to be as follows. The bulbar respiratory centre in fish has its own basic periodic activity. This develops after profound de-afferentation of the respiratory centre. During the first 5–10 min after de-afferentation the rhythmic activity of the respiratory centre retains the characteristic activity of the intact centre. Later, these bursts are generally replaced by bursts of a different rate and differing in a number of features—duration, frequency and number of impulses in the bursts. An interesting point is that in a great majority of the experiments the new bursts of impulses appeared several seconds after disappearance of the short bursts characteristic of the intact centre.

It is still difficult to state the exact functional significance of this automatic movement as the activity itself is not responsible for gill movements.

A question of fundamental importance is how the rhythmical activity of the centre underlying the normal respiration of fish and, for convenience of explanation, termed by us the respiratory rhythmical activity of the centre, is developed. Is it merely a modification of the basic automatic activity of the centre or is it a different kind of new rhythmic activity in the centre determined by afferent influences?

We cannot on the evidence available to us give any conclusive answer to this question. We can only state that switching of the centre from automatic to respiratory rhythmic activity required, first, the arrival of rhythmic afferent influences in the centre and, secondly, the existence of a certain level of afferent effects, the purpose of which may possibly be to increase the sensitivity of the centre to the rhythmically arriving influences. It was only under such conditions that rhythmic bursts of impulses capable of eliciting gill movements developed in the centre. In what way these afferent influences interact with the basic automatic activity under such circumstances is still obscure. We were unable to obtain satisfactory evidence on this point either when the centre changed over to automatic activity or when it developed respiratory rhythmical activity. It may be that this was due to limitations imposed by the method we used: we assessed the state of the centre from its electrogram and it proved impossible to demonstrate the change-over from one form of activity to the other by this method.

It can be stated on the evidence afforded by our findings that the bulbar respiratory centre in fishes is capable of adjusting itself to the rate of preceding afferent impulses and of maintaining this rhythm for several (5–10) minutes. This property of the centre may explain the maintenance of its activity at the rate of respiration for the period indicated after de-afferentation.

We shall not discuss in this paper the importance of our findings in relation to existing ideas about the nature of rhythmic activity of the respiratory centre in warm-blooded animals and fishes. This will be discussed in subsequent papers dealing with the analysis of various questions arising from the experimental results described.

REFERENCES

IRVING, O., O. S. SOLAND and O. M. SOLAND, *J. Physiol.* **84**, 187 (1935).

KOSHTOYANTS, KH. S., *Principles of Comparative Physiology* (Osnovy sravnitel'noi fiziologii). Vol. 2, Moscow 1957.

KRAVCHINSKII, B. D., Advances in Biology (*Uspekhi sovrem. biol.*) **19** (1945).

LUTZ, B. and R. BRENTON, *Am. J. Physiol.* **90**, 439 (1929).

POWERS, E. B., *Am. J. Physiol.* **138**, 104 (1942).

PUCHKOV, N. V., *Physiology of Fishes* (Fiziologiya ryb). Moscow 1954.

*SERBENYUK, TS. V., B. A. SHISHOV and T. K. KIPRIYAN, Biophysics (*Biofizika*) **4**, 657 (1959).

ANAEROBIC METABOLISM OF CARBOHYDRATES IN CARDIAC MUSCLE TISSUE IN THE NORMAL STATE AND IN EXPERIMENTAL MYOCARDITIS

S. Ye. Severin and L. A. Tseitlin

Institute of Pharmacology and Chemotherapy,
U.S.S.R. Academy of Medical Sciences, Moscow

Translated by Dr. R. Crawford

UNDER normal conditions the heart is an organ with very pronounced aerobic metabolism. Anaerobic glycogenolysis, while undoubtedly occurring in normal cardiac muscle (Haarman, 1932; Haarman and Brink, 1935; Wu and Chang, 1948; Buzard et al., 1956; Barron et al., 1953), plays a quite inconsiderable part in providing energy for functional activity and processes of plastic metabolism in this organ.

In the presence of various pathological states of the myocardium, associated with the development of hypoxia, the heart begins to use glycogenolysis as a compensatory mechanism. Bing (1956) observed increased glycolysis in embolism of the coronary arteries in patients with chronic cardiac insufficiency. A number of investigations afford evidence of the activation of glycogenolysis in cardiac muscle in the presence of aortic stenosis (Meerson et al., 1955; Vyalykh and Meerson, 1960) and in experimental myocardial infarct (Raiskina, 1958). There are also references to reduction of glycogen with simultaneous increase of lactic acid in cardiac muscle affected by myocarditis (Saratikov, 1953). On the other hand, no increase of glycogenolytic activity in the myocardium was observed in shock from haemorrhage (Bing, 1956). The importance of the glycogenolytic process for the pathologically altered heart and the possibility of its control by pharmacological substances (Koralev, 1951) encouraged us to make a detailed investigation of this process in relation to experimental myocarditis.

METHOD

Experimental myocarditis was produced in female rabbits weighing about 2–2·5 kg by a single injection of 1 per cent theophylline solution, 20 mg/kg into an ear vein and then, after 2 min, injection of 0·2 ml adrenaline hydrochloride (1 : 1000). The adrenaline was injected over a period of 3–5 min. The experiments were carried out on the 3rd, 4th or 5th day after the injection. The animals were killed by decapitation, the heart was extracted rapidly and, after preliminary perfusion with 0·9 per cent NaCl solution cooled to 0°C, was dried with filter paper, freed from connective tissue and fat and cut up into small pieces with scissors in the cold. Suspensions containing 300 mg of the finely divided cardiac tissue were incubated in phosphate buffer solution (pH 7·7) for 30–60 min at a temperature of 37°C in an atmosphere of nitrogen. The substrates used were glycogen, fructose diphosphate (FDP) (15 mg per test) and phosphoglyceric acid (PGA) (5 mg per test). Experiments were carried out both with and without glycolytic poisons. The final concentrations of fluoride and mono-iodoacetate in the experimental tests were respectively 0·025 and 0·002 M. The enzyme process was arrested by the addition of an equal volume of 5 per cent trichloroacetic acid. The intensity of glycogenolysis was assessed from the increase of inorganic phosphate as determined by the method of Peel and Loughman (1957) and from the increase of lactic acid as determined with p-oxydiphenyl (Barker and Summerson, 1941).

Estimations of the intermediate products of glycolysis were made at the same time: fructose diphosphate was estimated by the colour reaction given by fructose with resorcin; and phosphoglyceric acid was estimated by a modification of the Rappoport method (Meshkova and Aleksakhina, 1954). Adenosine triphosphatase activity was examined in bicarbonate buffer solution, pH 7·7, under anaerobic conditions and in the presence of mono-iodoacetate. Phosphorylase activity was estimated in freshly prepared aqueous extracts of cardiac muscle in the presence of fluoride. The intensity of glycogen synthesis was determined from the increase of glycogen and from increase of inorganic phosphorus from the breakdown of Cori ester.

RESULTS

Published reports indicate that the intravenous infusion of adrenaline or theophylline produces marked changes in the myocardium of the rabbit, which can reasonably be treated as experimental myocarditis (Mentova, 1939). The heart in myocarditis is generally much enlarged: in occasional cases its weight is increased 1·5 times. Histological investigations show that more or less marked changes of inflammatory nature, often associated with phenomena of regeneration, can be observed in all cases.

Our experiments showed that there was very little esterification of inorganic phosphate when pulped cardiac muscle was incubated under anaerobic conditions without the addition of glycogen and without glycolytic poisons, and sometimes even none. This applied equally to the experimental and the control animals. The values for the formation of lactic acid under these conditions were somewhat lower in the myocarditic animals. An average of 7·6 μM lactate was formed when pulped cardiac muscle from control animals was incubated for 30 min, whereas the average formation of lactic acid on incubation of cardiac muscle pulp from myocarditic animals was only 5 μM per test (Fig. 1). Quite intense linkage of inorganic phosphate was noted when glycogen was added to the experimental tests. The intense esterification of inorganic phosphate in cardiac muscle pulps from control animals was not, however, accompanied by a corresponding accumulation of lactic acid. The intensity of phosphorylation in pulp of cardiac muscle from myocarditic animals was only about one-half of the

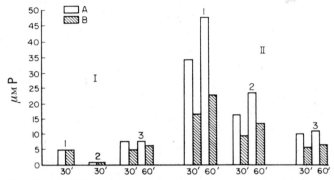

FIG. 1. Esterification of inorganic phosphate (1), formation of fructose diphosphate (2) and of lactic acid (3) in pulped cardiac muscle, normal (A) and myocarditic (B), without (I) and with (II) the addition of glycogen.

intensity seen in the control animals (Fig. 1). Averages of 34 and 48 μM phosphate became bound when pulp of cardiac muscle from control animals was incubated for 30 and 60 min respectively, whereas only 16 and 22 μM phosphate became bound in the pulp of cardiac muscle from myocarditic animals. The values for the formation of lactic acid in cardiac muscle pulp from myocarditic animals averaged 30–40 per cent less than those for the control animals, but in this case also the increase of lactic acid was disproportionately low in relation to glycogen utilization. The addition of glycogen to cardiac muscle pulp from the myocarditic animal did not produce any appreciable increase in the formation of lactic acid in comparison with its formation in endogenic substrates (Fig. 1).

About 50 per cent (even up to 70 per cent in occasional experiments) of the inorganic phosphate which had disappeared was found in the form of fructose diphosphate. The binding of a smaller quantity of inorganic phosphate in myocarditic muscle pulp was associated with reduced formation of fructose diphosphate. The glycogenolytic process as a whole was thus disturbed in myocarditis. The addition of various intermediate substrates of glycolysis and various glycolytic poisons instead of glycogen to the experimental tests revealed the most vulnerable link in the chain of glycolysis reactions.

Binding of inorganic phosphorus in glycogenolysis is observed in the stages of glycogen phosphorolysis and of glycolytic oxidoreduction. It can, therefore, be postulated that the reduced binding of inorganic phosphorus observed in the pulp of myocarditic muscle is determined by disturbance of the ability to link inorganic phosphorus in both these stages. This hypothesis was examined in experiments in which mono-iodoacetate was added to the experimental tests in order to exclude the process of glycolytic oxidoreduction. Figure 2 shows that the addition of mono-iodoacetate to the experimental tests led to considerable reduction in the binding of mineral

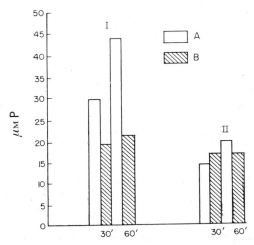

FIG. 2. Esterification of inorganic phosphate in normal myocardium (A) and in myocarditis (B) without (I) and with (II) the addition of mono-iodoacetate.

phosphate in the cardiac muscle pulp from the control animals (from averages of 30 and 44 after 30 and 60 min incubation respectively to 14 and 19 μM per test).

When mono-iodoacetate was added to the cardiac muscle pulp from myocarditic animals, there was little or no reduction in the binding of inorganic phosphate. Consequently, in the presence of mono-iodoacetate, the difference between the binding of mineral phosphate by pulp of cardiac muscle from control and from experimental animals tended to be reduced and sometimes disappeared completely. The results of these experiments pointed to disturbance of the reaction of glycolytic oxidoreduction in the presence of myocarditis.

The disturbance of glycolytic oxidoreduction in myocarditis was also confirmed in direct experiments in which the conversion of fructose di phosphate to phosphoglyceric acid was examined. The experiments in this series were carried out in the presence of fluoride and creatine (the latter was added to preserve adenosine diphosphate in the experimental tests).

Figure 3 shows that a much smaller quantity of phosphoglyceric acid than in the case of control animals was formed when pulp of cardiac muscle from myocarditic animals was incubated. Fructose diphosphate, added to the tests, was utilized intensively by the cardiac muscle pulps from both control and myocarditic animals, the loss of fructose diphosphate in both cases being considerably greater than the quantity of phosphoglyceric acid formed. This discrepancy between the reduction in fructose diphosphate and the increase of phosphoglyceric acid is apparently explained by the different rates of the enzyme processes—the quite considerable speed of

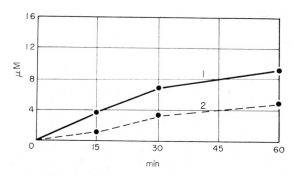

FIG. 3. Formation of phosphoglyceric acid from fructose diphosphate in normal myocardium (1) and in myocarditis (2).

the aldolase breakdown of fructose diphosphate and the comparatively slow reaction of glycolytic oxidoreduction. As only very slight differences in the esterification of mineral phosphate in the presence of mono-iodo-acetate were observed between the cardiac muscle pulp from control and pulp from myocarditic animals, there was no reason to believe that there was any important disturbance of glycolytic reactions preceding oxidoreduction. The question of possible disturbance in the terminal links of glyco-genolysis (by conversion of phosphoglyceric to lactic acid) remained open. In experiments to clarify this point phosphoglyceric acid was added as substrate. Figure 4 shows that no appreciable differences in the formation of lactic acid when phosphoglyceric acid was used as substrate could be observed between cardiac muscle pulps from control and myocarditic animals respectively. The quantity of lactic acid formed from phosphoglyceric acid in cardiac muscle pulp from control animals was of approximately the same order as when glycogen was added to the tests. A different picture was presented by cardiac muscle pulp from myocarditic animals. The quantity of lactic acid formed when phosphoglyceric acid was added to the tests was always greater than the quantity formed when glycogen was added and was almost the same as the quantity formed in the case of control animals. The results of this series of experiments thus indicate invulnerability of the end stages of glycogenolysis (phosphoglyceric acid, lactic acid) in experimental myocarditis.

It has already been stated that fructose diphosphate is reduced along with the reduced esterification of mineral phosphate in myocarditis. One possible reason for the reduced formation of fructose diphosphate would appear to be disturbance of the glycolytic resynthesis of adenosine triphosphate. But disturbed utilization of the adenosine triphosphate formed, for example, as a result of increased adenosine triphosphatase activity, could not lead to this result.

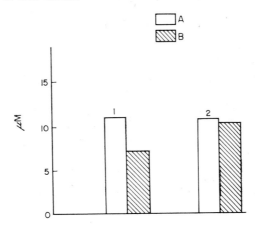

FIG. 4. Formation of lactic acid from glycogen (1) and from phosphoglyceric acid (2) in normal cardiac muscle (A) and in myocarditis (B).

TABLE 1. Adenosine triphosphatase activity of cardiac muscle tissue in the normal state and in myocarditis

| | | Pulp | | Water-soluble | | Water-insoluble | |
| | | μg P/300 mg tissue | | μg P/20 mg tissue | | | |
		15	30	15	30	15	30
Normal		960	1416	36	54	152	248
		1000	1700	42	77	149	244
		950	1700	74	124	132	218
		1150	1850	57	107	107	185
	Average	1015	1666	52	90	135	223
Myocarditis		1000	1350	46	77	127	235
		1000	1650	37	57	122	212
		1000	1560	32	62	122	235
		850	1350	37	57	112	198
	Average	962	1477	38	63	120	220

10 a*

Preliminary experiments on adenosine triphosphatase activity were carried out with cardiac muscle pulp.

Table 1 shows that the values for the adenosine triphosphatase activity for normal cardiac muscle pulp and for myocarditic pulp were of the same order. In normal cardiac muscle 1·0 mg P/300 mg tissue was released from adenosine triphosphate by incubation for 15 min and 1·6 mg P by incubation for 30 min, the corresponding values for myocarditic muscle being 0·96mg and 1·48 mg P.

In the actual experimental conditions difference in enzyme activity might not have been evident because of the high enzyme content of the tissue pulp. Experiments were, therefore, carried out in which adenosine triphosphatase activity was examined for small quantities of tissue (20 mg per test), the water-soluble and water-insoluble adenosine triphosphatase activities being determined separately in these experiments by the method of Zbarskii and Brisker (1948). Table 1 shows that, with the experiments

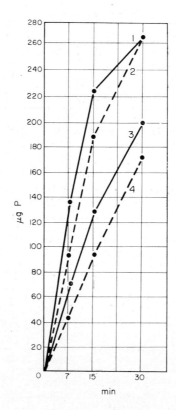

FIG. 5. Phosphorylase activities of extracts of cardiac muscle, normal (continuous line) and myocarditic (interrupted line).

1 and 2—dilution of extracts 1:4.   3 and 4—dilution of extracts 1:16.

so arranged, we were unable to demonstrate any changes whatever in the activity either of water-soluble or water-insoluble adenosine triphosphatase in myocarditis. The results given in Table 1 also indicate that much the greater part of the adenosine triphosphatase activity was in relation to the insoluble residue both in the normal state and in the presence of myocarditis.

It can, therefore, be inferred from this experimental material that the reduced formation of fructose diphosphate seen in myocarditis is not due to change in adenosine triphosphatase activity but is a consequence of reduced adenosine triphosphate formation, associated with disturbance of the reaction for glycolytic oxidoreduction.

It was also of interest to examine phosphorylase activity in experimental myocarditis as a number of investigators have established a connexion between the functional state of the heart and the activity of this enzyme (Hess and Haugaardt, 1958; Ellis, 1956).

A considerable difference in their glycogen-synthesizing activity was observed when fresh extracts of cardiac muscle from normal rabbits and rabbits with experimental myocarditis were examined (Fig. 5). The cardiac muscle extracts from myocarditic rabbits had less phosphorylase activity than similar extracts from control animals. Figure 5 shows that the difference in the increase of mineral phosphate when control and experimental extracts acted on Cori ester was most pronounced during the first 7 min of incubation. The increase of inorganic phosphorus for the rabbits with myocarditis was 45 μg after 7 min and 167 μg after 30 min of incubation, as compared with 70 and 199 μg after the same intervals for the control animals. The difference in the phosphorylase activities of the extracts was rendered slightly more evident by dilution of the extracts.

DISCUSSION

Our initial assumption in this investigation was that, as glycogenolysis is quite a complex process, consisting of a chain of successive and mutually determined reactions, it was of some importance to establish the most vulnerable link in the conditions afforded by experimental myocarditis. This is important as it is only by discovering which process and which links in the process are disturbed that we shall be able to find effective means of restoring normal metabolism.

Examination of the process of glycogenolysis in cardiac muscle tissue of control animals revealed a marked discrepancy between the quantity of mineral phosphate esterified and the accumulation of lactic acid. This was connected with retardation of the process of glycogenolysis at some intermediate stage or other. The considerable reduction (about 50 per cent) in the esterification of mineral phosphate in the presence of mono-iodoacetate indicated that the intensity of this process was due in about equal degree to phosphorolysis and glycolytic oxidoreduction. It could, therefore, be assumed that restriction of glycogenolysis occurred in some stage after oxidoreduction. The use of phosphoglyceric acid as substrate revealed that the quantity of lactic acid formed from it differed very little from the quantities formed from endogenous substrates. The quantity of lactic acid formed in endogeneous substrates was equivalent to 7·6 μM per test and 8·3 and 9·6 μM lactic acid when phosphoglyceric acid was added after 30 and 60 min of incubation respectively. Numerous investigations of lactic dehydrogenase activity showed that this was quite high in cardiac muscle tissue. It can only be assumed, therefore, that the factors limiting the formation of lactic acid from glycogen in cardiac muscle tissue are the reactions catalysed by enolase or pyruvate kinase.

Disturbance of the process of glycogenolysis, as shown by reduced esterification of inorganic phosphate, reduced accumulation of fructose diphosphate and lactic acid, has been demonstrated in experimental myocarditis. No reduction in the utilization of mineral phosphate in the presence of mono-iodoacetate was observed in cardiac muscle pulp from myocarditic animals, and in this respect they differed from the controls.

It follows, therefore, that one of the reasons for inhibition of the process of glycogenolysis in experimental myocarditis is disturbance of glycolytic oxidoreduction. Disturbance of this process was also demonstrated in the direct experiment in which the conversion of fructose diphosphate to phosphoglyceric acid was investigated. As the cardiac muscle pulp from control and from myocarditic animals exhibited no appreciable differences in respect of orthophosphate in the presence of mono-iodoacetate, there would not appear to be any serious grounds for thinking that phosphorylase activity was disturbed.

By using very dilute extracts (1:16) and short periods of incubation we were, however, able to demonstrate reduction of the activity of this enzyme, particularly in the first few minutes of incubation (by 30–35 per cent).

The reduced formation of fructose diphosphate seen in the cardiac muscle pulp from myocarditic animals thus had two causes, namely inhibition of phosphorolysis leading to reduced formation of fructose-6-phosphate and inhibition of glycolytic oxidoreduction leading to reduced formation of adenosine triphosphate.

Our examination of the direct formation of phosphoglyceric acid from fructose diphosphate enabled us to conclude that the disturbance of glycolytic oxidoreduction was not connected with change in phosphorylase activity. As factors which limit the formation of phosphoglyceric acid are extremely varied, demonstration of the manner in which glycolytic oxidoreduction is disturbed in experimental myocarditis must be the subject of further investigation.

CONCLUSIONS

(1) Examination of the process of glycogenolysis in pulp of rabbit cardiac muscle revealed a sharp discrepancy between the quantity of mineral phosphate esterified and the accumulation of lactic acid.

(2) Inhibition of glycolysis, as shown by reduced esterification of inorganic phosphate and the formation of lactic acid, was observed in cardiac muscle tissue in experimental myocarditis. This inhibition of glycolysis in myocarditis was determined by disturbance of glycolytic oxidoreduction.

(3) Reduced phosphorylase activity could be demonstrated when very dilute extracts of cardiac muscle were used.

(4) The adenosine triphosphatase activity in the cardiac muscle was unchanged in myocarditis.

REFERENCES

BARKER, S. and W. SUMMERSON, *J. Biol. Chem.* **138**, 535 (1941).

BARRON, E., W. SIGHTS and V. WIDLER, *Arch. Expl. Path. Pharmacol.* **219**, 338 (1953).

BING, R., *Fortschr. d. Kardiol.* **1**, 52 (1956).

BUZARD, I., P. NYTH, F. KORKA and M. PAUL, *Proc. Soc. Expl. Biol. Med.* **93**, 1, 156 (1956).

ELLIS, S., *Pharmacol. Rev.* **8**, 485 (1956).

HAARMAN, W., *Biochem. Z.* **255**, 103, 142 (1932).

HAARMAN, W. and H. BRINK, *Biochem. Z.* **282**, 419 (1935).

HESS, M. and N. HAUGAARDT, *J. Pharmacol. Expl. Therap.* **122**, 169 (1958).

KOROLEV, R., Papers of the 8th Scientific Conference of students of the Naval Medical Academy (Trudy 8-i nauchnoi konf. kursantov i slushatelei Voenno-Morskoi med. akad.) 12 (1952).

MEERSON, F. Z., M. YEGOROVA and S. GUZ, Problems of Medical Chemistry (*Voprosy med. khim.*) **1**, 5 (1955).

MENTOVA, V., Pharmacology and Toxicology (*Farmakol. i toksikol.*) **2**, 5, 51 (1939).

MESHKOVA, N. P. and N. ALEKSAKHINA, Advances in Biological Chemistry (*Uspekhi biol. khim.*) **2**, 277 (1954).

PEEL, L. and B. LOUGHMAN, *Biochem. J.* **65**, 709 (1957).

RAISKINA, M. YE., Papers of the All-Union Congress of Physicians (Trudy Vses. s"ezda terapevtov), Moscow 1958.

SARATIKOV, A. S., New medicinal plants of Siberia (*Novyye lekarstvennyye rasteniya Sibiri*) **4**, 155 (1953).

VYALYKH, M. F. and F. Z. MEERSON, Problems of Medical Chemistry (*Vopr. med. khim.*) **6**, 19 (1960).

WU, I. and I. CHANG, *Quart. J. Expl. Physiol.* **34**, 2, 91 (1948).

ZBARSKII, I. and N. BRISKER, Biochemistry (*Biokhimiya*) **13**, 2, 185 (1948).

THERAPEUTIC ACTION OF THIOL
COMPOUNDS IN THE INFECTIVE PROCESS

T. A. SPERANSKAYA

Institute of Animal Morphology, U.S.S.R. Academy of Sciences, Moscow

Translated by Dr. R. Crawford

THERE is a considerable volume of experimental material demonstrating the dependence of a number of physiological and biochemical processes on the state of the tissue sulphydryl (SH) groups. Investigations on the importance of SH-groups in the production of nerve effects are of particular interest (Koshtoyants and Turpayev, 1946; Turpayev, 1952; Koshtoyants, 1950; Smirnov *et al.*, 1952; Medyanik *et al.*, 1955; Galoyan, 1956; Nistratova, 1959), as are also investigations demonstrating the importance of SH-groups for the enzyme activity of thiol enzymes (Bersin, 1935; Barron and Singer, 1945; Haugaardt, 1946; Belen'kii and Rozengart, 1949; Gol'd-shtein, 1950; Barron, 1951; Poglazov *et al.*, 1958).

A comprehensive theoretical assessment of the importance of the reactive groups of proteins in vital processes was put forward by Koshtoyants (1951). Findings relating to the therapeutic action of substances containing free SH-groups in various pathological states are of interest in connexion with this concept. The injurious effects of certain toxic substances could be abolished by 2,3-dimercaptopropanol (Hughes, 1946; Eagle *et al.*, 1946; Batton *et al.*, 1947; Graham *et al.*, 1947). This same preparation was found to be effective in the treatment of hepatolenticular degeneration, an illness connected with disturbance of copper metabolism in the body and increased adsorption of the metal by brain tissue (Streifler and Feldman, 1953). The protective actions of cysteine and cysteinamine have been demonstrated in relation to radiation sickness in animals (Patt *et al.*, 1947; Rugh and Wang, 1953; Kirrmann, 1955). Compounds containing free sulphydryl groups have been shown to have hypotensive effects (Schroeder and Menhard, 1951; Konstantinova, 1955) and to be capable of counteracting the diabetogenic effect of alloxan (Sen and Bhattacharya, 1952). Cysteinamine (Kluyskens, 1953), and cysteine hydrochloride (Speranskaya, 1955) reduce the toxicity of streptomycin considerably. Bergol'ts (1955), in a paper reviewing the importance of sulphur-containing compounds in cancerogenesis, refers to evidence that the injection of substances containing free

SH-groups into animals suppresses and prevents the development of experimental tumours. Meyer-Doring (1954) synthesized a complex compound, cysteyl ascorbic acid, in an attempt to combine the antibacterial properties of ascorbic acid and the therapeutic activity of cysteine. His experiments showed that cysteyl ascorbic acid had a curative effect in various experimental infective processes. Unfortunately, the material presented by the author does not allow us to assess to what extent the results obtained were connected with the use of the complex compounds and what significance should actually be attached to each of the constituents, cysteine and ascorbic acid.

There is now, therefore, a considerable amount of material indicating that the state of the tissue sulphydryl groups determines the course of many vital processes and that a number of pathological phenomena are dependent on disturbance of the metabolism of thiol compounds.

This was the basis for our examination of the effects of substances containing free sulphydryl groups on the course of an experimental infective process.

The work was based on the Institute of Antibiotics, U.S.S.R. Academy of Medical Sciences. We take this opportunity of expressing our gratitude to Prof. V. A. Shorin, director of the Chemotherapy Division of the Institute, for making the work possible and for help therein.

METHOD

Standard models of infective processes in white mice were used in the experiments. Mice weighing 16–18 g were infected by the intraperitoneal injection of 0·1 ml diluted pneumococcus culture (*Diplococcus pneumoniae*, type I) or of 0·25 ml of a culture of dysentery bacilli (*Sh. paradysenteriae*, strain No. 7650). In lethal dose, each of these bacteria produced a fulminant infective process in white mice, leading to their death 24–48 hours after infection.

Some of the animals were infected with a suspension of the bacterial culture in increasing dilution and were not treated. The mortality in these groups of mice enabled us to establish the number of lethal doses of the bacterium injected into the animals in the experiments.

Substances containing free sulphydryl groups, namely free cysteine, cysteine hydrochloride and unithiol, and also cystine, which contains SS-groups, were administered to the experimental animals. These preparations were injected once 30–60 min after infection. The preparations were dissolved in normal saline and were injected subcutaneously in the abdominal region in volumes of 0·2 ml. The survival rate of the mice constituted the index of the therapeutic effect.

The antibacterial activity of the substances containing SH-groups was examined in addition to the testing of their therapeutic effect. For this the bacterial cultures were sown on solid media (beef peptone agar and

nitrate agar) containing free cysteine in various concentrations. Staphylococci and coli bacilli were used in this series of experiments. The growth
of the bacterial film in the presence of cysteine was the index of its antibacterial properties.

RESULTS

The effects of substances containing free SH-groups on the termination
of pneumococcal septicaemia in white mice were examined in the first
series of experiments. The results are given in Table 1.

TABLE 1. Therapeutic effects of substances containing SH-groups on pneumococcal
septicaemia in mice

Number of lethal doses of pneumococcus	Preparation	Dose—mg per mouse	Number of animals	
			Dying	Surviving
7·5	Free cysteine	6; 12	0	8
	Free cysteine	1·5; 3; 6	1	11
25	Cysteine hydrochloride	1·5; 3; 6	0	24
	Unithiol	1·5; 3; 6	0	12
500	Free cysteine	3; 6; 12	1	24
	Cysteine hydrochloride	3; 6; 12	6	22
	Free cysteine	0·12; 0·25; 0·5; 1; 2; 3; 6	41	7
750	Unithiol	0·12; 0·25; 0·5; 1; 2	15	5
1000	Free cysteine	0·25; 0·5; 1; 2; 3	20	0

These results indicate that the substances containing free SH-groups had
definite therapeutic effects in pneumococcal septicaemia in white mice.
At the same time the number of animals recovering diminished as the dose
of infection increased. Animals which had received 1000 lethal doses of
pneumococcus could not generally be cured. The results are not presented
separately for each dose employed as, within the limits of the doses tested,
the therapeutic effect did not appear to depend on the quantity of the
SH-preparation injected. In this and the following series of experiments the
animals which survived as a result of the administration of thiol compounds
were kept under observation for 10 to 12 days after infection and then killed.
The mice did not exhibit any signs of illness during this period.

The therapeutic effect of substances containing free SH-groups in illness
produced by gram-negative bacteria was examined in the next series of
experiments.

Table 2 shows that substances containing free SH-groups had also some
therapeutic activity in illness produced by gram-negative bacteria. This

effect was not, it is true, very pronounced. In assessing the effectiveness of the substances tested in this case one must remember that the dysentery bacillus, unlike the pneumococcus, is classed as of low virulence and is injected in larger numbers (millions of bacterial cells); its pathogenic effect increases as the bacteria die and large quantities of endotoxin are liberated.

TABLE 2. Therapeutic effects of substances containing SH-groups in mice infected with cultures of dysentery bacilli

Number of lethal doses of dysentery bacilli	Preparation	Dose—mg per mouse	Number of animals	
			Dying	Surviving
1	Free cysteine	3; 6	3	5
	Unithiol	3; 6	5	3
2	Free cysteine	3; 6	8	0
	Unithiol	3; 6	6	2
3	Cysteine hydrochloride	5; 7	8	0

Note: The average survival period of mice receiving therapeutic preparations was about 150 per cent that for the animals of the control group used to determine the dose of infection.

We carried out a series of experiments (Table 3) in which the animals, infected with pneumococci, were given cystine, instead of cysteine, by injection in order to determine to what extent free SH-groups were responsible for the effect obtained.

TABLE 3. Use of cystine in pneumococcal septicaemia of mice

Number of lethal doses of pneumococcus	Cystine	Number of animals	
		Dying	Surviving
7·5	6; 12	5	3
10	3; 6; 12; 24	16	0

The experiments showed that the curative effect of cystine was very poor compared with that of cysteine in pneumococcal septicaemia (see Table 1). Whereas cysteine cured 86 per cent of animals given 500 lethal doses of pneumococcus, cystine was quite without effect in mice infected with 10 lethal doses.

The very slight curative effect which was nevertheless obtained with cystine was, we suggest, due to the fact that this substance may possibly have undergone partial reduction in the bodies of the animals, being converted into cysteine.

The last question which we examined concerned the mode of action of these substances. An attempt was made to determine whether the therapeutic effect observed was due to the antibacterial activity of the substances containing sulphydryl groups or to their direct influence on the organism of the infected animal.

To determine this, free cysteine was titrated by the method of serial dilution (in test tubes). These experiments showed that when the bacteria were cultured on beef peptone agar or on nitrate agar, free cysteine in all the strengths tested (from 0·0009 to 1 per cent) had no bacteriostatic effect on either staphylococcus or coli bacillus cultures. Equally good growth of the bacterial culture was noted in all tubes 24 hours after seeding of the medium containing free cysteine in various concentrations.

DISCUSSION

It should first of all be noted that it was possible to overcome an infective process by means of a naturally occurring metabolic substance, the amino acid, cysteine. This fact is of interest in connexion with the organism's defensive powers. It can be assumed that the cysteine present in proteins and participating in metabolism is capable of having a positive effect in infection as well as injected cysteine.

It is likewise important to emphasize that the infected mice survived as a result of the administration of a relatively simple substance, a single amino acid, apparently because of its sulphydryl groups, inasmuch as cystine, which contains no SH-groups, has practically no therapeutic property. This circumstance affords us an opportunity to examine the delicate biochemical mechanisms which, it may be assumed, constitute the essential link in the development of an infective process. Our results may be of some interest in connexion with the general question of the importance of amino acids in the course of physiological and pathological processes, a problem on which much biochemical work has been done (Braunshtein, 1950).

The second point noted by us is that cysteine has no antibacterial activity *in vitro*. In other words, the curative effect observed was not determined by the bacteriostatic activity of the injected cysteine. The latter figures as a non-specific agent stimulating the defensive powers of the organism. We have likewise been unable to find any references in the literature to cysteine as having antibacterial action. On the other hand, there is evidence (Libenson *et al.*, 1953) that cysteine and other compounds containing sulphydryl groups (glutathione, thioglycolic acid) neutralize the bacteriostatic effect of sulphur as seen in relation to haemolytic streptococci, *Clostridia*, *Brucella* and other bacteria. The authors of this paper suggest that compounds containing SH-groups abolish the inactivating effect of sulphur on the thiol enzymes of the bacterial cells. It is well known that cysteine also reduces the bacteriostatic effects of a number of antibiotics.

This effect is usually ascribed to protection by cysteine of the thiol enzymes of the bacteria from the inhibiting effect of the antibiotic.

Research on the possibilities of therapeutic intervention in infective processes by the mobilization of the defensive powers of the sick organism is an important task. And this is all the more urgent in that the use of specific chemotherapy is leading with ever increasing frequency to the development in bacteria of resistance to the chemotherapeutics, a serious obstacle to the clinical use of antibiotics (Molchanov and Yaroshevskii, 1955; Lazarev, 1957). A theoretical basis for the development of methods of non-specific therapy is afforded by Pavlov's doctrine on physiological methods for the control of disease.

CONCLUSIONS

(1) Substances containing free sulphydryl groups—free cysteine, cysteine hydrochloride, unithiol—had definite curative effects in acute experimental infective processes produced by gram-positive bacteria (*Diplococcus pneumoniae*, type I).

(2) Substances containing SH-groups also had therapeutic effects in illnesses caused by gram-negative bacteria (*Sh. paradysenteriae*, strain No. 7650).

(3) The amino acid cystine had practically no therapeutic action. The curative effect obtained by the use of compounds containing sulphydryl groups would appear to be specifically connected with the presence of these groups in their molecules.

(4) Titration of free cysteine *in vitro* showed that this amino acid had no bacteriostatic effect either on gram-positive (staphylococci) or on gram-negative (coli bacilli) bacteria. The curative effect of cysteine in pneumococcal septicaemia and dysentery would appear to be produced through change in the reactive properties of the sick organism and mobilization of its defensive powers.

REFERENCES

BARRON, E., *Advances in Enzymology* **11**, 201 (1951).
BARRON, E. and T. SINGER, *J. Biol. Chem.* **157**, 221 (1945).
BARRON, E., Z. MILLER, G. BARTLETT and T. SINGER, *Biochem. J.* **41**, 69 (1947).
BELEN'KII, M. L. and V. I. ROZENGART, Advances in Biology (*Usp. sovrem. biol.*) **28**, 387 (1949).
BERGOL'TS, V. M., Advances in Biology (*Usp. sovrem. biol.*) **39**, 47–64 (1955).
BERSIN, T., *Erg. Enzym.* **4**, 68 (1935).
BRAUNSHTEIN, A. YE., Ukrainian Biochemical J. (*Ukr. biokhim. zh.*) **22**, 3, 273–295 (1950).
EAGLE, H., H. MAGNUSON and R. FLEISCHMAN, *J. Clin. Invest.* **25**, 451 (1946).
GALOYAN, SH. A., Papers of the Armenian S.S.R. Academy of Sciences (*Dokl. Akad. Nauk Arm. SSR*) **22**, 3, 141 (1956).
GOL'DSHTEIN, B. I., Ukrainian Biochemical J. (*Ukr. biokhim. zh.*) **22**, 349 (1950).
GRAHAM, A., LEVY and A. CHANGE, *Biochem. J.* **41**, 352 (1947).

HAUGAARDT, N., *J. Biol. Chem.* **164**, 1, 265 (1946).
HUGHES, W., *J. Clin. Invest.* **25**, 541 (1946).
KIRRMANN, I., *Bull. Biol.* **89**, 4, 491 (1955).
KLUYSKENS, P., *Nature* **172** (4385), 912 (1053).
KONSTANTINOVA, M. M., *Effect of Ferritin on Blood Pressure* (O Vliyanii ferritina na krovyanoye davleniye), Moscow 1955.
KOSHTOYANTS, KH. S., Papers of the U.S.S.R. Academy of Sciences (*Dokl. Akad. Nauk SSR*) **72**, 5, 981–984 (1950).
KOSHTOYANTS, KH. S., *Proteins, Metabolism and Nerve Regulation* (Belkovyye tela, obmen veshchestv i nervnaya regulyatsiya) (1951).
KOSHTOYANTS, KH. S. and T. M. TURPAYEV, Papers of the U.S.S.R. Academy of Sciences (*Dokl. Akad. Nauk SSSR*) **54**, 2, 181 (1946).
LAZAREV, N. V., J. of Microbiology Epidemiology and Immunobiology (*Zh. microbiol., epidemiol. i immunobiol.*) **10**, 41 (1957).
LIBENSON, L., F. HADLEY, A. MCILROY, V. WETZEL and R. MELLON, *J. Infect. Dis.* **93**, 1, 28–35 (1953).
MEDYANIK, I. A., L. A. MEDYANIK and YA. V. OLEINIK, Reports and Communications, L'vov Univ. (*Dokl. i soobsch. L'vovsk Un-ta*), **6**, 2, 50 (1955).
MEYER-DORING, H., *Nature* **174** (4429), **555** (1954).
MOLCHANOV, N. S. and A. YA. YAROSHEVSKII, Therapeutic Archives (*Terapevticheskii arkhiv*) **27**, 8, 5 (1955).
NISTRATOVA, S. N., *Biochemical Nature of Cholinoreceptor in Connexion with the Mechanism of Acetylcholine Action* (Ob biokhimicheskoi prirode kholinoretseptora v svyazi s mekhanizmom deistviya atsetilkholina), Moscow 1959.
PATT, H., E. TYREE, R. STRAUBE and D. SMITH, *Science* **2852**, 213 (1947).
PATT, H., E. TYREE, R. STRAUBE and D. SMITH, Science **2852**, 213 (1947).
POGLAZOV, B. F., V. BILUSHI and A. A. BAYEV, Biochemistry (*Biokhimiya*) **23**, 2, 269 (1958).
RUGH, R. and S. WANG, *Proc. Soc. Expl. Biol. Med.* **83**, 2, 411 (1953).
SCHROEDER, H. and E. MENHARD, *Fed. Proc.* **10**, 122 (1951).
SEN, P. B. and G. BHATTACHARYA, *Science* **115** (2976), 41 (1952).
SMIRNOV, G. D., A. L. BYZOV and YU. I. RAMPAN, Reports of U.S.S.R. Academy of Sciences (*Dokl. Akad. Nauk SSSR*) **87**, 1, 155 (1952).
SPERANSKAYA, T. N., *Proceedings of 8th All-Union Congress of Physiologists, Biochemists and Pharmacologists* (Tez. dokl. VII vses. s"ezda fiziol., biokhim. i farmakol.) 583 (1955).
STREIFLER, M. and S. FELDMAN, *Arch. Neurol. Psychol.* **69**, 1, 84 (1953).
TURPAYEV, T. M., Papers of the Institute of Animal Morphology, U.S.S.R. Academy of Sciences (*Trudy IMZh. Akad. Nauk SSSR*) **6**, 19 (1952).

FUNCTIONAL AND BIOCHEMICAL ANALYSIS OF THE ACTIONS OF ACETYLCHOLINE AND ATROPINE ON CARDIAC MUSCLE

T. M. Turpayev, T. G. Putintseva and S. N. Nistratova

Institute of Animal Morphology, U.S.S.R. Academy of Sciences, Moscow

Translated by Dr. R. Crawford

Elucidation of the biochemical processes underlying the action of chemical transmitters on the effector cell is one of the urgent problems in contemporary neurophysiology and pharmacology. The solution of this problem would bring us much closer to an understanding of the essential nature of the effect of the nervous system on functioning organs and would provide a rational approach to the synthesis of new pharmacological and therapeutic substances.

A concept developed by Koshtoyants and his co-workers was that the process for the transmission of nerve influences to the effector cell was built up of a chain of enzymochemical reactions.

The first link in this chain is the synthesis of the transmitter by nerve tissue and its liberation in free form, with finally, inclusion of the transmitter in the metabolic processes responsible for the functional activity of the effector cell (Koshtoyants, 1951).

An important link in this chain of reactions is the interaction of the transmitter with the structures in the effector cell sensitive to it, with receptors or receptive substance of Langley.

In respect of one transmitter, acetylcholine, there are now experimental results defining some of the properties of the cholinoreceptive substance in the muscle cell. It has been shown that the acetylcholine receptor is a substrate of protein nature (Turpayev, 1955a, 1958; Turpayev and Nistratova, 1959), situated on the outside of the muscle fibre membrane (Castillo and Katz, 1955) and occupying a very small part of its surface (Clark, 1926, 1933; Ginetsinskii, 1947; Castillo and Katz, 1955).

The reaction between acetylcholine and cholinoreceptive substance is similar in character to the interaction between enzyme and substrate; the kinetics of this reaction are similar to the kinetics of enzyme processes (Segre, 1957; Turpayev, 1958); the reaction has a temperature optimum (Turpayev, 1955b) and occurs when acetylcholine interacts with tissue homogenate (Turpayev and Nistratova, 1959) as well as with intact muscle.

The SH-groups of the cholinoreceptor play an important part in the production of the acetylcholine effect (Turpayev, 1955a; Nistratova and Turpayev, 1959).

Less has been discovered on the process by which acetylcholine is involved in the metabolism responsible for the contractile act of the muscle fibre, although there is indirect evidence of a connexion between acetylcholine and the metabolism of adenosine triphosphate (ATP) (Raab, 1959; Raiskina, 1959).

An indication of the involvement of acetylcholine in tissue metabolism is afforded, more particularly, by the liberation from heart muscle as a result of the action of acetylcholine of substances (or a substance) similar to energy-rich compounds in the nature of its action on another heart (Putintseva and Turpayev, 1960).

This paper describes experimental results obtained by two lines of investigation, namely (1) further examination of the interaction between acetylcholine and cholinoreceptors in cardiac muscle and the effect of atropine on this reaction and (2) study of the natures of the substances stimulating cardiac activity which are secreted in the ventricle of the frog heart acted on by acetylcholine.

KINETICS OF THE REACTION OF ACETYLCHOLINE WITH CHOLINORECEPTOR EFFECT OF ATROPINE ON THIS REACTION

When acetylcholine acts on the effector cell, the first reaction is that of acetylcholine with the specific protein—the cholinoreceptor. If we assume that acetylcholine (A) and receptor (R) form a compound (AR)

$$A + R \rightleftarrows AR$$

and that the effectiveness of the action of acetylcholine (y, expressed as a percentage) depends on the relative quantity of this compound, i.e. $y = \dfrac{100\,(AR)}{(R)}$, then, according to the law of mass action, the dissociation constant for the compound $AR\,(K_A)$ is

$$K_A = \frac{k_{-1}}{k_1} = \frac{(A)\,(R - AR)}{(AR)}$$

in which $(R - AR)$ is the concentration of free cholinoreceptors and k_1 and k_{-1} are the constants for the speeds of the direct and reverse reactions.

By solving this expression for $\dfrac{100\,(AR)}{(R)} = y$ we obtain the equation

$$y = \frac{100\,(A)}{K_A + (A)} \tag{1}$$

which is identical with the equation of Michaelis and Menton (1913) for enzyme reactions. A more convenient form of equation (1) for determination of the constant K_A is

$$\frac{1}{y} = \frac{K_A}{100} \times \frac{1}{(A)} + \frac{1}{100} \tag{1'}$$

which is similar to the form of the Michaelis and Menton equation suggested by Lineweaver and Burk (1934) for determination of the constants of enzyme reactions.

It follows from equation (1) that if the reciprocal of the effectiveness of acetylcholine action $(1)/y$ is plotted against the reciprocal of the acetylcholine concentration $(1)/A$, the slope of the line connecting the experimental points will be $K_A/100$.

In a preceding investigation (Turpayev, 1958) it was shown in experiments on the isolated frog ventricle that the effectiveness of acetylcholine action as determined from the degree of depression of the contractions of cardiac muscle was $y = 100\,(H - h)/H$, in which H, the amplitude of the myocardial contractions before the injection of acetylcholine, and h, the minimum amplitude of the contractions (after the injection of acetylcholine into the cannula), depend on the acetylcholine concentration given by equation (1) (Fig. 1, A). Thus, in the action of acetylcholine on cardiac muscle, one molecule of acetylcholine reacts with one active centre in the receptor molecule.

Further work on the kinetics of the reaction of acetylcholine with receptors in frog cardiac muscle afforded experimental evidence that in some frogs the effectiveness of the acetylcholine action on isolated ventricle had a more complex relationship to the concentration of acetylcholine than that represented by equation (1). Mathematical analysis of this relationship showed that the reciprocals of the effectiveness of acetylcholine action $(1)/y$ were in linear relationship, not with the reciprocals of the acetylcholine concentration $(1)/A$ but with the reciprocals of the squares of the acetylcholine concentration $1/(A)^2$ (Fig. 1, B), in accordance with the equation

$$y = \frac{100\,(A)^2}{K_{2A} + (A)^2} \tag{2}$$

or

$$\frac{1}{y} = \frac{K_{2A}}{100} \times \frac{1}{(A)^2} + \frac{1}{100} \tag{2'}$$

Equation (2) for the kinetics of the reaction of acetylcholine with receptors of the effector cell indicates that one active centre of the receptor molecule reacts with two molecules of acetylcholine, and not one:

$$2A + R \underset{k_{-1}}{\overset{k_1}{\rightleftarrows}} A_2R,$$

in which $K_{2A} = k_{-1}/k_1$, the dissociation constant for the compound A_2R, which has the dimensions of the square of the concentration.

The kinetics of the reaction between acetylcholine and receptors in the presence of atropine which, according to modern conceptions, is a competitive antagonist of acetylcholine (Segre, 1953; Timms, 1956; Hall, 1959), were studied in the next series of experiments.

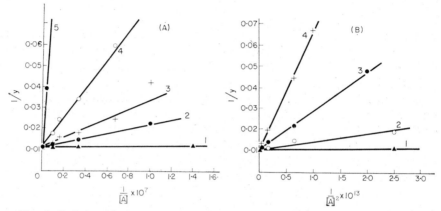

FIG. 1. Relationship between the effectiveness of acetylcholine and its concentration.

A—experiments on four hearts. The lines 1, 2, 3 and 4 connecting the experimental points correspond to equation (1') with constants equal to 2.2×10^{-8}, 1.5×10^{-8}, 0.9×10^{-8} and 0.3×10^{-8} g/ml. Abscissa — reciprocals of the concentration (g/ml) of acetylcholine $1/A$. Ordinate — reciprocals of the effectiveness of acetylcholine action. B — experiments on four hearts. The lines 1, 2, 3, 4 connecting the experimental points correspond to equation (2') with constants equal to $(3.0 \times 10^{-8})^2$, $(1.2 \times 10^{-8})^2$, $(1.0 \times 10^{-8})^2$ and $(0.6 \times 10^{-8}$ g/ml$)^2$. Abscissa—reciprocals of the squares of the acetylcholine concentration (g/ml) $(1/A^2)$.
Ordinate—reciprocals of the effectiveness of acetylcholine action $1/y$.

The effect of various concentrations of atropine on both types of interaction between acetylcholine and cholinoreceptors was investigated and the results were subsequently analysed by the method of binary reciprocal coordinates.

Analysis of the curves for the relationship between effectiveness of acetylcholine action and its concentration by this method showed that the reduction in the effectiveness of the acetylcholine action in the presence of atropine was due to increase in the value of the constant K. These changes in the constant show themselves in Fig. 2 by change in the inclination of the curves to the abscissa, which means that in the presence of atropine the equations (1) and (2) assume the forms

$$y = \frac{100\,(A)}{K_1 + (A)} \quad \text{or} \quad \frac{1}{y} = \frac{K_1}{100} \times \frac{1}{(A)} + \frac{1}{100} \tag{3}$$

and

$$y = \frac{100\,(A)^2}{K^2 + (A)^2} \quad \text{or} \quad \frac{1}{y} = \frac{K^2}{100} \times \frac{1}{(A)^2} + \frac{1}{100} \tag{4}$$

in which K_1 and K_2 are the apparent constants for the reaction.

We suggest that the following reactions take place in the action of acetyl-choline and atropine on cholinoreceptor of the first type:

$$A + R \rightleftarrows AR$$
$$At + R \rightleftarrows AtR,$$

in which $K_A = \dfrac{(A)\,(R-AR-AtR)}{(AR)}$, the dissociation constant for the acetyl-choline–cholinoreceptor complex and $K_{At} = \dfrac{(At)\,(R-AR-AtR)}{(AtR)}$, the dis-sociation constant for the atropine–cholinoreceptor complex, and $(R-AR-AtR)$ is the concentration of free receptors. Then, substituting the value AtR has in the first equation in the second equation and solving it for $(AR)/(R) \times 100 = y$ we obtain the equation:

$$\frac{1}{y} = \frac{K_A}{100}\left(1 + \frac{(At)}{K_{At}}\right)\frac{1}{(At)} - \frac{1}{100}$$

Consequently, the apparent equilibrium constant K_1 in equation (3) will be: $K_1 = K_A\left(1 + \dfrac{(At)}{K_{At}}\right)$, whence it is easy to calculate the dissociation constant K_{At} for the atropine–cholinoreceptor complex.

The following are the likely reactions occurring in the interaction of atropine and acetylcholine with cholinoreceptors of the second type:

$$2A + R \rightleftarrows A_2R$$

and

$$2At + R \rightleftarrows At_2R$$

Reasoning in the same way, we obtain the equation for competitive inhibition

$$\frac{1}{y} = \frac{K_{2A}}{100}\left(1 + \frac{(At)^2}{K_{2At}}\right) \times \frac{1}{(A)^2} + \frac{1}{100}$$

whence the apparent constant K_2 in equation (4) will be

$$K_2 = K_{2A}\left(1 + \frac{(At)^2}{K'_{2At}}\right)$$

Figure 2, A shows experiments in which acetylcholine and atropine acted on cholinoreceptor, the active centre of which interacted with ace-tylcholine, $A + R \rightleftarrows AR$. The dissociation constant for the complex

$AR = 10^{-8}$ g/ml or $6 \cdot 1 \times 10^{-8}$M. The dissociation constants of the complex AtR for curves 2, 3, 4 and 5 are $1 \cdot 7 \times 10^{-9}$, $2 \cdot 25 \times 10^{-9}$, $2 \cdot 0 \times 10^{-9}$ and $1 \cdot 65 \times 10^{-9}$ with an average value $K_{At} = 1 \cdot 9 \times 10^{-9}$ M. Thus, for this ventricle the affinity of receptor for atropine $(1)/K_{At}$ was approximately 32 times greater than the affinity of the receptor for acetylcholine $(1)/K_A$.

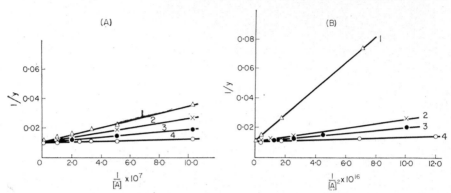

FIG. 2. Effect of atropine on the effectiveness of acetylcholine action in relation to concentration.

A — experiment on isolated ventricle the cholinoreceptors of which interact with acetylcholine in accordance with the equation $A + R \rightleftarrows AR$: 1—the normal state. 2—atropine 5×10^{-9} g/ml. 3—atropine $1 \cdot 5 \times 10^{-8}$ g/ml. 4—atropine $4 \cdot 0 \times 10^{-8}$ g/ml. 5—atropine $6 \cdot 0 \times 10^{-8}$ g/ml.
B—experiment on isolated ventricle the cholinoreceptors of which interact with acetylcholine in accordance with the equation $2A + R \rightleftarrows A_2R$: 1—normal state. 2—atropine 1×10^{-9} g/ml. 3—atropine 2×10^{-9} g/ml. 4—atropine 4×10^{-9} g/ml. Ordinate—reciprocals of the effectiveness of acetylcholine action $(1/y)$.
Abscissa—reciprocals: A—of the concentration (g/ml) of acetylcholine $(1)/A$ and B—of the square of the concentration (g/ml) of acetylcholine $(1)/A^2$.

Calculations of the dissociation constants of the complexes of acetylcholine and atropine with receptor for the reaction of the type $2A + R \rightleftarrows A_2R$ showed that the constants K_{2A} and K_{2At} were in this case greater than the corresponding constants K_A and K_{At}, while $(K_A)^2 \approx K_{2A}$ and $(K_{At})^2 \approx K_{2At}$. The dissociation constants of the complex At_2R for curves 2, 3 and 4 were respectively $(3 \cdot 8 \times 10^{-10}$ M$)^2$, $(4 \cdot 0 \times 10^{-10}$ M$)^2$ and $(4 \cdot 2 \times 10^{-10}$ M$)^2$.

Consequently, in this example the affinity of the active centre of the receptor for atropine $(1)/K_{2At}$ was $11 \cdot 5 \times 10^4$ times greater than the affinity for acetylcholine $(1)/K_{A2}$. If, however, these dissociation constants for the second type of reaction are calculated for interaction of the active centre of receptor with only one molecule of acetylcholine and atropine, we obtain values for the constants K_{2A} and K_{2At} of the same order as for the first type of reaction $A + R = AR$. For the findings given in Fig. 2, B the affinity of receptor for atropine was 340 times greater than the affinity for acetylcholine.

INTERACTION OF ACETYLCHOLINE AND ATROPINE
WITH CHOLINORECEPTORS IN TISSUE HOMOGENATE

In 1946 Koshtoyants and Turpayev first demonstrated the important part played by SH-groups in the production of vagus nerve and acetylcholine effects on the heart. This problem was subsequently pursued by quite a number of investigators (Koshtoyants and Logunova, 1950; Koshtoyants, 1951; Turpayev, 1952; Demin, 1952; Della Bella and Bacq, 1953; Bel'gova, 1954; Nistratova, 1959). It was shown that blocking of SH-groups with various thiol poisons led to loss of the transmitter action; on the other hand, there was, in the presence of acetylcholine, reduced reactivity of some of the tissue sulphydryl groups (Turpayev, 1955a). Acetylcholine reduces the reactive powers of some of the protein SH-groups in whole heart muscle of the frog (Turpayev, 1952; 1955a; Nistratova, 1959) and also in tissue homogenate (Turpayev and Nistratova, 1959). Normally the curve for the mercurimetric titration of the SH-groups of homogenate consists of a horizontal line corresponding to complete binding of mercury ions, a bend and a straight line inclined at an angle to the abscissa, at which time the thiol groups have already been titrated out. The character of the

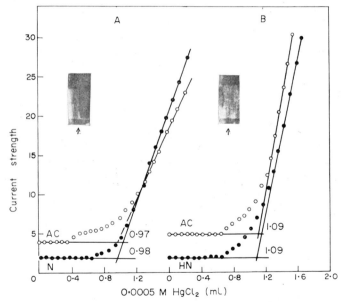

FIG. 3. Curve for the mercurimetric titration of SH-groups in homogenate of frog ventricle in the normal state (N) and in relation to the action of acetylcholine (AC) in final concentration of 10^{-4} g/ml.

A—homogenate from ventricles with normal sensitivity to acetylcholine (see kymogram). B—homogenate from ventricles the acetylcholine sensitivity of which had been destroyed by heat (see kymogram). The arrow indicates the injection of acetylcholine 10^{-6} g/ml into the cannula. Abscissa—quantity of 0·0005 M solution of HgCl₂ (ml). Ordinate—microammeter reading for current strength.

curve is altered in the presence of acetylcholine: the rise of the curve begins earlier and there is development of the "acetylcholine wave" (Fig. 3, A). The transfer of the curve to a new level indicates that, in the presence of acetylcholine, some of the tissue SH-groups become less reactive, as a higher concentration of sulphur in the solution is required for their interaction with mercury ions.

There is then the question of how specific this acetylcholine effect is: is the "acetylcholine wave" characteristic of the reaction between transmitter and cholinoreceptor or is it the result of some side-effect of acetylcholine. The influence of acetylcholine on the reactivity of SH-groups in homogenate of myocardium, previously heated, was therefore studied in experiments on frog heart. When the isolated frog ventricle had been heated three or four times to 40°C (for 3·5 min on each occasion), the cardiac muscle lost its sensitivity to acetylcholine as a result of heat denaturation of cholinoreceptors, although there was complete retention of excitability and contractile properties (Turpayev, 1958). The "acetylcholine wave" did not develop in the mercurimetric titration of SH-groups in homogenate prepared from ventricles with cholinoreceptors inactivated by heat: acetylcholine produced no change in the form of the titration curve (Fig. 3, B).

These findings indicate that acetylcholine reduced the reactivity of the SH-groups in cholinoreceptor in the same way as in whole cardiac muscle.

The specificity of this reaction was also indicated by experiments in which the sulphydryl groups of compounds which are not substrate for acetylcholine action were titrated—egg albumen, carp ventricle, which is not sensitive to acetylcholine (Shidlovskii, 1949) and non-protein thiol compounds, cysteine, glutathione and unithiol. There was no change in the form of the titration curve when acetylcholine was present in any of these experiments (Figs. 4, 5).

Results which at first sight were somewhat unexpected were obtained in the atropine experiments. Preliminary introduction of atropine into homogenate in a final concentration of 10^{-5} g/ml did not prevent the development of an "acetylcholine wave" when acetylcholine was subsequently added. Control experiments showed, however, that atropine itself produced a change in the form of the titration curve: the increase of the diffusion potential began earlier than under normal conditions; there was development of an "atropine wave" (Fig. 6, A). When the atropine concentration was reduced to 10^{-6} to 10^{-7} g/ml, the "atropine wave" became less pronounced and finally disappeared completely. The addition of acetylcholine 10^{-4} g/ml along with atropine to the homogenate did not alter the form or size of the "atropine wave." These findings suggested that atropine led to specific reduction of the reactivity of SH-groups in cholinoreceptors.

This view was supported by the following experiments. If the frog ventricle was exposed to heat to inactivate cholinoreceptors and a homogenate was then prepared from such acetylcholine-insensitive hearts, the addition of atropine did not produce any change in the form of the titration curve

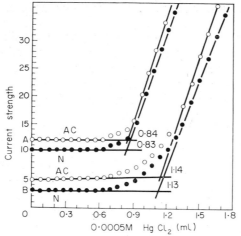

FIG. 4. Mercurimetric titration of SH-groups in the normal state (N) and in the presence of acetylcholine (AC) in concentration 10^{-4} g/ml.

A—homogenate from carp ventricle. B—egg albumen.

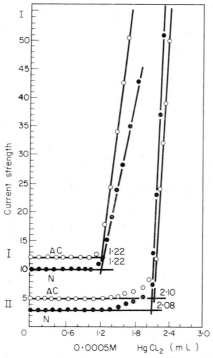

FIG. 5. Curves for the mercurimetric titration of the SH-groups of cysteine (1) and unithiol (sodium salt of 2,3-dimercaptopropanesulphonic acid) (II) under normal conditions and in the presence of acetylcholine (AC) in concentration 10^{-4} g/ml.

Abscissa–quantity of 0·0005 M solution of $HgCl_2$ (ml).
Ordinate—microammeter reading for current strength.

(Fig. 6, B). These results indicated that there was reduction of the reactivity of the same sulphydryl groups, the SH-groups of cholinoreceptors, when acetylcholine and atropine respectively acted on cardiac muscle homogenate. The abolition of the acetylcholine effect by atropine is apparently explained by the fact that the reaction between atropine and cholinoreceptor is associated with a change in the structure of the latter (recognized by us from the reduced reactivity of the SH-groups) which prevented interaction between cholinoreceptor and transmitter.

Our results also indicated that acetylcholine and atropine could react with receptor in structureless tissue homogenate as well as in tissue with its structure undisturbed.

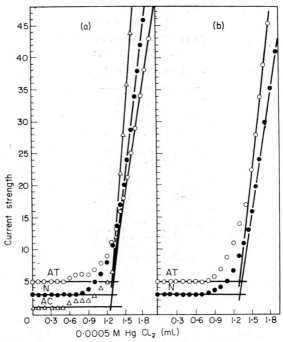

FIG. 6. Effect of atropine (AT) and acetylcholine (AC) on the reactivity of sulphydryl groups in homogenate of frog ventricle.

A—homogenate from ventricles with normal sensitivity to acetylcholine. B—homogenate from ventricles with cholinoreceptors inactivated by heat.

THE NATURE OF THE SUBSTANCE STIMULATING CARDIAC ACTIVITY SECRETED FROM THE FROG VENTRICLE WHEN ACTED ON BY ACETYLCHOLINE

Our preceding investigations (Putintseva and Turpayev, 1960) showed that when acetylcholine acted on isolated frog ventricle (*Rana temporaria*) a substance (X-factor) which had a stimulating effect on another isolated and previously atropinized frog heart was discharged into the perfusion fluid (Fig. 7). X-factor is not a sympathomimetic substance in that its action on the isolated heart, unlike that of adrenaline, noradrenaline and sympathin secreted on stimulation of the vagus nerve (Hoffman *et al.*, 1945; McDowall, 1946; Koshtoyants and Putintseva, 1957; Putintseva, 1958; Putintseva, 1960), is not abolished by the sympathicolytic, Redergan*.

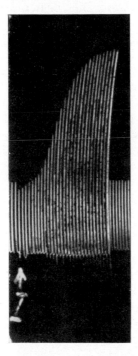

FIG. 7. Effect of X-factor, secreted from frog ventricle acted on by acetylcholine, on the isolated atropinized frog heart. Arrow–introduction of perfusate obtained after 20 min of acetylcholine 10^{-5} g/ml action on the isolated ventricle.

Atropine prevented the secretion of X-factor from the ventricle but had no effect on the secretion of sympathin. A considerable quantity of X-factor was present in the frog ventricle as X-factor was secreted from the ventricle even after the 12th or 15th injection of acetylcholine. It was shown that the muscle elements of the heart were responsible for the secretion of X-factor.

X-factor is much more stable than adrenaline since adrenaline solution, which produces the same stimulating effect as a solution of X-factor, is completely inactivated after keeping at room temperature for 1 to 1·5 hours, whereas the activity of X-factor was quite unchanged after keeping for

* Redergan, a preparation of the Hungarian chemical firm Gedeon-Richter, is the dehydrogenated alkaloid of ergot, the main active principle of which is dehydroergo-toxin-ethanesulphonate.

6 to 7 hours. Though much reduced, the positive inotropic effect of X-factor was still present even after the perfusate had been kept for 20 to 24 hours.

Experiments to compare the resistances of this stimulating substance and adrenaline and noradrenaline to high temperatures at various pH values showed that heating of perfusate containing X-factor on the water bath in neutral and acid (pH 5–6) media for 10 to 45 min merely reduced its activity, whereas heating of adrenaline or noradrenaline solutions under the same conditions for only 1 min inactivated these substances completely. There was complete loss of activity when a solution of X-factor was boiled for 10 to 15 min in a weakly alkaline medium (pH 8–9). When, however, X-factor was first adsorbed by activated charcoal and then removed from the charcoal with ethyl alcohol (Putintseva, 1960), the boiling of X-factor in weakly alkaline solution produced no change in its activity. It would appear that the perfusate contains, along with X-factor, other substances which alter the properties of X-factor. When X-factor was purified from associated substances, it became thermostable. Similar thermostability was observed when solutions of adenosine triphosphate, uridine triphosphate and uridine diphosphate were boiled.

We then attempted to determine the importance of muscle fibre structures in relation to the formation of X-factor. A series of experiments was performed to examine the effect of acetylcholine on frog ventricle homogenate. It was found that, with acetylcholine 10^{-5} g/ml, there was no formation of X-factor under these circumstances.

The fact that X-factor dialysed through a colloid membrane indicates that its molecules are small.

Having thus determined some of the properties of X-factor, we were faced with the problem of determining the links in the metabolic process responsible for the secretion of this stimulating substance. One method by which to determine the nature of X-factor was to study the secretion of this substance by cardiac muscle elements in relation to the action of various metabolic poisons which disturb definite processes in cardiac muscle tissue metabolism.

Experiments were carried out in the following manner. A metabolic poison was introduced for 5 min into the donor-ventricle, the source of X-factor, after which a mixture of acetylcholine and the poison was introduced into the same ventricle for 20 min. If the particular concentration of the poison produced no change in the amplitude of the contractions of the isolated recipient-heart on which testing of the perfusate taken from the ventricle was being carried out, or if the change produced was only very slight, the perfusate was tested on a recipient heart without previous treatment of the latter with the metabolic poison. If, however, the particular concentration of the poison led to considerable reduction in the amplitude of the recipient-heart contractions, it was subjected to preliminary action of the metabolic poison and then, on a background of reduced amplitude, perfusate from the donor-heart ventricle, obtained as a result of the simultaneous action of acetylcholine and the metabolic poison on this heart, was introduced into it. Of the substances with which we were concerned, this perfusate contained acetylcholine, metabolic poison and X-factor. The acetylcholine effect did not develop as the recipient-heart had been treated with atropine, which is known to abolish the acetylcholine effect on the heart; likewise the metabolic poison produced no change in the amplitude of contractions as the recipient-heart had already been treated with Ringer's solution containing this poison before introduction of the perfusate. The only substance that could increase the amplitude of the contractions of the isolated frog heart was, therefore, X-factor.

This series of experiments yielded the following results. Sodium fluoride, which inactivates enolase and thus inhibits the process of glycolysis (Warburg and Christian, 1942), acting on the ventricle in a concentration of 10^{-3} g/ml, did not arrest the secretion of X-factor by this ventricle when acted on by acetylcholine. Similar effects were produced by mono-iodoacetic acid (10^{-3} g/ml) which more particularly inactivates phosphoglyceric aldehyde dehydrogenase by binding its sulphydryl groups and thus leads to suppression of the glycolytic process (Segal and Boyer, 1953; Ushakov and Korolenko, 1954), and also by malonate (10^{-3} g/ml), which is known to inhibit succinic dehydrogenase and thus disturb the Krebs cycle, and by potassium cyanide (3×10^{-4} g/ml), which suppresses tissue respiration to the extent of almost 90 per cent.

The so-called uncoupling poisons, 2,4-dinitrophenol and sodium azide, had quite different effects on the secretion of X-factor. This type of poison inhibits the process of oxidative phosphorylation (Ronzoni, 1936; Seits and El'tsina, 1951). In addition, 2,4-dinitrophenol intensifies the breakdown of high-energy phosphoric compounds such as adenosine triphosphoric acid and phosphocreatine (Witter et al., 1953). In a concentration of 10^{-5} g/ml, this metabolic poison produced complete arrest of cardiac activity after 10–12 min, but cardiac activity could be restored to normal by washing for 30–40 min with Ringer's solution or by the introduction of a solution of adenosine triphosphate.

In view of these properties of 2,4-dinitrophenol, the experiment was carried out in the following manner. A solution of 2,4-dinitrophenol 10^{-5} g/ml was introduced into the ventricle of the donor-heart for 12–15 min; the solution was then extracted from the ventricle and, after repeated washing, acetylcholine solution 10^{-5} g/ml was introduced for 20 min into the ventricle of the donor-heart. It was found that there was no secretion of X-factor under these conditions and there was no change in the amplitude of the contractions of the recipient-heart. If, however, the ventricle was washed out for 30–40 min with Ringer's solution, the introduction of acetylcholine into the ventricle again led to the appearance of X-factor in the perfusate (Fig. 8).

11*

The ability to secrete X-factor was restored very rapidly by the introduction of adenosine-triphosphoric acid (10^{-6} to 10^{-5} g/ml) into the ventricle which had been treated with 2,4-dinitrophenol.

Like 2,4-dinitrophenol, sodium azide suppresses oxidative phosphorylation; in addition, it has depressing effects on cell respiration and glycolytic processes. Because suppression of cell respiration and glycolysis does not affect the secretion of X-factor, sodium azide was used by us as a substance which inhibits oxidative phosphorylation. Like 2,4-dinitrophenol, sodium azide abolished the secretion of X-factor by the muscle elements of the heart completely. Secretion was restored after washing of the ventricle of the donor-heart free from the poison with Ringer's solution for 20–25 min.

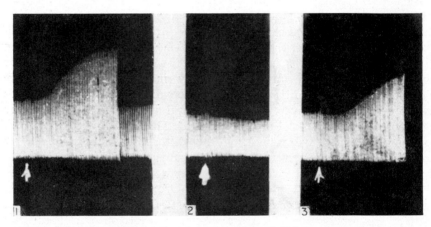

Fig. 8. Effect of 2,4-dinitrophenol on secretion of X-factor from the ventricle of the frog heart acted on by acetylcholine.

I—introduction of perfusate obtained after acetylcholine 10^{-5} g/ml had acted on the isolated ventricle for 20 min. II—the same after treatment of the ventricle with 2,4-dinitrophenol 3×10^{-4} g/ml for 15 min. III—the same after washing out of 2,4-dinitrophenol with Ringer's solution for 40 min.

DISCUSSION

The findings reported in this paper together with our earlier observations on the effect of acetylcholine on the isolated frog ventricle enable us to give the following description of the primary reaction between acetylcholine and the effector cell, the interaction of acetylcholine with cholinoreceptive substance.

Cholinoreceptor is a substrate of protein nature (Turpayev, 1958) containing SH-groups which are necessary for the activity of this protein (Turpayev, 1955a). Cholinoreceptor is inactivated by heat. When a ventricle is heated once to 40°C for 3–3·5 min there is complete but reversible inactivation of cholinoreceptors. Heating to 40°C three or four times (for

3–3·5 min on each occasion) leads to irreversible inactivation of cholino-receptors. The acetylcholine-sensitivity of the cardiac muscle is then lost but the myocardium retains its normal excitability and contractile pro-perties (Turpayev, 1958; Turpayev and Nistratova, 1959).

Study of the kinetics of the reaction between acetylcholine and the muscle cell showed that there are two types of interaction between acetylcholine and receptor. The ventricular cholinoreceptors enter into a reaction with acetylcholine in which one active centre of receptor reacts with one molecule of acetylcholine in the case of some frogs and with two molecules in the case of others.

The interaction between acetylcholine and cholinoreceptive protein is accompanied by a change in the structure of this protein which was demon-strated by us from change in the reactive power of the SH-groups. Experi-ments on intact cardiac muscle (Turpayev, 1955a) and on tissue homogenate (Nistratova and Turpayev, 1959; Nistratova, 1959) demonstrated reduction of the reactivity of SH-groups in cholinoreceptors in the presence of acetyl-choline. Whether or not acetylcholine enters into reaction with SH-groups directly is difficult to say. The possibility of the formation of an ion con-nexion between the positively charged nitrogen of the acetylcholine molecule and the electronegative SH-groups of cholinoreceptor protein cannot be excluded (Turpayev, 1955a).

Like acetylcholine, atropine reacts with cholinoreceptor and changes the structure of this protein. An "atropine wave," indicative of reduction in the reactivity of some of the tissue SH-groups, appears in the curve when SH-groups of frog ventricle homogenate are titrated in the presence of atro-pine. This wave is identical in form and size with the "acetylcholine wave". Neither the "acetylcholine" nor the "atropine" wave appears when homo-genate is prepared from ventricles with cholinoreceptors inactivated by heat. These findings indicate that acetylcholine and atropine act on the same substrate, namely cholinoreceptor. The view that both these substances act on the same part of the cholinoreceptor molecule, the active centres, is supported by the experiments on the kinetics of the reaction of acetyl-choline with receptors in the presence of atropine, demonstrating the com-petitive nature of the relationship between acetylcholine and atropine.

As regards our attempt to study the inclusion of acetylcholine in meta-bolic processes of cardiac muscle connected with the production of the contractile act, it should be noted that the findings are merely those of the first stage in this investigation.

According to modern conceptions, the metabolism of high-energy com-pounds and particularly adenosine triphosphate metabolism occupies the central position in the energy metabolism of cardiac muscle responsible for the contractile act (Hegglin, 1959; Gertler, 1959). The results described in this paper suggest that acetylcholine is concerned in the metabolism of high-energy compounds. Acted on by acetylcholine, the myocardium secretes some highly active substance (X-factor), many properties of which resemble those of the high-energy compounds, adenosine triphosphate, uridine triphosphate and uridine diphosphate. Like these nucleotides, X-factor produces prolonged intensification of cardiac activity, is adsorbed by activated charcoal and is removed from the charcoal with alcohol. The X-factor removed from charcoal is not destroyed by boiling at pH 5–9 and dialyses readily.

The identity of X-factor with one of the high-energy substances is supported by the experiments with poisons disturbing the synthesis of these substances in the cell. It was shown, for example, that uncoupling poisons (2,4-dinitrophenol, sodium azide) abolished secretion of X-factor associated with the action of acetylcholine and that adenosine triphosphate restored its secretion. It would appear that definition of the biochemical nature of X-factor would be facilitated by discovery of the actual enzyme processes through which acetylcholine realizes its depressing effect on the contractile act of the myocardium.

REFERENCES

BEL'GOVA, I. N., Bull. Exp. Biol. and Med. (*Byull. eksp. biol. i med.*) **37**, 12 (1954).
CASTILLO, J. and B. KATZ, *J. Physiol.* **128**, 157 (1955).
CLARK, A. J., *J. Physiol.* **61**, 530 (1926).
CLARK, A. J., In: *Mode of Action of Drugs on Cells.* p. 234. London 1933.
DELLA BELLA, D. and L. M. BACQ, *Arch. Expl. Pathol. Pharmacol.* **219**, 366 (1953).
DEMIN, N. N., *Biochemical Activity of Acetylcholine* (Biokhimicheskaya aktivnost' atsetilkholina), Moscow 1952.
GERTLER, M. M. (Editor), *Metabolic Factors in Cardiac Contractility*, New York 1959.
GINETSINSKII, A. G., Physiol. J. U.S.S.R. (*Fiziol. zh. SSSR*) **33**, 413 (1947).
HALL, E. K., *J. Cell. Comp. Physiol.* **53**, 31 (1959).
HEGGLIN, R. (Editor), *Advances in Cardiology*, Moscow 1959.
HOFFMANN, F., E. I. HOFFMANN et al., *Am. J. Physiol.* **144**, 1, 189 (1945).
KOSHTOYANTS, KH. S., Physiol. J. U.S.S.R. (*Fiziol. zh. SSSR*) **36**, 92 (1950).
KOSHTOYANTS, KH. S., *Protein, Metabolism and Nerve Regulation* (Belkovyye tela, obmen veshchestv i nervnaya regulyatsiya) (1951).
KOSHTOYANTS, KH. S. and K. S. LOGUNOVA, Papers of the U.S.S.R. Academy of Sciences (*Dokl. Akad. Nauk SSSR*) **73**, 439 (1950).
KOSHTOYANTS, KH. S. and T. G. PUTINTSEVA, Physiol. J. U.S.S.R. (*Fiziol. zh. SSSR*) **43**, 414 (1957).
KOSHTOYANTS, KH. S. and T. M. TURPAYEV, Papers of the U.S.S.R. Academy of Sciences (*Dokl. Akad. Nauk SSSR*) **54**, 161 (1946).
LINEWEAVER, H. and D. BURK, *J. Am. Chem. Soc.* **56**, 658 (1934).
McDOWALL, R. I. S., *J. Physiol.* **104**, 392 (1946).
MICHAELIS, L. and M. L. MENTON, *Biochem. Z.* **49**, 333 (1913).
NISTRATOVA, S. N., *Biochemical Nature of Cholinoreceptor in Connexion with the Mechanism of Acetylcholine Action* (O biokhimicheskoi prirode kholinoretseptora v svyazi s mekhanizmom deistviya atsetilkholina), Moscow 1959.
NISTRATOVA, S. N. and T. M. TURPAYEV, Biochemistry (*Biokhimiya*) **24**, 171 (1959).
PUTINTSEVA, T. G., Physiol. J. U.S.S.R. (*Fiziol. zh. SSSR*) **44**, 438 (1958).
PUTINTSEVA, T. G., Physiol. J. U.S.S.R. (*Fiziol. zh. SSSR*) **46**, 1064 (1960).

Putintseva, T. G. and T. M. Turpayev, Papers of the U.S.S.R. Academy of Sciences (*Dokl. Akad. Nauk SSSR*) **129**, 1442 (1959).
Putintseva, T. G. and T. M. Turpayev, Physiol. J. U.S.S.R. (*Fiziol. zh. SSSR*) **46**, 84 (1960).
Raab, V., In: *Advances in Cardiology*. Edited by Hegglin, R., Moscow 1959.
Raiskina, M. Ye., Problems of Medical Chemistry (*Vopr. med. khim.*) **5**, 83 (1959).
Ronzoni, E., *J. Biol. Chem.* **115**, 749 (1936).
Segal, H. L. and V. P. D. Boyer, *Biol. Chem.* **204**, 265 (1953).
Segre, G., *Boll. Soc. Ital. Biol. Spirim.* **29**, 1266 (1953).
Segre, G., *Arch. Ital. Sci. Farmacol.* **7**, 141 (1957).
Seits, I. F. and N. V. El'tsina, Biochemistry (*Biokhimiya*) **16**, 62 (1951).
Shidlovskii, V. A., *Trudy DGZ*. **1**, 49 (1949).
Timms, A. R., *Brit. J. Pharmacol. Chemotherap.* **11**, 273 (1956).
Turpayev, T. M., Papers of the Institute of Animal Morphology, U.S.S.R. Academy of Sciences (*Trudy IMZh Akad. Nauk SSSR*) **6**, 19 (1952).
Turpayev, T. M., Biochemistry (*Biokhimiya*) **20**, 456 (1955a).
Turpayev, T. M., Papers of the U.S.S.R. Academy of Sciences (*Dokl. Akad. Nauk SSSR*) **102**, 323 (1955b).
Turpayev, T. M., Biochemistry (*Biokhimiya*) **23**, 71 (1958).
Turpayev, T. M. and S. N. Nistratova, *Proceedings of Conference on thiol compounds in medicine* (Trudy Konf. "Tiolovyye soedineniya v meditsine"), p. 65, Kiev 1959.
Ushakov, B. P. and S. A. Korolenko, Physiol. J. U.S.S.R. (*Fiziol. zh. SSSR*) **40**, 208 (1954).
Warburg, O. and W. Christian, *Biochem. Z.* **310**, 384 (1942).
Witter, R. F., Newcomb, E. H. and E. Stotz, *J. Biol. Chem.* **202**, 291 (1953).

CONFIGURATIONAL AND HYDROLYTIC CHANGES IN PROTEINS CAUSED BY CELLULAR STIMULATION AND INJURY

GEORGES UNGAR

Houston, Texas, U.S.A.

ONE of the basic problems of general physiology is the relation between living matter and its environment. We still know very little of the mechanism by which the living cell maintains its morphological and chemical integrity and identity in spite of a continuous exchange of matter and energy with the external world. It is known, of course, that living organisms are submitted to external forces to which they have to adapt themselves if they are to stay alive. Some of these forces, such as, for example, gravity or atmospheric pressure may remain constant enough for a given organism, in its natural habitat, to be ignored. Other environmental factors, however, are subject to periodical or irregular variations which may, more or less abruptly, alter the steady state relationship between the cell and the extracellular medium. Such factors are temperature, light and other radiations, mechanical impact, chemical composition, ecological conditions and others.

A change in any of these environmental factors represents a stimulus capable of eliciting in the cell an excitatory response. It is generally stated that all living matter is excitable but in complex organisms excitability is, to a large extent, delegated to specialized structures whose function is to receive impulses, conduct them, or to react to them rapidly. For this reason, excitation phenomena have been studied almost exclusively in nerve and muscle. It should be kept in mind, however, that excitation plays an essential role in a great variety of processes, particularly in fertilization of the ovum, cell division, glandular secretion and hormonal regulations (for a broad survey of this problem, see Ungar, 1963).

An arbitrary distinction is usually made between physiological and injurious stimuli. This distinction, however useful it may be from a medical point of view, has no valid biological basis. The main purpose of this paper is to emphasize the fundamental unity of the modifications in cell proteins observed in physiological and pathological excitation.

REST, EXCITATION, RECOVERY AND INJURY

By definition, a cell is in a state of rest when it is not submitted to the action of a stimulus. The resting state, however, is not a state of thermo-dynamic equilibrium of zero energy but a steady state in which the flow of energy from the environment to the cell is about equally balanced with the flow in the opposite direction.

Living matter at rest is in a state of high energy and low entropy. Rest is therefore a less probable and more labile state than excitation; it could more appropriately be called a state of alert in which the cell is ready to respond to the slightest change in the environment.

Excitability, which is an essential characteristic of the resting state, is maintained by means of the electrochemical gradient for potassium and sodium ions, the resting potential and the high content in energy-rich phos-phate bonds. All these conditions require the expenditure of metabolic work. In the absence of this work, the cell surface is depolarized, potassium is lost, sodium is gained and excitability declines. The commonly accepted explanation is that metabolic energy is required to operate an ionic "pump" which keeps sodium out of the cell and accumulates potassium (Hodgkin, 1957).

At the onset of excitation, the cell loses energy and gains entropy. Its surface is depolarized, sodium enters, potassium goes out and the high-energy phosphate bonds are hydrolyzed. All this is accompanied by a decreased excitability which may reach absolute refractoriness.

Typical excitation is characterized by its self-propagating action potential. It appears now, however, that too much emphasis was laid in the past on the all-or-none character of excitation. In reality, this remarkable property belongs only to such highly specialized structures as the axon and the skeletal muscle fiber. The large majority of cells, including those of the central ner-vous system, respond to stimuli in a graded manner and the conduction of the impulse is decremental (Bishop, 1956; Grundfest, 1957).

Typically, excitation is a discontinuous process consisting of trains of alternating activity and restoration of the resting state. During the latter phase, the high energy level is re-established as indicated by the reappearance of the resting potential and cessation of the inward flux of sodium.

There are undoubtedly many excitable systems, especially those involved in pathological excitation, which behave differently from nerve and striated muscle. In these systems, excitation is not accompanied by refractoriness. This means that they are not protected against overstimulation so that a prolonged stimulus can result in exhaustion or even disruption of the cell.

The last few years have brought forward the idea that chemical agents are among the most important natural stimuli. Chemical transmission has been demonstrated at the synaptic level, the neuro-muscular junction and chemical processes are likely to occur at most sensory receptors. Chemical

stimulation is also predominant in pathological excitation in which biological factors play the most important role and act by modifying the chemical composition of the cell environment.

A given chemical agent becomes a stimulus if it has the ability to combine
with some cell constituent. This, of course, is the basis of the receptor
theory, well-known to pharmacologists, but has also wider implications,
especially in pathological excitation. It explains, for example, that a substance which normally fails to stimulate a given cell, becomes a powerful
stimulus as soon as the cell develops an antibody to it.

TRANSCONFORMATION AND PROTEOLYSIS

The idea of the participation of cell proteins in excitation goes back to
the turn of the century (Lugaro, 1895; Carlson, 1902) but it failed to attract
any attention because of the inadequate information then available on
protein structure.

As a result mainly of the work of Pauling (1953), Linderstrøm-Lang
(1952, 1959) and their associates, we are beginning to have some idea of
the structure of protein molecules. It is customary to consider this structure
at three different levels:

(a) the primary structure is essentially the chain of amino acids linked
end to end by means of peptide bonds;

(b) the secondary structure adds a third dimension to the alignment of
amino acids by arranging it in a helix stabilized by hydrogen bonds linking
adjacent peptide linkages;

(c) the tertiary structure concerns the disposition of amino acid side
groups linked together by hydrogen bonds, van der Waals forces, salt
linkages, disulfide and phosphate bridges, etc. It also includes, linked to the
side groups, other molecules such as fat, carbohydrates, pigments and,
most important in the present context, inorganic ions and water.

Although our present knowledge of protein configuration is still based
on hypotheses, it may serve, to a certain extent, as a basis on which structural changes can be correlated with biological function.

It has been known for a very long time that, under a number of conditions, proteins can undergo a change called "denaturation." This was,
however, believed to be a process occurring only in artificial circumstances
and to have no bearing on the function of the proteins. The possible biological significance of protein denaturation was first suggested by Rapkine
(1931) and by Mirsky (1936). At the same time, it became apparent that
denaturation is a change in the secondary and tertiary structures of the
protein which are designated by the terms configuration or conformation.
Lumry and Eyring (1954) proposed to replace the term denaturation by
that of "transconformation" to express the idea of structural change and

also to remove the stigma of artificiality from a process which may play an important biological role.

Protein chemists admit readily today that some proteins show "configurational adaptability" (Karush, 1950), "fluctuations" or "motility" (Linderstrøm-Lang and Schellman, 1959). All these designations mean that protein molecules can undergo more or less extensive and more or less reversible structural changes. These occur when a zymogen is converted into an active enzyme, when proteins bind smaller molecules, probably during enzyme action and, as we assume, in the excited cell.

Transconformation is essentially a loosening of the native structure, for example, the conversion of the ordered helix into a random coil. It need not, however, go that far; it may consist in the rupture of a few weak bonds with partial unmasking of ionized side groups. Such a change, although not altering the molecule markedly, is comparatively easy to detect if the side groups can be determined by some chemical or physical means.

The affinity of the ionized side groups for certain dyes was used by Nassonov and his co-workers in the experiments which form the foundation of the denaturation theory of excitation (1959). A similar method was also utilized recently by Fischer and Zeman (1959).

Among the amino acid side groups, the phenolic hydroxyl of tyrosine and the sulfhydryl of cysteine are comparatively easy to detect and this was put to use by Wald and Brown (1952) and by ourselves (Ungar et al., 1957). There are many other and better methods to measure transconformation, reviewed recently by Kauzmann (1959), but most of them are applicable only to pure proteins and therefore are not suitable for biological work.

An important concept that helps to understand the role of proteins in the cellular response to stimulation and injury is the interdependence of transconformation and proteolysis. Linderstrøm-Lang (1952) was the first to suggest that denaturation may be the initial stage of enzymatic breakdown of the protein molecule. He represented the passage from the native (N) to the denatured (D) form of proteins and their ultimate hydrolysis by enzymes (E) as follows:

$$N \rightleftharpoons D \xrightarrow{E} \text{Hydrolysis}$$

He also suggested the possibility of denaturation itself being initiated by proteases:

$$N \underset{E}{\rightleftharpoons} D \xrightarrow{E} \text{Hydrolysis.}$$

Interrelation between transconformation and hydrolysis is also shown by the frequent occurrence of "limited proteolysis" in the course of structural rearrangement, for example in the activation of zymogens.

In the following sections we shall apply these concepts to cellular excitation.

11 a*

PROTEIN CHANGES IN PHYSIOLOGICAL EXCITATION

As mentioned above, there are indications in the older literature that configurational changes may occur in stimulated nerve cells. The findings of Soula (1913) and Hirschberg and Winterstein (1919) suggest also the probability of a breakdown in the primary structure of proteins.

The full significance of protein changes associated with cellular excitation was understood by Nassonov and his co-workers. In a series of investigations, started about twenty-five years ago, they laid the groundwork for a theory of excitation which attributed an essential role to protein denaturation. It is unfortunate that until very recently their work remained unknown in the West.

Increased breakdown of proteins during excitation was observed by Geiger, Yamasaki and Lyons (1956) and by ourselves (Ungar *et al.*, 1957). This was in agreement with the increased turnover of proteins in excited nerve cells, described by Friedberg, Tarver and Greenberg (1948), Gaitonde and Richter (1955) and Palladin (1956), and with the microspectrophotometric observations of Hydèn (1955) (see recent reviews by Richter, 1959, and Waelsch and Lajtha, 1961).

It has been known since Harris (1923) that sulfhydryl groups have a special significance in the denaturation of proteins. In 1946, Koshtoyants and Turpayev found that the blocking of SH groups prevented the inhibitory effect of vagus stimulation on the heart. The effect could be restored by an excess of cysteine (Koshtoyants, 1946). Similar observations were made in skeletal muscle and sympathetic ganglia (Koshtoyants, 1953).

More recent work on this subject has confirmed the importance of sulfhydryl groups in the heart (Reynolds, Chenoweth and Ellman, 1958; Takahashi, Murai and Sasaki, 1958) and in nerve (Smith, 1958). Wald and Brown had observed in 1952 the appearance of SH groups in visual purple stimulated by light. All these findings can be interpreted in relation either to protein structure or to the particular significance of SH groups in many important enzyme systems. It is likely that both aspects are linked together in a manner which is still unknown.

Our own work on physiological excitation came about as the logical sequence of our investigations on tissue reactions to injury which will be

TABLE 1. Protein breakdown by electrical stimulation of rat sciatic nerve

	Protein	S.D.	Breakdown products	S.D.
Resting*	72·7	6·8	35·8	3·3
Stimulated†	65·0	5·8	47·4	4·2

Results expressed in optical density at 280 mμ per g of wet weight.
* means of 6 experiments.   † means of 10 experiments.

mentioned below. By 1955, we became convinced that injurious stimuli invariably elicit a proteolytic response and we set out to determine whether a similar reaction occurs on electrical stimulation of nerves (Ungar *et al.*, 1957). Table 1, summarizing our results, shows that prolonged stimulation of isolated rat sciatic nerves causes a decrease in protein content of the tissue with simultaneous increase in the acid-soluble protein breakdown products.

Subsequently, the enzymatic nature of protein breakdown was investigated in rat cerebral cortex stimulated *in vivo* through its afferent nerves. Rat brain contains a protease which hydrolyzes the synthetic substrate *N*-acetyl-L-tryptophan ethyl ester so that enzymatic activity could be determined in the extracts of brain collected at rest or after stimulation. The results, summarized in Table 2, show that after stimulation for one minute, there is no detectable proteolysis, although protease activity is increased. After 20 minutes' stimulation both values show an increase. Chapman and Wolff (1958) observed the appearance of a protease in the cerebrospinal fluid after intense peripheral stimulation.

TABLE 2. Protease activity and protein breakdown by electrical stimulation of rat brain

	Protease activity*	S.D.	Breakdown products †	S.D.
Resting	10·9	2·9	14·2	2·8
Stimulated 1 min	16·4	2·1	12·7	2·5
Stimulated 20 min	23·2	2·0	18·2	4·2

* Expressed in μM of the synthetic substrate *N*-acetyl-L-tryptophan ethyl ester hydrolyzed per hour per gram of wet weight.

† Expressed in optical density at 280 mμ of the trichloracetic filtrate per g of wet weight.

In view of what was said above on the relation between proteolysis and transconformation, the results just summarized suggest that physiological excitation may be associated with a change in protein configuration. The hypothesis was tested first by an ultraviolet spectrophotometric method based on the findings of Crammer and Neuberger (1943). These workers showed that unmasking of the ionized side group of tyrosine causes a shift in the 280–300 mμ region of the spectrum. We found a similar shift in the 240–245 mμ region for the ionization of cysteine. The results were expressed by the ratio of optical densities at pH 12 and pH 7, which we called "side group ionization ratio" (SGIR). Table 3 shows some of our results. Increase in the SGIR indicates the degree of unmasking of OH groups of tyrosine and SH groups of cysteine. This change is reversible if the stimulation is stopped. Figure 1 shows an example of the reversibility and also of the way in which side group ionization affects the ultraviolet spectrum. These results

TABLE 3. Increase in side group ionization by electrical stimulation

	245 mμ			
	Resting ±	S.D.	Stimulated ±	S.D.
Frog sciatic	—	—	—	—
Rat sciatic	1·39	0·08	1·85	0·16
Rat brain	1·52	0·11	1·85	0·14
Cat brain	2·16	0·39	2·54	0·41

	300 mμ			
	Resting ±	S.D.	Stimulated ±	S.D.
Frog sciatic	1·45	0·11	2·05	0·38
Rat sciatic	1·56	0·16	1·73	0·22
Rat brain	1·37	0·14	1·52	0·14
Cat brain	1·50	0·22	1·81	0·22

For experimental details see Ungar et al. (1957).

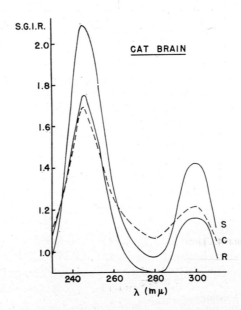

FIG. 1. Side group ionization ratio (SGIR) in cat brain.

From resting cortex (C); after stimulation of corresponding brachial plexus for 2 min (S); and after the same stimulation followed by 2 min rest (R). From Ungar et al. (1957). Originally published in *J. Gen. Physiology* **40**, 635 (1957) and reprinted here by kind permission of the Rockefeller Institute Press, New York, U.S.A.

were confirmed by Luxoro (1959), Benetato *et al.* (1961) and similar data were obtained by means of different methods by Kayushin, Lyudkovskaya and Shmelev (1960), and Vinnikov and Titova (1961).

In further work (Ungar and Romano, 1958) direct estimation of the unmasked SH groups was done by the amperometric titration method of Benesch, Lardy and Benesch (1955). Some of the results obtained by this method in rat cerebral cortex are shown in Fig. 2. Sulfhydryl groups were also estimated in resting and stimulated skeletal muscle and Table 4 shows the results obtained in the rat diaphragm.

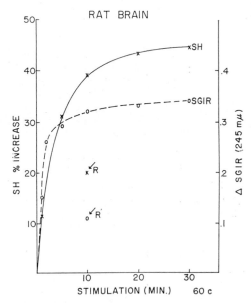

FIG. 2. Changes in ionizable sulfhydryl groups and side group ionization ratio in rat brain.

Abscissa: duration of electrical stimulation of the central end of the sciatic nerves. Ordinate: on the left, per cent increase in SH groups (x———); on the right, increase of SGIR at 245 mμ (o ·····). The points marked R indicate the tendency to recovery after 30 min stimulation followed by 20 min rest. Each point represents means of at least 6 experiments.

TABLE 4. Titration of sulfhydryl groups in rat diaphragm

	μM/g	± S.D.	N*
Resting	5·32	1·08	48
Stimulated	8·53	2·05	20

Each hemidiaphragm was stimulated through the phrenic nerve with a 60 cycle, 2 volt current for 20 min. The opposite hemidiaphragm was the resting sample.
* Number of animals.

More recently, we took advantage of the fluorescence changes described during protein denaturation (Konev, 1957; Teale, 1961) to demonstrate transconformation in stimulated nerve fibers (Ungar and Romano, 1962). Figure 3 shows the fluorescence and activation spectra of extracts from resting and stimulated frog sciatic nerves. The most significant results, however, were obtained in live nerve fibers, the fluorescence of which was measured before, during and after electrical stimulation. Figure 4 shows that stimulation reduces the fluorescence in a reversible manner. Within the limits of the physiological characteristics of the nerve, the reduction in fluorescence is related to the number of impulses. These observations show that transconformation does actually occur in living system and is not an artifact observable only in tissue extracts.

Transconformation, as detected by SGIR and sulfhydryl changes, was observed in other systems: submaxillary gland, urinary bladder, retina and recently in kidney tubules stimulated by adrenocortical hormone (Canessa and Fischer, 1959).

It was mentioned earlier that Rapkine described changes in SH groups in the fertilized ovum. Proteolytic phenomena were observed under the

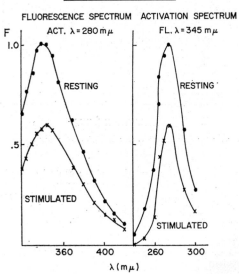

FROG NERVE EXTRACT

FIG. 3. Fluorescence changes produced by electrical stimulation of frog sciatic nerves.

Abscissa: wave-length in mμ; ordinate: relative fluorescence of the extracts of resting and stimulated nerves (the peak being taken arbitrarily as 1·0). On the left, fluorescence spectrum with activation at 280 mμ; on the right, activation spectrum with fluorescence at 345 mμ. Electrical stimulation for 2 hr at 2 V, 180 cycles.

Originally published in *J. Gen. Physiology*, **45**, 2 (1962) and reprinted here by kind permission of the Rockefeller Institute Press, New York, U.S.A.

same circumstances by Runnström (1949), Gross (1952) and Lundblad (1954). It appears, therefore, that structural and hydrolytic changes in proteins are associated with the excited state of a wide variety of biological systems.

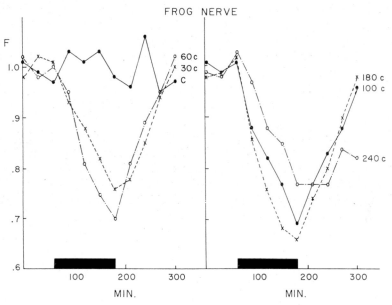

FIG. 4. Fluorescence of live nerve fibers before, during and after electrical stimulation.

Frog sciatic nerves with their fibers teased apart were suspended in a quartz microcuvette of the spectrophotofluorometer and attached to an electrode. Abscissa: time in min. Block shows stimulation at 2 V and at the frequencies indicated with each curve. C, control nerves treated identically but not stimulated. Ordinate: relative fluorescence at 345 mμ (activation, 280 mμ). The mean fluorescence measured during a preliminary resting period was taken as 1·0. Each point represents means of at least 6 experiments. Originally published in *J. Gen. Physiology*, **45**, 2 (1962) and reprinted here by kind permission of the Rockefeller Institute Press, New York, U.S.A.

PROTEIN CHANGES INDUCED BY PATHOLOGICAL STIMULATION

The most common response of tissues to noxious stimuli follows the pattern traditionally designated by the term inflammation (Ungar, 1952, 1953). This is a somewhat vague concept which includes such quasi-physiological phenomena as the triple response of Lewis (1927) and such profound pathological changes as granulation tissue formation or suppuration. There is fairly general agreement that the various inflammatory manifestations are produced by chemical mediation: the stimulus elicits in the cells the liberation of active substances such as histamine, 5-hydroxytryptamine (serotonin), vaso-active peptides (Lewis, 1960) or proteins (Menkin, 1956). These mediators are responsible for spreading the inflammatory process from the cells originally stimulated to the neighboring structures.

Inflammation can be produced by a variety of stimuli: radiation, heat, chemical irritants, animal venoms, bacterial toxins and antigen-antibody reaction. It is the latter type of stimulus that was used in most of our own work. We showed first that proteolytic activity appears in isolated tissues on addition of the stimulating agent (Ungar, 1947). These observations were made in guinea pig tissue slices by a technique described earlier (Ungar and Parrot, 1936). Subsequently (Ungar and Damgaard, 1955, Ungar, 1956) similar observations were made in perfused organs and a parallel was established between proteolysis and the release of mediators, particularly histamine. Figure 5 shows an example of these experiments in which the release of K^+ ions was also determined. More recently, protease activation was shown in human skin slices (Ungar et al., 1961).

These observations were confirmed by Herberts (1955), Weimar (1955) and especially by Hayashi, Tokuda and Udaka (1960) who were able to

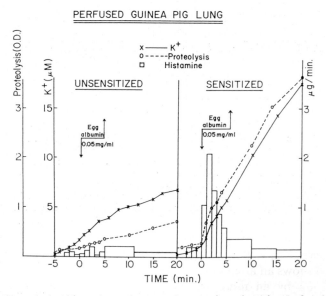

PERFUSED GUINEA PIG LUNG

FIG. 5. Proteolysis, histamine release and potassium loss in perfused guinea pig lung.

Left, normal guinea pig; right, guinea pig sensitized to egg albumin. Abscissa: time in min (0 time is the beginning of the perfusion with egg albumin containing Ringer's solution). Ordinate (from left to right): proteolysis, expressed in optical density units per min of the trichloracetic acid filtrate of the perfusate; potassium loss (K^+ content of the perfusate in μM/min); histamine released in μg/min. From: Ungar, 1961 a.

Originally published in *Federation Proceedings* **20** (suppl. 9), 153 (1961) and reprinted here by kind permission of the Federation of American Societies for Experimental Biology, Washington, U.S.A.

demonstrate protease activation in cultures of sensitized cells to which the antigen had been added. Protease activation has also been demonstrated in tissues submitted to thermal stimulation (Ungar and Damgaard, 1954).

As mentioned above, cells submitted to injurious stimuli release various cellular constituents which can act as mediators. This liberation can be considered an integral part of the cellular excitatory process. It is, therefore, not surprising that anoxia (Parrot, 1940) and a number of metabolic inhibitors (Mongar and Schild, 1957; Mota, 1959) which abolish cellular excitability, also inhibit the release of histamine.

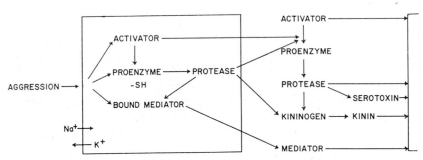

Fig. 6. Diagram of the changes initiated by cell injury and their role in the transmission of excitation.

The aggression elicits K^+ release and Na^+ uptake, activates cell proteases and modifies the conformation of cell proteins. These changes result in the release of activators, enzymes and active substances which were bound to macromolecules. The material released, by interacting with constituents of the extracellular medium, results in the production of new active substances, plasma proteases, serotoxin and plasma kinins. These in turn can stimulate other cells and spread the excited state to neighboring or remote structures. From: Ungar 1961 a.

Originally published in *Federation Proceedings* **20** (suppl. 9), 153 (1961) and reprinted here by kind permission of the Federation of American Societies for Experimental Biology, Washington, U.S.A.

An important characteristic of some of the cellular proteases activated by injurious stimuli is their SH-dependence: they are blocked by SH-inhibitors and the block can be abolished by excess cysteine (Herberts, 1955; Hayashi, 1956).

Figure 6 shows an attempt at representing the sequence of events of cellular excitation by an injurious stimulus. As a result of the stimulation, proteases become active in the cell. Whether this activation results from a preceding structural change unmasking SH groups, is at present a matter of speculation. Whatever may be the case, some protein molecules undergo rearrangements in their configuration. Such a rearrangement liberates smaller molecules loosely attached to the protein and these will become the mediators.

Some of the cellular enzymes also escape from the cell and may become stimuli for other structures or activate circulating enzyme precursors. They may also activate extracellular enzymes, act on extracellular substrates and give rise to kinins and serotoxins which together with the mediators released from the cell can transmit the excited state to neighboring or even remote structures. The intricate interrelations between cellular and humoral enzymatic factors and their role in inflammation and shock have been reviewed by Hayashi and Ungar (1958) and Ungar (1961a).

Heilbrunn (1956) believed in a similarity between cellular reaction to injury and coagulation of the blood. The analogy may have been pushed too far but it is interesting to note that Bettex-Galland and Lüscher (1959) have observed some interesting protein changes in blood platelets. They found that platelets contain a contractile protein, analogous to actomyosin. When they are stimulated by thrombin, this protein forms fine threads which slowly contract. The whole process can be interpreted as platelet excitation in which potassium is lost and proteins undergo structural rearrangements.

These few examples illustrate the widespread occurrence of configurational and hydrolytic changes in pathological excitation. It is probable that these changes will ultimately be shown to play a fundamental role in many disease processes.

CONCLUDING REMARKS

In the preceding pages an attempt was made to summarize some of the observations showing the role of protein modifications in excitation. The facts known today suggest that stimulation can affect cellular proteins in two ways;

(a) by causing transconformation, that is more or less pronounced rearrangement of the secondary and tertiary structures;

(b) by hydrolytic breakdown of the primary structure. It is probable that the two types of effect are not fundamentally different but represent varying degrees of the same process.

There are, of course, still many problems to be solved concerning the precise role of the protein changes in the mechanism of excitation. One of them, the relation between cellular proteins and the movement of ions has been extensively studied by Troshin (1958). Our work in this field was summarized recently (Ungar, 1959) and some new developments have been added (Ungar and Romano, 1963, Ungar, 1961b). There seems to be a definite correlation between the state of the proteins and the ability of the cells to maintain a concentration gradient of potassium and sodium.

The most difficult problem is that of the energy relationships between protein changes and the excitatory process. Under physiological conditions the energy input of the stimulus is very small compared to the total expenditure of energy of the excitation process. One can, perhaps, represent the cell proteins as the essential parts of an amplifying system. Like an electronic amplifier, it is traversed by two currents of energy: one is of metabolic origin while the other consists of signals received from the extracellular medium. The metabolic current, involving high levels of energy, amplifies the signals and supplies power for their conduction, transmission and conversion into various types of responses, such as muscular contraction, glandular secretion, etc. Under pathological conditions, a high energy input of signals may wreck the whole delicately balanced system.

One can also view the role of the proteins in term of their high information content and Hydèn (1959) has recently formulated a theory of memory based on the storage of information in the structure of the proteins of the nerve cell.

REFERENCES

BENESCH, R. E., H. A. LARDY and R. BENESCH, *J. Biol. Chem.* **216**, 663 (1955).
BENETATO, G., V. NESTIANU, V. BENETATO and O. MAIOR, *5th Internat. Congress Biochem.*, Moscow, p. 209 (1961).
BETTEX-GALLAND, M. and E. F. LÜSCHER, *Nature* **184**, 276 (1959).
BISHOP, G. H., *Physiol. Rev.* **36**, 376 (1956).
CANESSA, M. and S. FISCHER, *21st Internat. Congress Physiol. Sci.* Buenos Aires (abstr.), p. 52 (1959).
CARLSON, A. J., *Amer. J. Anat.* **2**, 341 (1902).
CHAPMAN, L. F. and H. G. WOLFF, *Science* **128**, 1208 (1958).
CRAMMER, J. L. and A. NEUBERGER, *Biochem. J.* **37**, 302 (1943).
FISCHER, R. and W. ZEMAN, *Nature* **183**, 1337 (1959).
FRIEDBERG, F., H. TARVER and D. GREENBERG, *J. Biol. Chem.* **173**, 355 (1948).
GAITONDE, M. K. and D. RICHTER, *Biochem. J.* **59**, 690 (1955).
GEIGER, A., S. YAMASAKI and R. LYONS, *Amer. J. Physiol.* **184**, 230 (1956).
GROSS, P. R., *Biol. Bull.* **103**, 293 (1952).
GRUNDFEST, H., *Ann. N.Y. Acad. Sci.* **66**, 537 (1957).
HARRIS, L. J., *Proc. Roy. Soc. London*, B **94**, 426 (1923).
HAYASHI, H., *Mié Med. J.* **6**, 195 (1956).
HAYASHI, H., A. TOKUDA and K. UDAKA, *J. Exp. Med.* **112**, 237 (1960).
HEILBRUNN, L. V., *The Dynamics of Living Protoplasm.* New York, Acad. Press 1956.
HERBERTS, G., *Acta Allergol.* **9**, 167 (1955).
HIRSCHBERG, E. and H. WINTERSTEIN, *Z. Physiol. Chem.* **108**, 9 (1919).
HODGKIN, A. L., *Proc. Roy. Soc. London*, B **148**, 1 (1957).
HYDÈN, H. in *Neurochemistry* (Elliott, K. A. C., Page, I. H. and Quastel, J. H. Eds.), Springfield, Ill. C. C. Thomas, p. 204 (1955).
HYDÈN, H. in *Biochemistry of the Central Nervous System.* London, Pergamon Press, p. 64 (1959).
KARUSH, F., *J. Amer. Chem. Soc.* **72**, 2705 (1950).
KAUZMANN, W., *Adv. Protein Chem.* **14**, 1 (1959).
KAYUSHIN, L. P., R. G. LYUDKOVSKAYA and I. P. SHMELEV, *Biophysics* **5**, 323 (1960).
KONEV, S. V., *Dokl. Akad. Nauk. SSSR* **116**, 594 (1957).
KOSHTOYANTS, KH. S., *Nature* **158**, 836 (1946).
KOSHTOYANTS, KH. S., *Physiol. Bohemoslov.* **3**, 382 (1954).
KOSHTOYANTS, KH. S. and T. M. TURPAYEV, *Dokl. Akad. Nauk SSSR.* **54**, 181 (1946).
LEWIS, G. P., *Physiol. Rev.* **40**, 647 (1960).
LEWIS, T., *Blood Vessels of the Human Skin and Their Responses*, London, Shaw 1927.
LINDERSTRØM-LANG, K. U., *Proteins and Enzymes.* Stanford Univ. Press 1952.

LINDERSTRØM-LANG, K. U. and J. A. SCHELLMAN, in *The Enzymes* (Boyer, P. D., Lardy, H. and Myrback, Eds.), New York Acad. Press 1, 443 (1959).

LUGARO, E., *Arch. ital. Biol.* 24, 258 (1895).

LUMRY, R. and H. EYRING, *J. Phys. Chem.* 58, 110 (1954).

LUNDBLAD, G., *Ark. Kemi.* 7, 127 (1954).

LUXORO, M., 21*st Congress Physiol. Sci.* Buenos Aires (abstr.), p. 171 (1959).

MENKIN, V., *Biochemical Mechanisms in Inflammation.* Springfield, Ill., C. C. Thomas 1956.

MIRSKY, A. E., *Proc. Nat. Acad. Sci., Wash.* 22, 439 (1936).

MONGAR, J. L. and H. O. SCHILD, *J. Physiol.* 135, 301 (1957).

MOTA, I., *Immunology* 2, 403 (1959).

NASSONOV, D. N., *Local Reaction of the Protoplasm and Propagated Excitation.* Izdat. Akad. Nauk SSSR, Moscow–Leningrad (1959).

PALLADIN, A. V., 20*th Internat. Physiol. Congress.* Brussels, p. 378 (1956).

PARROT, J. L., *C. R. Soc. Biol.* 136, 361 (1942).

PAULING, L., in *Les Protéines* (Stoops, R. Ed.) Bruxelles, Inst. Internat. Chimie Solvay, p. 63 (1953).

RAPKINE, L., *Ann. Physiol. Physicochim. Biol.* 7, 382 (1931).

REYNOLDS, R. C., M. B. CHENOWETH and G. L. ELLMAN, *Proc. Soc. Exp. Biol. Med.* 99, 185.

RICHTER, D., *Brit. Med. J.* 2, 1255 (1959).

RUNNSTRÖM, J., *Adv. Enzymol.* 9, 241 (1949).

SOULA, L. C., *J. Physiol. Path. Gen.* 15, 267 (1913).

TAKAHASHI, H., T. MURAI and T. SASAKI, *Nature* 182, 1675 (1958).

TEALE, F. W. J., *Biochem. J.* 80, 14 P (1961).

TROSHIN, A. S., *Das Problem der Zellpermeabilität*, Jena, Fischer (1958).

UNGAR, G., *Lancet* 1, 708 (1947).

UNGAR, G., *Lancet* 2, 742 (1952).

UNGAR, G., in *The Mechanism of Inflammation* (Jasmin, G. and Robert, A. Eds.). Montreal, Acta, p. 151 (1953).

UNGAR, G., *Tsitologiya* 1, 627 (1959).

UNGAR, G., in *Recent Progress and Present Problems in the Field of Shock.* Washington Fed. Am. Soc. Exp. Biol., p. 151 (1961 a).

UNGAR, G., in *Membrane Transport and Metabolism* (A. Kleinzeller and A. Kotyk, Eds.) Prague, Czechosl. Acad. Sci., p. 160 (1961 b).

UNGAR, G., *Excitation.* Springfield, Ill. C. C. Thomas (1963).

UNGAR, G., E. ASCHHEIM, S. PSYCHOYOS and D. V. ROMANO, *J. Gen. Physiol.* 40, 635 (1957).

UNGAR, G. and E. DAMGAARD, *Proc. Soc. exp. Biol. Med.* 87, 378 (1954).

UNGAR, G. and E. DAMGAARD, *J. Exp. Med.* 101, 1 (1955).

UNGAR, G. and H. HAYASHI, *Ann. Allergy* 16, 542 (1958).

UNGAR, G. and J. L. PARROT, *C. R. Soc. Biol.* 123, 676 (1936).

UNGAR, G. and D. V. ROMANO, *Proc. Soc. exp. Biol. Med.* 97, 324 (1958).

UNGAR, G. and D. V. ROMANO, *J. Gen. Physiol.* 46, 267 (1962).

UNGAR, G. and D. V. ROMANO, *Biochim. Biophys. Acta* 66, 110 (1963).

UNGAR, G., T. YAMURA, J. B. ISOLA and S. KOBRIN, *J. Exp. Med.* 113, 359 (1961).

VINNIKOV, YA. A. and L. I. TITOVA, *Organ of Corti; Histophysiology and Histochemistry.* Moscow-Leningrad, Izdat. Akad. Nauk. SSSR. English translation in preparation by Pergamon Press (1960).

WAELSCH, H. and A. LAJTHA, *Physiol. Rev.* 41, 709 (1961).

WALD, G. and P. K. BROWN, *J. Gen. Physiol.* 35, 797 (1951/52).

WEIMAR, V., *Arch. internat. Pharmacodyn.* 103, 419 (1955).

THE VARIOUS TYPES
OF CATECHOLAMINE CONVERSION
IN ANIMAL TISSUES

A. M. UTEVSKII, V. O. OSINSKAYA and P. A. KALIMAN

Kharkov Medical Institute and the Ukrainian Institute of
Experimental Endocrinology, Kharkov

Translated by Dr. R. Crawford

ACETYLCHOLINE and catecholamines are generally recognized mediators of nervous processes both in the transmission of the nerve impulse from neuron to effector organ and in peripheral and central synaptic formations. Catecholamines are known to play an important part in neurohumoral regulation, in the mediation of sympathetic nerve processes and in the trophic function of the nervous system. These substances are hormone-mediators.

According to modern conceptions, the conversion of catecholamines can take place in different directions and in different ways: (1) the "catechin–quinoid" type of oxidation whereby dehydroadrenaline, adrenochrome, leucoadrenochrome, oxoadrenochrome and leuco-oxoadrenochrome are formed from adrenaline and demethylated "quinones" are formed from noradrenaline; (2) the "amine oxidase" type of catecholamine conversion with the formation of homoprotocatechuic aldehyde and homo-protocatechuic acid; (3) linkage of adrenaline and noradrenaline with sulphuric or glycuronic acid (formation of conjugated compounds) and also the formation of methoxy compounds ("metanephrine" and "normeta-nephrine") with their subsequent oxidation or with the formation of con-jugated compounds; and (4) various "proteinization" processes both of unchanged catecholamines and of various intermediate products of their oxidation.

The "catechin–quinoid" route for the oxidation of adrenergic hormone-mediators is of special interest to physiologists as intermediate products with catalytic properties and functions appear in the course of the conversion of catechins (Utevskii and Osinskaya, 1955; Green and Richter, 1937; Meyerhof and Randall, 1948; and others). Several reversible oxidation–reduction systems are thus formed.

We still do not know very much about the enzymes participating in these processes. It is suggested that cytochromes and cytochrome oxidases are concerned. The possibility that phenoloxidase (tyrosinase) plays some part cannot be excluded; there are also indications of certain autocatalytic processes.

In the opinion of some investigators the "amine oxidase" type of catecholamine conversion is the main factor in the rapid inactivation, the "switching-off" of adrenergic hormone-mediators. Blashchko (1952) and other investigators have discussed the properties, distribution and function of amine oxidase in a number of papers. The view of investigators who have noted a certain similarity in functions between amine oxidase and cholinesterase are summarized by Davison (1958): "It has long been suggested that monoamine oxidase can inactivate a neurohumoral mediator such as, for example, noradrenaline or dopamine in the same way as cholinesterase is responsible for the splitting of excess acetylcholine."

There are a number of reports which indicate that many processes of catecholamine conversion in the body cannot be readily explained by the action of amine oxidase (monoamine oxidase). The results of experiments in which substances suppressing the action of amine oxidase (iproniazide, etc.) were injected into animals afford strong evidence against this enzyme being regarded as the main factor in the inactivation of adrenaline and noradrenaline. The results obtained by a number of investigators indicate that the injection of amine oxidase inhibitors into animals has no material influence on the physiological effects, secretion or rate of destruction of injected adrenaline or noradrenaline. Yet at the same time these enzyme inhibitors were effective in relation to the action and excretion of tyramine.

Attention is merited by the findings of Axelrod (1959) and others on the formation from adrenaline and noradrenaline of methoxy derivatives which may constitute a better substrate for the action of tissue monoamine oxidase than naturally occurring catecholamine. An enzyme, catechol-orthomethyl-transferase, has been described which, in a system containing S-adenosyl methionine, transfers a methyl group to the orthophenol radical of adrenaline and noradrenaline.

3-Methoxy-4-hydroxymindolic acid has been demonstrated in the urine of man and certain animals. Whether orthomethylation precedes deamination or whether the products of deamination are methylated secondarily is still not altogether clear, but most of the evidence is for recognition of orthomethylation as a process preceding the action of monoamine oxidase.

Conjugated compounds of catecholamines with sulphuric or glycuronic acid can undoubtedly be formed in the body. The early investigations of Richter (1940) and others suggested considerable formation of such compounds. It was, however, found in the later investigations of Euler *et al.* that conjugated catecholamine compounds were formed to a very limited extent in the body. Nevertheless, when investigating adrenergic substances in the urine, we found a certain quantity of these substances in bound state (Kaliman, 1957).

The possible combination of several routes and "mechanisms" for the conversion of catecholamines is not excluded. It may be, for example, that the process begins by the "catechin–quinoid" route and switches at some stage to the "amine oxidase" conversion or to the formation of conjugated compounds. In relation to the formation of methoxy compounds there is also the question of whether these processes are primary and whether there may not be *ortho*methylation of certain intermediate products of catecholamine metabolism as well as of the naturally occurring catecholamines.

A characteristic feature of adrenergic hormone-mediators is thus the multiplicity of possible routes for their conversion, routes which are not completely isolated from one another and may intersect in some degree in intermediate stages.

In this paper, which is a part of our investigations on the metabolism of adrenaline and noradrenaline in animals and man, we describe certain findings on the "fate" of catecholamines injected into animals (rabbits), on the rate of transfer of these substances from the blood to the tissues and on their accumulation or conversion in these tissues (heart, liver). We correlate these findings with estimations which we have made of monoamine oxidase activity in cardiac and hepatic tissue in relation to tyramine, adrenaline and noradrenaline.

Catecholamines were estimated by the method of fluorescent analysis developed by V. O. Osinskaya, whereby it is possible to differentiate and to estimate quantitatively adrenaline, noradrenaline and substances present in the tissues with the properties of "catechin–quinoid" products of catecholamines oxidation. Estimations were made in blood, liver, heart, skeletal muscle, brain and other organs.

The estimations in the experiments for examination of monoamine oxidase activity were made in tissue homogenates (liver, heart) prepared in a Potter–Elvejem homogenizer. The homogenate (10 per cent in phosphate buffer, pH 7·17) was placed in the small vessels of a Warburg apparatus, usually with added cyanide (0·2 ml KCN, 0·01 N, per test), semicarbazide (0·2 ml 0·1 N per test), tyramine as substrate, and adrenaline or noradrenaline in various quantities (500–1000 μg per test). Experiments were also carried out without the addition of cyanides (but with semicarbazide), without cyanides and without semicarbazide, and also experiments with boiled tissue, experiments with single reagents and so on. Enzyme activity was determined manometrically (from O_2 absorption when the action of other oxidation enzymes, with the exception of monoamine oxidase was blocked) and also from the formation of ammonia by the isothermic distillation method (and in the case of oxidation of adrenaline, from the appearance of methylamine).

The experiments in which adrenaline and noradrenaline were injected into animals revealed the following. When adrenaline or noradrenaline (about 30 μg/kg) was injected subcutaneously into rabbits, no accumulation of these substances in the blood or tissues could be demonstrated. The slow absorption of the catecholamines was apparently completely balanced by processes of elimination and conversion.

When adrenaline or noradrenaline was injected directly into the blood stream (from 30 to 80 μg into the vessels of the ear), the experimental rabbits might exhibit appreciable but transient adrenalinaemia (or noradrenalinaemia). This accumulation of catecholamines in the blood could only be demonstrated during the first few minutes after the injection of adrenaline or noradrenaline. When the examination was made after 5–10 min, it was found that they had already disappeared from the blood stream and the blood only contained the traces of adrenaline-like substances which are generally present in rabbit blood.

Appreciable quantities of the hormone could be demonstrated in the heart of rabbits into which adrenaline had been injected intravenously (see Fig. 1, which shows the average findings in a number of experiments). According to V. O. Osinskaya, the rabbit heart usually contains noradrenaline but no appreciable quantities of adrenaline. The appearance of adrenaline in the heart when this hormone was injected into the blood indicated that the heart had a considerable capacity for extraction of catecholamines from the blood. At the same time the hearts of the experimental animals usually contained larger quantities of catecholamine oxidation products than the hearts of control rabbits. This indicated that not only did the heart extract adrenaline actively from the blood and store it but that it also subjected adrenaline gradually to certain processes of oxidation, probably of "catechin–quinoid" type (as is indicated by the increase of the oxidation product fraction). This increase in the heart of substances with the properties of the oxidation products of adrenaline was very small and was only observed in relation to repeated injection of the hormone. An interesting point is that injection of adrenaline was also sometimes accompanied by increase of noradrenaline in the heart, this probably being the result of a general increase of sympathetic nervous system tone and not of the direct conversion of the adrenaline injected into noradrenaline in the heart.

When noradrenaline was injected into animals there was a considerable increase of this catecholamine in the heart. We were unable to note the appearance of adrenaline in the hearts of the experimental animals under these conditions (Fig. 1).

Examination of the livers of the experimental animals yielded somewhat different results (Fig. 2). The injection of catecholamines into the animals did not lead to accumulation of these substances (in the form of adrenaline or noradrenaline) in the hepatic tissue. At the same time there was in the liver a certain increase of oxidation products, a point which may be regarded as indicating that the liver, while it eliminates injected catecholamines from the blood, probably subjects them to conversion relatively rapidly. It must be assumed (from the increase in the oxidation product fraction) that at any rate some fraction of injected adrenergic hormones is subjected to conversion by the "catechin–quinoid" route in the liver. Investigations by Osinskaya on some of the properties of this oxidation product fraction

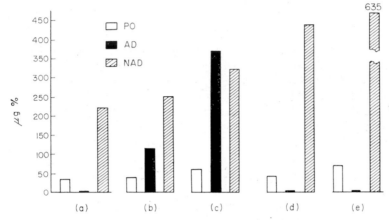

FIG. 1. Effect of the injection of adrenaline (AD) and noradrenaline (NAD) and products of catecholamine oxidation (PO) into the blood of animals on the content of these substances in the heart.

a—control. b—single injection of adrenaline 80 μg/kg. c—repeated (4–6 times) injection of adrenaline at intervals of 15 min in quantities of 30–50 μg/kg. d—single injection of noradrenaline (80 μg/kg). e—repeated (4–6 times) injection of noradrenaline at intervals of 15 min in quantities of 30–50 μg/kg.

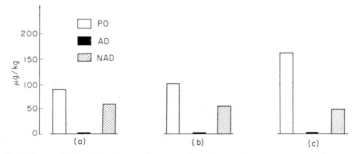

FIG. 2. Effect of the injection of adrenaline into the blood of animals on the adrenaline content of the liver.

a—control. b—single injection of adrenaline 80 μg/kg. c—repeated injection of adrenaline (4–6 times) in quantities of 30–50 μg/kg at intervals of 15 min. Remaining notation as in Fig. 1.

revealed that these substances differed somewhat from the oxidation products usually found in the liver (for example, they were labile when oxidized by iodine). Identification of this oxidation product fraction is one of the tasks in our research.

Our examination of the "amine oxidase" activities of hepatic and cardiac tissue yielded the following results. When monoamine oxidase activity developed, the liver tissue exhibited fairly high enzyme activity in relation to tyramine. The "amine oxidase" oxidation of noradrenaline was much feebler and hepatic monoamine oxidase failed almost completely to oxidize adrenaline (Fig. 3).

In view of the feeble "amine oxidase" activity of the liver in relation to noradrenaline and adrenaline, particularly the latter, it must be assumed that other processes for the conversion of catecholamines proceed with greater intensity in liver tissue. That such processes must proceed quite energetically in the liver is supported by numerous published reports and by our observations that, when relatively large quantities of catecholamines are injected into the body, they cannot be demonstrated in the liver. It must be assumed that the oxidation of catecholamines in the liver proceeds by the "catechin–quinoid" and, to a small extent (for noradrenaline), through "amine oxidase" activity. Along with these, there are apparently other processes in the liver leading, for example, to the formation of various conjugated compounds, like the catecholamines themselves, and also certain products of their oxidation or methylation.

Examination of the "amine oxidase" activity of cardiac tissue revealed the following. In conditions in which monoamine oxidase

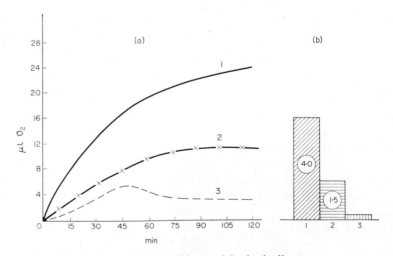

FIG. 3. Amine oxidase activity in the liver.

a—oxygen consumption in a Warburg apparatus. b—liberation of ammonia (μM per test). For adrenaline—methylamine: 1—tyramine; 2—noradrenaline; 3—adrenaline.

activity could develop, cardiac tissue oxidized all three substrates examined (tyramine, adrenaline, noradrenaline) very feebly. Relationships here were, however, slightly different from those seen in the liver. There was practically no oxidation of noradrenaline (Fig. 4). Tyramine was oxidized fairly actively, although its "amine oxidase" conversion in the heart was much less than in hepatic tissue. Adrenaline behaved in a curious manner under these conditions. To judge from O_2 absorption, adrenaline appeared to be subjected to some (slight) "amine oxidase" oxidation in cardiac tissue. Yet it was almost impossible to detect methylamine under these

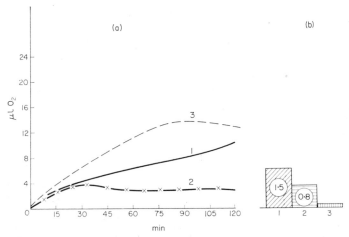

FIG. 4. Activity of amine oxidase in the heart.

Notation as in Fig. 3.

conditions. There was intense O_2 absorption and the appearance of coloured "quinoid" products of adrenaline oxidation in experiments set up without the addition of cyanides. One was almost forced to think that, although the conditions excluded the action of other oxidation enzymes apart from monoamine oxidase (addition of cyanides and semicarbazide), there was still present in the heart some catalytic or autocatalytic process for the oxidation of catecholamines, with which some of the O_2 absorption ascribed to the action of monoamine oxidase was also connected. As there was considerable accumulation of injected adrenaline and noradrenaline in the heart and the increase of oxidation products was greater than in the control animals, it had to be assumed that there were fairly active "anti-oxygen" systems in the heart stabilizing the catecholamines and retarding their conversion to some extent. Investigations carried out in our laboratory by Gaisinskaya (1952, 1957) point to the presence in various tissues of such "stabilizing systems" for adrenaline and noradrenaline.

It should, however, be remembered that the appearance in the heart of the experimental animals of considerable quantities of adrenaline or increase in its noradrenaline content may also depend on rapid (in the conditions of the experiments described above) transfer of catecholamines from the blood into the heart tissue in quantities exceeding the "through capacity" of the oxidation systems in the heart in relation to the adrenergic hormone-mediators. In order to investigate this question, we are now carrying out investigations on the catecholamine and oxidation product contents of the heart of animals at longer intervals after the injection of adrenaline and noradrenaline than in the case of the experiments described above. All the findings contained in experiments in which catecholamines are injected cannot, of course, be applied without corresponding investigations and corrections for processes of endogenous adrenaline and noradrenaline conversion.

Comparison of our findings on the content and conversion of catecholamines in heart and liver with findings or the "amine oxidase" activities of these tissues forces us to recognize that the monoamine oxidase of the heart and liver cannot be the only, or even the main factor in the conversion of adrenergic hormone-mediators in these tissues (organs). We suggest that there are no adequate grounds for an analogy between the functions of cholinesterase and monoamine oxidase in neurohumoral processes. As already stated, a characteristic feature of catecholamines is that they can undergo conversion in several ways.

In whatever way the conversion of catecholamines proceeds, there is no doubt that processes of "proteinization" play an important part in their metabolism and functioning. This was demonstrated for adrenaline by the early investigations of A. M. Utevskii and his co-workers. Subsequently, Barts (1957), working in our laboratory, used various methods for the precipitation and fractionation of proteins and demonstrated the presence of noradrenaline linked to proteins in the rabbit heart. When sympathetic nerves were stimulated, there was a shift in the content of bound noradrenaline, with increased "proteinization", this phenomenon being noted when the nerve stimulation was accompanied by the physiological (inotropic) effect. Corticosteroids (cortisone, deoxycorticosterone acetate) influence this process of noradrenaline "proteinization" in the heart.

The oxidation products demonstrated by Osinskaya (1957, 1959) in various tissues were also apparently present in these tissues, partly in the bound state.

It would appear that the linking of catecholamines in the heart and other organs by some proteins entails the inactivation of these highly active hormone-mediators whereas their linkage by other proteins leads to manifestation of catecholamine function and the appearance of the products of their metabolism.

Bound forms of adrenaline and noradrenaline have also been found by ourselves and by other authors in the suprarenal glands. There are reports of the presence of complexes consisting of catecholamines with proteins and adenosine triphosphate in the granules of chromaffin tissue (Hillarp, 1959). Similar complexes apparently play a part in the secretion of adrenaline and noradrenaline, in their deposition and protection from processes of oxidation.

The investigations of Tsukernik (1956), carried out in our laboratory, merit attention in connexion with the possible oxidation of catecholamines in chromaffin tissue; these investigations demonstrated the presence of amine oxidase in the suprarenal glands. It must be assumed that the function of this enzyme in chromaffin tissue is somewhat different from its function in other organs.

Despite the large number of investigations dealing with the role of monoamine oxidase in the conversion of adrenaline and noradrenaline, its functional significance still remains very obscure. In the case of the heart "catechin–quinoid" oxidation is most probably the main form. This oxidation process may apparently also operate to some extent in the liver along with other processes (formation of methoxy derivatives and conjugated catecholamine compounds, "amine oxidase" oxidation, etc.). One cannot exclude the possible occurrence of several processes for the conversion of catecholamines in the heart also, but their capacity must be regarded as small in comparison with the main process. And it must be postulated that any such process is not one which leads to rapid inactivation, like the action of cholinesterase, but a process leading to the formation of numerous intermediate substances with catalytic properties—the "catechin–quinoid" form of metabolism. But this statement requires further proof, and most of all, differentiation of the oxidation products, identification and quantitative estimation of substances such as adrenochromes, oxoadrenochromes, etc. in the heart and other organs. Even now, however, reasoning from evidence of differing capacities for the oxidation of adrenaline and noradrenaline with the formation of quinones, and the presence of noradrenaline and oxidation products in the heart and other organs, we (Utevskii and Osinskaya, 1955) have expressed the view that noradrenaline is utilized in the animal body mainly as a sympathomimetic amine and adrenaline as a source of catalytically active "quinones" which enter directly into the biochemical dynamics of the effector organ. The most varied interrelationships and correlations are, however, possible between the metabolism and functions of adrenaline and noradrenaline.

As for the action of monoamine oxidase, the activity of which in relation to adrenergic hormone-mediators is comparatively slight, it is possible that this enzyme does not participate mainly at the level of natural catecholamines, but that the substrates for its activity are the intermediate products of the metabolism of adrenaline and noradrenaline, produced by other forms of conversion. The evidence of "amine oxidase" oxidation of methoxy derivatives of catecholamines is in particular agreement with this concept. The inclusion of monoamine oxidase function in this way is possible for the "catechin–quinoid" form of conversion, but only in the first stage, in which dehydro-adrenaline, still with a lateral chain—methyl-aminoethanol—is formed. In subsequent stages, when there is closure of the lateral chain with the formation of dehydro-indole and indoxyl rings (adrenochromes, etc.), such inclusion of monoamine oxidase is scarcely possible.

The "switching" of the metabolism of adrenergic hormone-mediators from one mode of conversion to another is of considerable theoretical and practical interest. We are at present working on this subject.

CONCLUSIONS

The accumulation in the blood and tissues (heart, liver) of adrenaline, noradrenaline and substances with properties of "catechin–quinoid" products of catecholamine oxidation was investigated in relation to the intravenous injection of adrenaline and noradrenaline in rabbits. The results were correlated with findings for monoamine oxidase activity in the heart and liver in relation to tyramine, adrenaline and noradrenaline.

When adrenaline (30–80 μg/kg) was injected intravenously into rabbits, the appearance of adrenaline in the heart was noted. When adrenaline was injected repeatedly, increased content of noradrenaline in the heart (in comparison with control animals) and some increase of the oxidation products was sometimes also noted.

The injection of noradrenaline (30–80 μg/kg) into animals led to considerable increase in the content of noradrenaline in the heart. Adrenaline was not then detected in the hearts of the experimental or control animals.

Adrenaline and noradrenaline could not be demonstrated in the liver of the experimental animals into which these catecholamines had been injected. Some increase of the oxidation product fraction was noted (after repeated injection of adrenaline).

Examination of the "amine oxidase" activity of the liver and heart showed that the monoamine oxidase of the liver was active in relation to tyramine, oxidized noradrenaline feebly and had practically no effect on adrenaline. The monoamine oxidase of the heart was of low activity, had no effect on noradrenaline and oxidized tyramine feebly. In conditions in which monoamine oxidase activity developed (cyanides, monosemicarbazide) there was some increase of O_2 absorption, which pointed to the "amine oxidase" oxidation of adrenaline, but other findings indicate that there may have been other processes for the oxidation of adrenaline (possibly autocatalytic) in these experiments.

Certain theoretical views on the importance of the various forms of catecholamine conversion and on the possibility of the "switching" from one process to another are examined.

REFERENCES

AXELROD, J., *Physiol. Rev.* **39**, 751 (1959).

BACQ, Z. M., *J. Pharm. Expl. Therap.* **95**, 1 (1949).

BARTS, M. P., Problems of Endocrinology and Hormone Therapy (*Problemy endokrinologii i gormonoterapii*) **2**, 33 (1957).

BLASCHKO, H., *Parmacol. Rev.* **4**, 415 (1952).

DAVISON, A. H., *Physiol. Rev.* **38**, 729 (1958).

EULER, U. S., *Noradrenaline*, Philadelphia 1956.

GAISINSKAYA, M. YU., Ukrainian Biochemical J. (*Ukr. biokhim. zh.*) **24**, 287 (1952).

GAISINSKAYA, M. YU., Collection of papers of Kharkov Med. Inst. (*Sbornik Khar'kovsk. med. in-ta*) **15** (1957).

GREEN, D. E. and D. RICHTER, *Biochem. J.* **31**, 596 (1937).

HILLARP, N. A., *Acta Physiol. Scand.* **47**, 271 (1959).

KALIMAN, P. A., Collection of papers of Kharkov Med. Inst. (*Sbornik Khar'kovsk. med. in-ta*) **15** (1957).

MEYERHOF, O. and L. O. RANDALL, *Arch. Biochem.* **17**, 171 (1948).

OSINSKAYA, V. O., Biochemistry (*Biokhimiya*) **18**, 56 (1953).

OSINSKAYA, V. O., Biochemistry (*Biokhimiya*) **22**, 57 (1957).

OSINSKAYA, V. O., Proceedings of Scientific Conference of UIEE (Materialy nauchnoi konf. UIEE), Kharkov 1959.

RICHTER, D., *J. Physiol.* **98**, 361 (1940).

TSUKERNIK, A. V., Ukrainian Biochemical J. (*Ukr. biokhim. zh.*) **28**, 338 (1956).

UTEVSKII, A. M., Advances in Biological Chemistry (*Usp. biol. khim.*) **1**, 433 (1950).

UTEVSKII, A. M., Problems of Endocrinology and Hormone Therapy (*Probl. endokrinol. i gormonoterap.*) **1**, 19 (1955).

UTEVSKII, A. M., Papers of the Kharkov Med. Inst. (*Sbornik Khar'kovsk. med. in-ta*) **15**, 139 (1957).

UTEVSKII, A. M., Proceedings of 8th Mendeleyev Congress (*Dokl. VIII Mendeleyevskogo s"ezda*) **8**, 141 (1959a).

UTEVSKII, A. M., Proceedings of 9th All-Union Congress of Physiologists (*Dokl. IX Vses. s"ezda fiziol.*) **3**, 147 (1959b).

UTEVSKII, A. M., *Hormones and Enzymes* (Gormony i fermenty) (In press).

UTEVSKII, A. M. and V. O. OSINSKAYA, Ukrainian Biochemical J. (*Ukr. biokhim. zh.*) **27**, 401 (1955).

COMPARATIVE NEUROPHYSIOLOGY,
ITS AIMS AND ITS PRESENT STATUS

C. A. G. WIERSMA

Division of Biology, California Institute of Technology
Pasadena, California

FROM time to time a good purpose can be served by taking stock of the achievements in a certain field of scientific endeavor and considering what its future may be. It may be shown that either too much attention is being given to it, so that the return obtained is not in proportion to the effort spent, or possibly the reverse is the case, with the result that not enough contributions are being made and the field, instead of keeping up with the demands of the present, lags behind. In many fields of comparative physiology the latter appears clearly to be the case. The reason for this situation is fairly obvious. The advances which have been made in vertebrate physiology during the early part of this century have been so great that in many cases the originally physiological problems have become biochemical or biophysical ones. As a result of underdevelopment of comparative physiology at that time, the same problems in comparative physiology were much less worked out and as a consequence we are still very poorly informed about such topics as blood circulation and its regulation in lower forms. In this example no significant contribution has been made to the general problem by comparative investigations. It may be held that none was possible in the first place because it was only in the vertebrates that the blood circulation became really important. But the fact that relevant data are even now so scarce is in itself a great handicap for comparative physiologists working with other organ systems, who thereby lack important information readily available for vertebrates. Whether the missing data will ever be provided and how long this may take is at present unpredictable. Such data would certainly be necessary to obtain a picture of the physiology of the animal as whole, but may be of minor importance with regard to other problems of more general significance, in the same animals.

Comparative neurophysiology finds itself in a much better but still by no means ideal, position. This is due to a number of factors. In the first place, purely physiological problems of nervous functioning are still very much in the foreground. Secondly, though certain aspects have now rightly been turned over to biophysicists and chemists, the latter often find it very useful to apply their arts to specific systems of invertebrates, which in a number of cases provide material which is easier to handle than that of vertebrates. Thirdly, whereas interest of vertebrate physiologists in other fields of comparative physiology has either been absent or has died almost completely down at present, that in comparative aspects of neurology has continued from the days of Richet, Biedermann and Pavlov, and has been carried on with success by such investigators as Adrian, Hill and their schools. Only in some other instances, such as photosensitive pigments has anything comparable taken place.

A considerable handicap to the neurophysiologist has been the diminished interest in the anatomical aspects of the invertebrate nervous systems after the early development from 1880–1890. Although this is to be regretted, perhaps less harm resulted than one would think at first sight. As in vertebrate neurology, the study of structure and function of the identical material is a necessity, and it helps but little if the anatomy of a rather distantly related form has been described in anatomical detail, because important features may differ considerably. But even more relevant is that many aspects which are now found to be of great physiological importance have often not been considered by older workers. It is therefore a very highly important event that lately a renewed interest has been aroused for this type of anatomy. In vertebrate physiology many people who started out as anatomists have since become concerned with physiological aspects, and a similar development in comparative approaches would be highly desirable. Since there are too few people in this field in the first place and because, in contrast to their vertebrate colleagues they find themselves with plenty of practically new, purely anatomical problems, this development may not become sufficiently strong. But insofar as the comparative physiologist cannot himself obtain the required data, he may be able to persuade an anatomist to help him.

For these reasons, it seems to me, the greatest successes of the comparative approach have so far come from the cases in which outstanding simplified systems have been discovered in invertebrates, so that its contribution to the biophysical and biochemical aspects of nervous function has been much greater than to more complex functional relationships. To mention such contributions in order of their levels, the first example is that of the giant motor fiber of the squid. Because these nerve fibers are so large that internal electrodes can be brought into them without noticeably impairing their function, the study of the membrane in rest and in activity has been possible with this preparation for a considerable time before comparable data on smaller axons could be obtained. Thus these investigations have been of the utmost importance for the development of our present insight into the nature of the conducted nerve impulse in general. It is rather amazing to have to state that the physiological effects of impulses in this axon are still greatly unknown, for though they are motor fibers there is no evidence available about the way they transmit their activity to the muscle fibers they innervate, other than this happens in a fairly strict all or none fashion. However, with this and other similar systems, transmission at the interneural junctions has been studied with advantage to a more general understanding of such transmission.

It has, for instance, lately been found that a type of transmission called electrical, which at one time was supposed to be the main way in which neuro-neural transmission came about, but which was then completely replaced by that of transmitter liberation, is present after all in certain structures which are clearly one-way conducting paths[1]. This occurs at synapses which are not formed by the ends of the presynaptic fiber, but in places where a lateral contact between the pre- and post-fiber exists. Only further study can tell if similar electrical transmission is present in other systems, where lateral synapses occur, of which there are certainly a number in invertebrates and perhaps also in vertebrates, or whether in these cases transmitter substances still do play the main role. Perhaps there exist places in which the two are simultaneously present and knowledge of this would deepen our insight into the evolution of the nervous system. A further study of the influence of different drugs on such transmissions may also be very worthwhile.

Another aspect opened by the comparative approach stems from the fact that the properties of nerve fibers can vary greatly from one to another even though the axons appear to be very similar. Thus it has been shown that although their mechanisms of conduction appear quite similar, the three motor fibers which innervate the muscles in the last joint of the crustacean leg respond quite differently to the same type of stimulation, so that each of them may be considered to be unique[2]. In the vertebrate such differences are known to exist between different categories of fibers, e.g. A and its divisions, B and C, but it is believed that in each class they are much the same. However, this may not be really the case, and any group that appears to be homogeneous may consist of a population of fibers in which differences between the extremes would be easily apparent were they not hidden by the "random" variation.

In the field of sensory perception and the transmission of external stimulation to action impulse sequences, the role of comparative physiology has also been considerable. At the simplest level, the stretch receptor of the crustaceans is probably the best example. It was one of the first objects in which the relation between the generator potential and the impulse sequence was elucidated, followed closely, if not preceded, by similar studies on the vertebrate muscle spindle and the Pacinian corpuscle. The crustacean stretch receptor has one advantage above the others, in that it possesses peripheral inhibitory fibers, which make it possible to study how secondary changes of the generator potential can result in suppression of the spike potentials, thus showing that there is a close relation between the height of the generator potential no matter how obtained, and the resulting firing of the axon[3]. This system also demonstrates how, by central control, it is possible to negate peripheral stimulation, but here the physiological importance has still to be discovered. In this respect the study of the responses of *Limulus* ommatids to light gives a much clearer answer. In this case the response of the cell which transmits the information to the central nervous system is most likely secondary, in contrast to the above-mentioned receptors. However, as in the case of the vertebrate motor neuron there is a recurrent pathway by which activity in one axon inhibits that of neighbouring ones, and this appears to be direct and not by intercalation of an inhibitory neuron as with the Renshaw cells[4]. This system has been analyzed with great success in terms of its over-all function and further progress can be looked for shortly in several respects. It has also been found here that depolarization of the receptive part of the transmitting neuron, no matter whether brought about by light, by internal depolarization, or by a combination of the two, results in similar discharge rates for similar amounts of depolarization[5].

Examples of this kind could be given for a number of other instances, but one of the main purposes of the present paper is to call attention to the contributions that can be expected from comparative investigations of the more complex functions of the central nervous system at the physiological level, as against that of the ethological[6]. In the latter field and also in that of "cybernetics", invertebrate material has been used rather frequently with good results. The situation at the physiological level was however, until very recently, much less satisfactory, though it would seem that here there is a much better chance to bridge the gap between the aspects of cellular physiology and behavior than anywhere else. Previous attempts made in this direction have in general been based on the methods used in vertebrate central nervous physiology. However, these have, on the whole, not contributed much to our understanding of reflexology and integration. This has been greatly due to an uncritical application of methods in use for vertebrates without sufficient understanding of the types of connections and the pathways involved, and partially to the fact that they have not been pursued intensively enough. At least in one type of invertebrate, the Cephalopods, it has more recently been possible to analyze higher functions of the central nervous systems by methods analogous to those of vertebrates, even though our knowledge of peripheral connections, such as the role played by the peripheral ganglia and the lack of information about nerve–muscle connections, puts certain restrictions on the interpretability of the results—except in a general behavioral analysis. But much more than in other invertebrates, the fundamental structure of the CNS of these molluscs appears to resemble that of the vertebrates as is immediately clear from the fact that the number of nerve cells of the CNS in them is larger by a high factor[7]. They, like vertebrates, appear to have whole tracts of interneurons of similar function. In the arthropods and presumably in the annelids, on the other hand, single interneurons, directly connected to the sensory input, often collect impulses from large sensory fields distributed over a large number and sometimes all body segments[8]. As a consequence each such interneuron is distinctly unique, and may replace a whole tract in the vertebrate sense. Because of the small number of motor fibers innervating the musculature and the limited number of interneurons, the total cell count of the CNS in these phyla is small. For these reasons it is more likely that the fate of a certain input can be followed closely throughout the system than it can in nervous systems with many more central fibers. The closest approximation to such a possibility has been obtained by a study of giant fiber systems, which are also present in molluscs and vertebrates. In such systems, the input is at least partially known. Single impulses in the giant fibers are often sufficient to cause contractions of a great number of muscles, appropriate for an escape reflex. In annelids and crustacea, as in the squid, a single muscle twitch in a large part of the musculature provides for the main part, and sometimes perhaps all, of the necessary body motion. In insects, like the cockroach, with a lower threshold for the interneurons, motor consequences are more complex and less easily released. As Roeder[9] has pointed out, such systems provide the quickest reflexes of which the animals are capable, and interesting correlations can be made between this "flight reflex" time and the similar time of the "catch mechanism" of predators.

At least for Crustacea it is quite clear that many of the other types of behavior are built up from similar elements. Stimulation—which then has to be repetitive—of different interneurons, leads to the activation of distinct movements performed by subsequent contractions of muscles. Thus the defence reflex can be obtained by stimulation at a frequency of 30 or more impulses per second of a single fiber in the circumesophageal commissure. That such motor patterns do not solely depend for their subsequent development on sensory feedback is well illustrated by experiments in which the swimmeret movements of the crayfish were studied[10]. It was found that the isolated tail of a crayfish would show these movements and the accompanying motor discharges electrically registered from the motor output even when all but one swimmeret nerve was cut. With all cut, rhythmic output was still present, but of a kind which would not have provided for regular coordinated swimmeret movement. However, when the abdominal cord was left in connection with the rest of the CNS, swimmeret movements and their accompanying motor impulses could be regularly triggered by stimulation of specific interneurons in the subesophageal commissure, whereas stimulation of others would stop such movements. It was found that rhythmic discharges, differing little if any from those with the peripheral nerves all intact, were obtained after all roots to the swimmerets had been cut, so that no feedback from swimmeret movements was possible. It has thus to be concluded that interneurons exist whose function is to release pre-existing motor patterns or to stop them. The name "command" fibers seems appropriate to describe their functions. As is known from investigation of vertebrate spinal cord such motor patterns also occur there[11].

There remain numerous problems to be solved before it will be possible to claim that at last a real beginning has been made in understanding a central nervous system as a whole. For instance it has been regularly observed that activity in a number of interneurons is rhythmical and that such activity can continue even when all apparent sensory input has been removed by isolation. In at least some crayfish interneurons, such spontaneity is very regular in timing and nearly identical in the same units in different preparations. Neither the genesis nor the functional importance of these impulses is as yet understood. But again the fact that they are so constant and can be obtained in isolation offers the hope that further investigations are feasible.

However, it is clear that at present the rate of progress being made is all too slow. For in this field there are some 100 investigators who work full time on the same kind of problems in vertebrates and especially mammals for each one who specializes in invertebrates. Thus many findings which at the present time could without much trouble be made in invertebrates and which would help to develop our insight in vertebrate physiology may well come again too late to be of more than supporting help in that field. Several findings have already shown that these nervous systems, though considerably different, do have factors in common, which makes it possible to ask the right kind of questions from either. But as long as no more effort is put into the invertebrate problems their usefulness to the general picture will remain very severely restricted.

Professor Kh. S. Koshtoyants was one well aware of the possibilities of comparative neurophysiology for these purposes and did much to stress them. It is with pride that the present author remembers him as a friend. It is to be hoped that his work along these lines will be continued by his successors as a further tribute to his memory.

REFERENCES

1. FURSHPAN, E. J. and D. D. POTTER, Transmission at the giant motor synapses of the crayfish. *J. Physiol.* **145**, 289–325 (1959).
2. WRIGHT, E. B., The subthreshold response of the single crustacean motor axon. *J. Cell Comp. Physiol.* **53**, 349–376 (1959).
3. KUFFLER, S. E., Synaptic inhibitory mechanisms, properties of dendrites and problems of excitation in isolated nerve cells. *Exp. Cell Res.*, Suppl. **5**, 493–519 (1958).
4. HARTLINE, H. K. and F. RATLIFF, Spatial summation of inhibitory influences in the eye of Limulus and the mutual interaction of receptor units. *J. Gen. Physiol.* **41**, 1049–1066 (1958).

5. FUORTES, M. G. F., Initiation of impulses in visual cells of *Limulus*. *J. Physiol.* **148**, 14–28 (1959).
6. BAERENDS, G. P., The contribution of ethology to the study of causation of behaviour. *Act. Physiol. Pharmacol. neerl.* **7**, 466-499 (1958).
7. WELLS, M. J., A touch-learning centre in Octopus. *J. Exp. Biol.* **36**, 590–612 (1959).
8. WIERSMA, C. A. G., On the functional connections of single units in the central nervous system of the crayfish, *Procambarus clarkii* Girard. *J. Comp. Neur.* **110**, 421–472 (1958).
9. ROEDER, K. D., A physiological approach to the relation between prey and predator. *Smithsonian miscellaneous collections* **137**, 287–306 (1959).
10. HUGHES, G. M. and C. A. G. WIERSMA, The coordination of swimmeret movements in the crayfish. *J. Exp. Biol.* **37**, 657–670 (1960).
11. WEISS, P., Autonomous versus reflexogenous activity of the central nervous system. *Proc. Am. Phil. Soc.* **84**, 53–64 (1941).

EVOLUTION OF PHYSIOLOGICAL
MECHANISMS OF TONUS
IN THE VERTEBRATES

Ye. K. Zhukov

Physiological Institute, State University, Leningrad

Translated by Dr. R. Crawford

THERE are numerous reports indicating that the physiological mechanisms responsible for skeletal muscle tonus differ in lower and higher vertebrates. Investigations by a number of authors have shown that muscle tonus in amphibians is produced through the activity of special "tonic" neuromotor units, and, in its mechanism, is a physiological acetylcholine contracture.

Conversely, the tonic contraction of mammalian muscle is due mainly to the activity of muscle fibres with extremely slow contractions and well marked powers of summation, and not fibres capable of acetylcholine contracture. The tonus of skeletal muscles in mammals would appear not to differ in the nature of its physiological mechanism from tetanus (Ginetsinskii, 1947; Zhukov, 1956a).

It was thought important for an understanding of the phylogenetic development of the physiological mechanisms of tone to examine the contractile activity of the skeletal muscles of reptiles, which constitute a transitional group of animals from amphibians to birds and mammals. Do reptiles have special motor mechanisms for tonus? What part does acetylcholine mechanism play in their activity?

We attempted to find the answers to these questions in experiments on the neuromuscular apparatus of the tortoise (*Testudo graeca*).

The Tonic Component of Contraction

Ginetsinskii and Mikhel'son (1937) and Vereshchagin and Zhukov (1948) showed that mixed muscles of the frog (gastrocnemius, semitendinosus, etc.) gave a rapid transient tetanic contraction (spike) accompanied by a long wave of tonic after-effect (tonic tail) in response to transient tetanization of the nerve trunk. Special investigations (Vereshchagin and Zhukov, 1947) revealed that this slow component of the contraction represented the contractile wave of specialized tonic muscle fibres, which was rendered clearly

evident by stimulation of this kind. Was this tonic component present
in the contraction of the tortoise muscles?

A tonic component was seen to be clearly evident in the contractions
of muscles such as the gastrocnemius and semitendinosus in the tortoise
(Fig. 1). It was never seen in the sartorius muscle (just as in the frog).
The contractions of the gastrocnemius and semitendinosus muscle in fresh
preparations under optimum stimulation conditions could be broken down
into a relatively rapid initial "spike" and a slow "tail" of very large area,
often appearing as an independently developing wave.

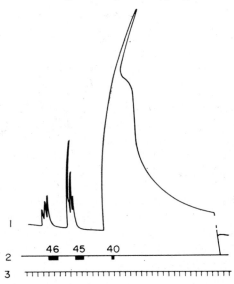

FIG. 1. Two-component curve of the contraction of the gastrocnemius muscle
in the tortoise.

1—myogram. 2—stimulation (the numbers indicate the distance in cm between the
induction coils). 3—time (1 sec). Stimulation frequency—50/sec.

It should, however, be noted that the term "rapid" applied to the initial
spike in this case is used in a relative sense. The spike in the skeletal muscles
of the tortoise was in fact very slow in comparison with the speed of the
corresponding component in the frog muscles. The length of a single
gastrocnemius muscle contraction in the tortoise is 0·6 sec, as compared
with 0·1 sec for the same muscle in the frog. With adequately prolonged
stimulation maximum tetanus in the sartorius muscle of the tortoise was
only achieved after 30 sec (see Fig. 3); it required less than a second to
attain maximum contraction of the frog sartorius.

Two-component curves of contraction were also demonstrated by Itina
(1938) in experiments on the retractor capitis muscle of the marsh tortoise.
Ginetsinskii and Itina (1938) demonstrated with a string galvanometer

that the spike was associated with fast action potentials whereas the tail developed on a background of prolonged depolarization of the muscle fibres.

Thresholds for the development of the rapid and slow components of contraction. Frog experiments revealed that much stronger stimulation was required to produce the tonic tails than the tetanic spike (Vereshchagin and Zhukov, 1948). In the case of stimulation from an induction apparatus the difference between the thresholds was equivalent to a coil separation distance of 20 cm or more. This difference in thresholds was determined by a difference in the excitability of the nerve fibres supplying tetanic and tonic muscle fibres (Kuffler and Gerard, 1947). By taking advantage of this circumstance, we could eliminate the tetanic neuromotor units from the system in the mixed muscle of the frog, leaving the potentially tonic fibres. All that was necessary was to select a nerve stimulation the strength of which was pessimal* for the tetanic apparatus but still optimal for the tonic apparatus (Zhukov, 1956b).

In contrast to what was observed in the frog, the difference between the thresholds for development of the spike and of the tail was very small in the tortoise—not usually more than 5 cm of coil separation (Fig. 1). In some cases the thresholds for the two components appeared to be approximately the same.

Consequently, the attempt to demonstrate differential phasic and tonic activity by increasing the strength of stimulation was unsuccessful. Even a very slight increase in the strength of stimulation which had proved pessimal for the tetanic component led to development of the tonic component, so that there was no transitional drop in the curve of the contraction.

Specialized Neuromotor Units

Numerous investigations of various kinds have shown that the two-component nature of the contractions of frog skeletal muscles is due to the fact that they contain two different contractile systems, one specialized for the function of phasic contraction and the other for the function of tonus (Zhukov, 1956a). Are there similar specialized systems in the muscles of the tortoise or is the two-component nature of the contractions of these muscles determined by the capacity of every muscle for both phasic and tonic activity, as Ginetsinskii and Itina (1938) suggested?

In an attempt to settle this we examined the changes in the responses of the gastrocnemius muscle of the tortoise when the nerve impulses were blocked in a segment of cathodal parabiosis (Fig. 2). It was found that, when the blocking current was of a certain strength, the first relatively rapid

---

* *Editor's note.* This phrase is understood to refer to the phenomenon known to British and American physiologists as Wedensky inhibition.

component of the contraction disappeared and the contraction assumed the character of pure tonus. This fact indicated that there are specialized neuromotor units in tortoises. Just as in frogs (Vereshchagin, 1948a), the nerve fibres supplying the tonic apparatus of the muscle were more resistant to the blocking action of the cathode of a steady current than the fibres supplying the tetanic apparatus.

Morphological findings likewise point to functional specialization of the contractile mechanisms in the tortoise. Kohlen (1938) demonstrated that there are two kinds of muscle fibre in the skeletal muscles of the tortoise (just as in the frog), fibres with "Fibrillenstruktur" and fibres with "Feldernstruktur". According to Kruger (1952) the fibres of the former kind effect rapid phasic contractions and the latter are specialized for the function of tonus.

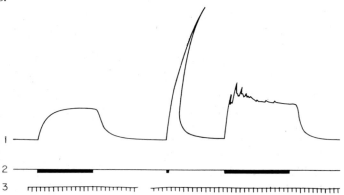

FIG. 2. Effect of blocking of the nerve impulses with a steady current on the nature of the contraction of the gastrocnemius muscle in the tortoise. The first contraction was recorded with a blocking current of strength 20 μA, the second with 10 μA and the third, 15 μA. Stimulation frequency—100/sec.

Notation as in Fig. 1.

Reaction of Muscles to Prolonged Stimulation

We know that in the frog different muscles react differently to prolonged tetanizing stimulation of their nerves. Tetanic muscles (e.g. sartorius) become fatigued relatively rapidly and relax despite continued stimulation. On the other hand, tonic muscles (e.g. the tonic bundle of the iliofibular muscle) are little prone to fatigue and can maintain contraction for many minutes.

This difference is little in evidence in the muscles of the tortoise. Even the sartorius muscle, contraction of which would not appear to have a tonic component, gives a prolonged, persistently maintained steady contraction, accompanied by little trace of contracture, on prolonged stimulation (Fig. 3).

In contrast to what happens in the frog (Zhukov, 1956b), more powerful stimulation was accompanied by very slight pessimal relaxation of the muscles in the tortoise—even of its sartorius.

The explanation of these differences is apparently that there is a considerable, slow reversible change in mechanical properties, somewhat similar to increase of viscosity, in the skeletal muscles of the tortoise during the process of contraction. These changes render relaxation of the muscle difficult and contribute to prolonged maintenance of the contracted state, despite developing fatigue and pessimum (Vereshchagin *et al.*, 1950; Zhukov, 1957).

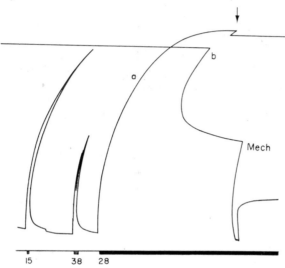

FIG. 3. Contractions of the sartorius muscle of the tortoise on short and prolonged (5 min) stimulation of the nerve.

a—commencement of prolonged stimulation. b—its end. The arrow indicates stopping of the kymograph for 2 min. Mech.—temporary relaxation of the muscle. Numbers—distance (cm) between induction coils. Stimulation frequency—80/sec.

Effects of Acetylcholine and Eserine

In the frog different muscles react differently to the application of acetylcholine (Sommerkamp, 1928; Vereshchagin, 1948b). While tonic and mixed muscles are quite sensitive to this agent and, exposed to its action, give persistent and prolonged contracture, tetanic muscles (e.g. sartorius) react to acetylcholine by variable and transient contractions.

All the tortoise muscles examined by us gave distinct prolonged contractions in response to painting with acetylcholine solution (10^{-4} to 10^{-6} g/ml). Even the sartorius exhibited stable and prolonged shortening. If it is accepted that the power of a muscle to react to acetylcholine by contracture

12b*

is an indication of the extent to which it is a tonic muscle, it should be recognized that the muscle fibres of the sartorius in the tortoise are capable of both phasic and tonic contraction.

Eserine, which inactivates cholinesterase, leads to development and intensification of the tonic component of the contractions of the gastro-cnemius and semitendinosus muscles in the tortoise. When, for example, a gastrocnemius muscle was kept for an hour in eserine solution 10^{-4} g/ml, the spike was reduced and the tonic tail was considerably increased. Similar findings were obtained by Ginetsinskii and Itina (1938) with the action of eserine on the muscle retracting the tortoise's head.

Damping of the Tonic Component of Contraction

When any mixed muscle of the frog is subjected to repeated stimulation every spike of contraction that develops is accompanied by a well marked tonic tail. The muscles of the tortoise give a quite different picture. Figure 4a shows that the powerful tonic component of contraction elicited on one occasion only did not develop in relation to further stimulations, being as it were damped out. Increasing the strength of stimulation did not generally lead to its reappearance.

Preliminary eserinization of the muscle stabilized the development of the tonic tails; each new stimulation was then accompanied by both a rapid component of contraction and a slow tonic component (Fig. 4, b). Stabili-

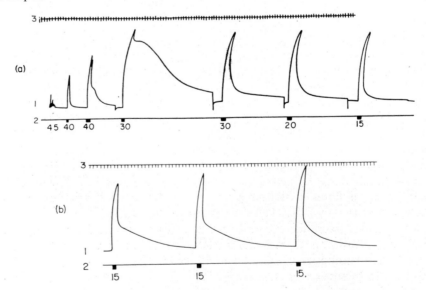

FIG. 4. Damping of the tonic component of contraction.

a—semitendinosus muscle of the tortoise. b—the same muscle after treatment for 45 min with eserine solution 10^{-4} g/ml. Notation as in Fig. 1.

zation of the tonic component of contraction by eserine has been described and investigated by Itina (1938) and by Ginetsinskii and Itina (1938) in relation to the retractor muscle of the head.

There are at least two possible causes for this phenomenon. First, the cholinoreceptive substance in the tonic fibres in the tortoise may be capable of rapid adaptation to the action of acetylcholine. It is, however, difficult to reconcile the capacity for the prolonged maintenance of contraction in response to the action of even weak acetylcholine solutions seen in the tortoise with this explanation. Secondly, it may be suggested that the source of acetylcholine in the muscles of the tortoise is rapidly exhausted. If this were the case, the required concentration of acetylcholine could be achieved either by some increase in the duration of stimulation or by inactivation of cholinesterase. In actual fact both contribute to greater stability of the tonic components.

DISCUSSION

As a result of these findings we are, we believe, able to give the following answers to the question formulated at the commencement of the investigation.

The motor apparatus in the tortoise, like that in amphibians and mammals, contains neuromotor units adapted for rapid and slow contractions respectively. The evidence of this is, first, that the process of contraction in many of the tortoise's muscles is clearly differentiated into two components, namely a relatively rapid spike and a slower tail. At the same time, the second component is absent in the contractile wave of some other muscles in the tortoise. The second piece of evidence is that those muscles of the tortoise, the contractions of which consist of two components, contain muscle fibres with two different types of structure (Kruger, 1952). Finally, this specialization reveals itself by the fact that, in the tortoise, the nerve fibres supplying the "rapid" and "slow" muscle fibres respectively differ in their properties, as is shown by their different resistances to the blocking effect of steady current. An interesting point is that such a combination of properties—only slight difference between excitability thresholds and a considerable difference in resistance—is characteristic of the "rapid" and "slow" nerve fibres in the cat as well as in the tortoise (Sharipova and Zhukov, 1954).

The skeletal muscles of the tortoises react to acetylcholine, whether pharmacological or physiological, by prolonged contraction, by contracture. Both "slow" and "rapid" (e.g. sartorius muscle) are found to be sensitive to this agent. But the mechanism for the reaction of contracture to nerve impulses is unstable, this instability being apparently dependent on rapid "exhaustion" of the source of physiological acetylcholine. We are, therefore, compelled to think that, even though it operates, the acetylcholine mechanism can hardly play any important part in the prolonged tonic contractions of the skeletal muscles in the tortoise. Such contractions are apparently provided for mainly by the slowness of the contractile act, a feature which is so characteristic in all the skeletal muscles of the tortoise, and by gradual increase in "viscosity" in the course of the maintenance of contraction.

The impression is thus created that, in accord with the phylogenetic position of reptiles, the contractile properties of their muscles and the mechanism for muscular tonus have features characteristic of amphibians on the one hand and of mammals on the other. Actually, the maintenance of muscular tonus in reptiles is provided for to some extent by the acetylcholine mechanism inherited from amphibians. On the other hand, an important part (possibly even a more important part) is played by the summation of slow waves of contraction and change in the physicochemical properties of the contractile substrate in the course of activity, which is in fact the tonus mechanism peculiar to the motor apparatus of mammals.

Might it be, however, that these features of contractile activity are not determined by the evolutionary level of these animals but are idioadaptational features arising in connexion with the peculiarities of locomotion and defence, which are so specific to these animals? In this connexion it is interesting to note that the functional properties of the skeletal muscles and the tonus mechanism in one of the slowly moving amphibians (toad) are similar to those seen in the relatively active frog and not those of the slow tortoise. The transient tetanic contraction of mixed skeletal muscle of the toad is clearly subdivided into a rapid spike and slow tonic tail, the latter being persistent and not disappearing on repeated stimulation. The threshold for the development of the tonic component is much higher than that for the tetanic. It was thus possible, by appropriate selection of the strength of stimulation, to demonstrate the activity of the tonic apparatus of this muscle in pure form by first bringing the tetanic apparatus to a state of pessimum. These facts indicate that the features of the motor apparatus in the tortoise are to some extent connected with the phylogenetic position of reptiles generally.

On the other hand, the tonic mechanism of a mobile reptile (lizard, *Ezemias arguta*) shows greater similarity to that of the tortoise. The stimulation thresholds for production of the tetanic and tonic components of contraction respectively are just as close to one another in the lizard as in the tortoise; a purely tonic optimum of contraction could not be demonstrated. True, the acetylcholine mechanism for tonus is much more stable in relation to repeated stimulation in the lizard. The importance of this becomes obvious when it is realized that the rate of the contractile act in the lizard is greater than in the tortoise.

These facts lead us to conclude that the particular features of the tonus mechanism in the skeletal muscles of the tortoise are determined more by its membership of the class of reptiles than by the features of the animal's motor activity. In reptiles we are apparently actually observing a transitional stage, the acetylcholine mechanism for muscular tonus peculiar to lower vertebrates being replaced by the "tetanic tone" characteristic of the higher vertebrates.

What are the reasons for the replacement of one tonus mechanism by another? In our opinion the replacement of the acetylcholine tonus mechanism by the mechanism of summation occurred in the course of the adaptational evolution of animals in connexion with the need to deal with the new motor tasks arising with the development of the vertebrate subtype.

According to Ruckert (1930), great aptitude for chemical contracture is a sign of phylogenetically young skeletal muscle. Itina (1959) has actually demonstrated in lower vertebrates (cyclostomes) both the power of the muscles to react by a contractile wave to a nerve impulse and their high sensitivity to the direct action of a number of chemical agents—acetylcholine, arecoline and others. In this respect, the skeletal muscles of cyclostomes are similar to the muscles of the embryos of higher vertebrates. Yet, the acetylcholine tonus mechanism is clearly reduced in near relatives of the cyclostomes (bony fishes). According to Itina (1959) and also Shamarina (1943), the muscles of the pectoral fins of bony fishes are almost insensitive to the direct action of acetylcholine. Only when a solution of acetylcholine was injected into the muscle vessels was there a transient tetanic contraction—much in the same way as in mammals. Reduction of the acetylcholine tonus mechanism in fishes has apparently been determined by the small demand for muscle tone in these animals generally as a result of the reduction of their weight in accordance with the principle of Archimedes.

An urgent problem in the first terrestrial vertebrates (amphibians) was the constant struggle with the force of gravity. The old chemical tonus mechanism was used and perfected to deal with this problem and there was development of specialized nerve and muscle structures for the function of tonus and of special tonic reflexes.

The ability to effect a considerable increase of mobility is characteristic of typical reptiles. Many of them raise their body from the ground when running and, while this promotes rapidity of movement, it also increases the demand for muscle tone because of the reduced angle of stability (Kesareva, 1959). There was increasing need for adaptation of body posture to the changing conditions of movement, for constant adjustment in accordance with tonic and phasic reflexes. It may be thought that, because of this, muscle tone in reptiles began to be maintained both by the acetylcholine mechanism and also by a mechanism of summation similar to that which is the basis of phasic movements. This unification of tonic and phasic mechanisms was apparently effected for the dynamic coordination of these forms of activity.

Because of the lengthening of the extremities and the straightening out of the joint angles, the centre of gravity of the body is situated much higher in mammals than in amphibians or reptiles; the angle of stability of the body of the mammal is reduced (Fig. 5). Body stability is often threatened because of the highly developed motor activity of these animals. Consequently, the need for tonic activity in the musculature of mammals is very great. In most cases, however, this tone must be highly dynamic, and not static.

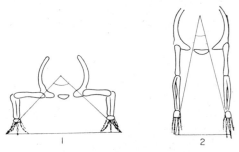

FIG. 5. Diagram of the position of the trunk and extremities and the angle of stability in the primitive terrestrial vertebrate (1) and in the mammal (2).

The problem of constantly adapting muscle tone to the needs and conditions of phasic motor activity becomes very real. Obviously the old slow mechanism of acetylcholine contracture is little suited to deal with this problem. The mobile nerve mechanism for tone, producing asynchronous tetani in different fibres of the muscle and capable of rapid switching to the innervation of phasic movements, acquires exceptional importance. At the same time, wherever there is tension, it must be constant and prolonged: use is then made of the slow "red" muscle fibres, which are capable of forming fused and continuous tetani at the expense of occasional bursts of excitation and with low energy expenditure.

REFERENCES

GINETSINSKII, A. G., Physiol. J. U.S.S.R. (*Fiziol. zh. SSSR*) **33**, 4, 413 (1947).
GINETSINSKII, A. G. and N. A. ITINA, Bull. Expl. Biol. and Med. (*Byull. eksp. biol. i med.*) **5**, 4, 386 (1938).
GINETSINSKII, A. G. and N. I. MIKHEL'SON, Recent Advances in Biology (*Usp. sovrem. biol.*) **6**, 3, 399 (1937).
ITINA, N. A., Physiol. J. U.S.S.R. (*Fiziol. zh. SSSR*) **25**, 5, 664 (1938).
ITINA, N. A., Functional properties of neuromuscular apparatuses in lower vertebrates (*Funktsional'nyye svoistva nervnomyshechnykh priborov nizshikh pozvonochnykh*). Izdat. Akad. Nauk SSSR (1959).
KESAREVA, YE. P., *Unconditioned and Conditioned Tonic Reflexes in their Connexion with Motor Activity in Man* (Bezuslovnyye i uslovnyye tonicheskiye refleksy v ikh svyazi s dvigatel'noi deyatelnost'yu cheloveka) (1959).
KOHLEN, H., Z. Zellforsch. **28**, 597 (1938).

KRUGER, P., *Tetanus und Tonus der quergestreiften Skelettmuskeln der Wirbeltiere und des Menschen*, Leipzig 1952.

KUFFLER, S. W. and R. W. GERARD, *J. Neurophysiol.* **10**, 383 (1947).

RUCKERT, W., *Pflüg. Arch.* **226**, 323 (1930).

SHAMARINA, N. M., Bull. of the U.S.S.R. Academy of Sciences, Biological Series (*Izv. Akad. Nauk SSSR, seriya biol.*) **2**, 116 (1943).

SHARIPOVA, R. R. and YE. K. ZHUKOV, Physiol. J. U.S.S.R. (*Fiziol. zh. SSSR*) **40**, 4, 445 (1954).

SOMMERKAMP, H., *Arch. Expl. Path. u. Pharm.* **128**, 99 (1928).

VERESHCHAGIN, S. M., Physiol. J. U.S.S.R. (*Fiziol. zh. SSSR*) **31**, 1, 73 (1948a).

VERESHCHAGIN, S. M., Physiol. J. U.S.S.R. (*Fiziol. zh. SSSR*) **31**, 1, 81 (1948b).

VERESHCHAGIN, S. M. and YE. K. ZHUKOV, Physiol. J. U.S.S.R. (*Fiziol. zh. SSSR*) **33**, 3, 335 (1947).

VERESHCHAGIN, S. M. and YE. K. ZHUKOV, Physiol. J. U.S.S.R. (*Fiziol. zh. SSSR*) **34**, 2, 207 (1948).

VERESHCHAGIN, S. M. and YE. K. ZHUKOV, Physiol. J. U.S.S.R. (*Fiziol. zh. SSSR*) **36**, 6, 673 (1950).

ZHUKOV, YE. K., *Investigation on Skeletal Muscle Tone* (Issledovaniye o tonuse skeletnykh myshts.) Medgiz (1956a).

ZHUKOV, YE. K., *Problems in Current Physiology of Nervous and Muscular Systems*. A collection commemorating the 70th birthday of I. S. Beritashvili (Problemy sovremennoi fiziologii nervnoi i myshechnoi sistem. Sbornik, posvyashch. 70-letiyu I. S. Beritashvili) p. 437. Tbilisi 1956b.

ZHUKOV, YE. K., Physiol. J. U.S.S.R. (*Fiziol. zh. SSSR*) **43**, 11, 1112 (1957).

NAME INDEX

SUBJECT INDEX